NOBEL PRIZE LIBRARY

PERSE

PIRANDELLO

PONTOPPIDAN

QUASIMODO

Nobel Prize Library

PUBLISHED UNDER THE SPONSORSHIP OF THE

NOBEL FOUNDATION & THE SWEDISH ACADEMY

St.-John Perse

Luigi Pirandello

Henrik Pontoppidan

Salvatore Quasimodo

ALEXIS GREGORY, *New York*, AND
CRM PUBLISHING, *Del Mar, California*

CONTENTS

St.-John Perse

Presentation Address 3
Acceptance Speech 7
SEAMARKS 11
The Life and Works of St.-John Perse 59
The 1960 Prize 67

Luigi Pirandello

Presentation Address 71
Acceptance Speech 77
THE EMPEROR (HENRY IV) 79
SIX CHARACTERS IN SEARCH OF AN AUTHOR 117
The Life and Works of Luigi Pirandello 157
The 1934 Prize 167

Henrik Pontoppidan

THE PROMISED LAND 173
The Life and Works of Henrik Pontoppidan 269
The 1917 Prize 276

Salvatore Quasimodo

Presentation Address 281
Acceptance Speech 285
DISCOURSE ON POETRY 289
POEMS 297
The Life and Works of Salvatore Quasimodo 365
The 1959 Prize 371

St.-John Perse

1960

"For the soaring flight and the evocative imagery of his poetry, which in a visionary fashion reflects the conditions of our times"

Illustrated by ZAO WOU-KI

PRESENTATION ADDRESS

By ANDERS ÖSTERLING

PERMANENT SECRETARY
OF THE SWEDISH ACADEMY

THE NOBEL PRIZE laureate for Literature for this year bears a name of unusual sound, which he chose at first to protect himself from the curious. St.-John Perse is the poet's name, made internationally famous by a private man who in civil life is called Alexis Léger and as such was to acquire great prestige in another domain of public life. Thus his life is divided into two periods, one of which has ended whereas the other is continuing: Alexis Léger, the diplomat, has been transformed into St.-John Perse, the poet.

Considered as a literary personage, he presents a biography remarkable in many respects. Born in 1887 in Guadeloupe, he belonged to a French family that came to settle there as early as the seventeenth century. He spent his childhood in this tropical Eden of the Antilles, all rustling with palms, but at the age of eleven he left for France with his family. He was educated at Pau and at Bordeaux, decided to take a degree in law, and in 1914 entered upon a diplomatic career. Sent first to Peking, he next found himself entrusted with increasingly important assignments. As Secretary General for the Ministry of Foreign Affairs for several years, with the rank of Councilor of State, he assumed major responsibilities during the political events that were the prelude to the Second World War.

After the defeat of France in 1940 he was abruptly suspended and went into exile, was considered a dangerous adversary by the Vichy regime, and was even deprived of his French citizenship. He found refuge in Washington, where he occupied a position as literary adviser to the Library of Congress. The French state was soon to reinstate him in his full rights, but the exile firmly refused to re-enter diplomacy. In recent years, however, he has repeatedly returned to France for private reasons.

Here is a career which opens vast vistas and which presupposes in the one who succeeds in it a breadth of perspective acquired under many conditions, combined with a spiritual tone of uncommon dynamic quality. This international versatility, the hallmark of the great traveler, constitutes moreover one of the themes often repeated in the poet's work. He owed his first success to the cycle of poems entitled *"Pour fêter une enfance"* ("To Celebrate a Childhood," 1910) whose dazzling imagery evokes in the golden dawn of childhood memories the exotic paradise of Guadeloupe, and its fabulous plants and animals. From China he brought back an epic poem, *Anabase* (*Anabasis,* 1924), which relates, in a form suggestive and hard as enamel, a mysterious warlike expedition into the Asian deserts. The same, uncompromisingly dense form, in which verse and prose are united in a solemn flow blending Biblical verse with the rhythm of the Alexandrine, is found again in the collections of poems which followed: *Exil* (*Exile,* 1942) and *Vents* (*Winds,* 1946), both written in America. They constitute an imposing statement of the uninterrupted cycle of degeneration and rejuvenation, while *Amers* (*Seamarks,* 1957) celebrates the sea, the eternal dispenser of power, the first cradle of civilizations.

These works are, it is true, of marked singularity, complicated in form and thought, but the master who created them is anything but exclusive, if one means by that that he immures himself in a satisfied autonomy and is interested only in himself. Quite the contrary; his dominating quality is the wish to express the human, seized in all its multiplicity, all its continuity; the wish to describe man, forever the creator, struggling from century to century against the equally perpetual insubordination of the elements. He identifies himself with all the races who have lived on our stormy planet. "Our race is old," he said in a poem, "our face is nameless. And time knows much about all the men that we may have been . . . the ocean of things besets us. Death is at the porthole, but our route is not there."

In this exaltation of man's creative power, St.-John Perse may sometimes recall the hymns of the German poet Hölderlin, who also was a magician of speech, filled with the grandeur of the poetic vocation.

It is very easy to treat the sublime faith in the power of poetry as a paradox in order to belittle it, especially when it seems to assert itself with a force inversely proportional to the need of arousing an immediate response to the thirst of human communion. On the other hand, St.-John Perse is an eloquent example of the isolation and estrangement which in our era are a vital condition for poetic creation when its aim is high.

One can only admire the integrity of his poetic attitude, the lofty insistence with which he perseveres in the only mode of expression that allows him to realize his intentions, an exclusive but always pertinent form. The inexhaustible luxuriance of the picturesque style of his rhapsodies is intellectually demanding and may weary the reader of whom the poet demands such efforts of concentration. He takes his metaphors from all disciplines, from all eras, from all mythologies, from all regions; his cycles of poems call to mind those great sea shells from which a cosmic music seems to emanate. This expansive imagination is his strength. Exile, separation—evocations whose voiceless murmur gives his poetry its general tonality; and through the double theme of man's strength and helplessness a heroic appeal can be perceived, an appeal which is perhaps expressed more distinctly than before in the poet's latest work, *Chronique* (*Chronicle,* 1960), filled with a breath of grandeur, in which the poet recapitulates everything, at the end of the day, while making veiled allusions to the present state of the world. And he even makes a prophetic appeal to Europe to have it consider this fateful moment, this turning point in the course of history. The poem ends with these words: "Great age, here we are. Take measure of the heart of man."

It is, then, correct to say that St.-John Perse, behind an apparent abstruseness and symbols frequently difficult to grasp, brings a universal message to his contemporaries. One has every reason to add that in his own way he perpetuates a majestic tradition in French poetic art, especially the rhetorical tradition inherited from the classics. In short, this honor awarded to him only confirms the position he has acquired in letters as one of the great leaders in poetry.

ACCEPTANCE SPEECH

By ST.-JOHN PERSE

I HAVE ACCEPTED in behalf of poetry the honor which has been given to it here and which I am anxious to restore to it. Without you poetry would not often be held in esteem, for there appears to be an increasing dissociation between poetic activity and a society enslaved by materialism. The poet accepts this split, although he has not sought it. It would exist for the scientist as well, were it not for the practical uses of science. But it is the disinterested thought of both scientist and poet that is honored here. In this place at least let them no longer be considered hostile brothers. For they are exploring the same abyss and it is only in their modes of investigation that they differ.

When one watches the drama of modern science discovering its rational limits in pure mathematics; when one sees in physics two great doctrines posit, the one a general theory of relativity, the other a quantum theory of uncertainty and indeterminism that would limit forever the exactitude even of physical measurements; when one has heard the greatest scientific innovator of this century, the initiator of a modern cosmology that reduces the vastest intellectual synthesis to the terms of an equation, invoke intuition to come to the aid of reason and proclaim that "the imagination is the true seed bed of science," going even so far as to claim for the scientist the benefit of a true artistic vision: is one not justified in considering the tool of poetry as legitimate as that of logic?

In truth, every creation of the mind is first of all "poetic" in the proper sense of the word; and inasmuch as there exists an equivalence between the modes of sensibility and intellect, it is the same function that is exercised initially in the enterprises of the poet and the scientist. Discursive thought or poetic ellipsis—which of these travels to, and returns from, more remote regions? And from that primal night in which two men born blind grope for their ways, the one equipped with the tools of science, the other helped only by the flashes of his imagination, which one returns sooner and more heavily laden with a brief phosphorescence? The answer does not matter. The mystery is common to both. And the great adventure of the poetic mind is in no way secondary to the dramatic advances of modern science. Astronomers have been bewildered by the theory of an expanding universe, but there is no less expansion in the moral infinite of the universe of man. As far as the frontiers of science are pushed back, over the extended arc of these frontiers one will hear the poet's hounds on the chase. For if poetry is not, as has been said, "absolute reality," it comes very close to it, for poetry has a strong longing for, and a deep perception of, reality, situated as it is at that extreme limit of cooperation where the real seems to assume shape in the poem. Through analogy and symbolism, through the remote illuminations of mediating imagery, through the interplay of their correspondences in a thousand chains of reactions and strange associations, and finally, through the grace of a language into which the very rhythm of Being has been translated, the poet invests himself with a surreality that cannot be that of science. Is there among men a more striking dialectic, one that engages them more completely? Since even the philosophers are deserting the threshold of metaphysics, it is the poets' task to retrieve metaphysics; thus poetry, not philosophy, reveals itself as the true "daughter of wonder," according to the words of that ancient philosopher to whom it was most suspect.

But more than a mode of perception, poetry is above all a way of life, of integral life. The poet existed among the cave men; he will exist among men of the atomic age, for he is an inherent part of man. Even religions have been born from the need for poetry, which is a spiritual need, and it is through the grace of poetry that the divine spark lives forever in the human flint. When mythologies vanish, the divine finds refuge and perhaps even continuation in poetry. As in the processions of antiquity the bearers of bread yielded their place to the bearers of torches, so now in the domain of social order and of the immediacies of human need it is the poetic imagination that is still illuminating the lofty passion of peoples in quest of light. Look at man walking proudly under the load of his eternal task; look at him moving along under his burden of humanity, when a new humanism opens before him, fraught with true universality and wholeness of soul. Faithful to its task, which is the exploration of the mystery of man, modern poetry is engaged in an enterprise the pursuit of which concerns the full integration of man.

There is nothing Pythian in such poetry. Nor is it purely esthetic. It is neither the art of the embalmer, nor that of the decorator. It does not breed cultured pearls, nor does it deal in semblances and emblems, and it would not be satisfied by any feast of music. Poetry allies itself with beauty—a supreme union—but never uses it as its ultimate goal or sole nourishment. Refusing to divorce art from life, love from perception, it is action, it is passion, it is power, and always the innovation which extend borders. Love is its hearth-fire, insurrection its law; its place is everywhere, in anticipation. It wants neither to deny nor to keep aloof; it expects no benefits from the advantages of its time. Attached to its own destiny and free from any ideology, it recognizes itself the equal of life, which is its own justification. And with one embrace, like a single great, living strophe, it clasps both past and future in the present, the human with the superhuman, planetary space with universal space. The obscurity for which it is reproached pertains not to its own nature, which is to illuminate, but to the night which it explores, the night of the soul and the mystery in which human existence is shrouded. Obscurity is banished from its expression and this expression is no less exacting than that of science.

Thus by his total adherence to that which is, the poet maintains for us a relationship with the permanence and unity of Being. And his lesson is one of optimism. For him the entire world of things is governed by a single law of harmony. Nothing can happen that by nature could exceed the measure of man. The worst upheavals of history are nothing but seasonal rhythms in a much vaster cycle of repetitions and renewals. And the Furies that cross the scene with lifted torches light only a fragment of the long historical process. Ripening civilizations do not die in the throes of one autumn: they merely change. Inertia is the only menace. The poet is the one who breaks through our habits. And in this way the poet finds himself tied to history despite himself. No aspect of the drama of his times is foreign to him. May he give all of us a clear taste of life in this great age. For this is a great and new time calling for a new self-appraisal. And, after all, to whom would we yield the honor of belonging to our age?

"Do not fear," says History, lifting one day her mask of violence, and with her hand making the conciliatory gesture of the Asiatic divinity at the climax of her dance of destruction, "Do not fear or doubt, for doubt is sterile and fear servile. Listen instead to the rhythmic beat that my high innovating hand imposes on the great human theme in the constant process of creation. It is not true that life can renounce itself. There is nothing living which proceeds from nothingness or yearns for it. But neither does anything ever keep form or measure under the incessant flux of Being. The tragedy lies not in metamorphosis as such. The true drama of the age is in the widening gap between temporal and eternal man. Is man illuminated on one side going to grow dark on the other? And will his forced maturation in a community without communion be nothing but a false maturity?"

It is up to the true poet to bear witness among us to man's double vocation. And that means holding up to his mind a mirror more sensitive to his spiritual possibilities. It means evoking in this our century a human condition more worthy of original man. It means, finally, bringing the collective soul into closer contact with the spiritual energy of the world. In the face of nuclear energy, will the poet's clay lamp suffice for his purpose? Yes, if man remembers the clay.

Thus it is enough for the poet to be the bad conscience of his age.

SEAMARKS

By ST.-JOHN PERSE

Translated by Wallace Fowlie

AND YOU, SEAS . . .

1

And you, Seas, who have read in wider dreams, will you leave us one evening at the rostra of the City, in the center of the public stone and the bronze vine leaves?

Larger, O crowd, our audience on this versant of an age without decline: the Sea, immense and green like a dawn to the orient of men,

The Sea, in celebration of its steps, like an ode of stone: vigil and celebration on our frontiers, murmur and celebration to the height of men—the Sea itself our vigil, like a divine promulgation . . .

The funeral smell of the rose will no longer lay siege to the grilles of the tomb; the life hour in the palms will no longer silence its soul of a stranger . . . Bitter? have our lips of living men ever been such?

I saw smiling in the fires of the open sea the great festive thing: the Sea as celebrated in our dreams, like an Easter of green grasses and like a feast day that we celebrate,

All the Sea in celebration on its confines, under its falconry of white clouds, like a tax-free domain and like entailed land, like a province of rank weeds that was wagered on the dice . . .

O breeze, flood my birth! And may my favor go to the circus of wider pupils! The javelins of Noon quiver in the gates of joy. The drums of nothingness yield to the fifes of light. And the Ocean, on all sides, trampling its weight of dead roses,

Over our terraces of calcium raises its head of a Tetrarch!

2

. . . I will make you weep, there is too much grace between us.

"Tears of grace, not of sorrow, says the Singer of the most beautiful song;
"And for that pure feeling of the heart whose source I ignore
"And for that pure instant of the sea which comes before the breeze . . ."

Thus spoke the man of the sea, talking a seaman's talk.
Thus did he praise, praising love and desire of the sea
And towards the sea, from all sides, this new flowing of the springs of pleasure . . .

"It is a tale I will tell, it is a tale you will hear;

"It is a tale I will tell as it should be told,
"And with such grace will it be told, that all must delight in it.

"Surely, a story that one would wish once more to hear in the carefreeness of death,
"And such and such, fresh as it is, in the heart of man without memory,
"That it will be to us a new favor, like the breeze from the estuary in sight of the lamps on land.

"And of those who will hear it, seating under the great tree of sorrow,
"There will be few who will not rise, will not rise with us and go, smiling,
"Among the ferns again of childhood and the unrolling of the curled fronds of death."

3

Poetry to accompany the march of a recitation in honor of the Sea.

Poetry to assist the song of a march round the circuit of the Sea.

Like the ritual round the altar and the gravitation of the chorus in the circuit of the strophe.

And it is a chant of the sea as has never been chanted, and it is the Sea in us that will chant it:

The Sea, borne in us, to the satiety of breath and the peroration of breath,

The Sea, in us bearing the silken sound of open seas and all the great freshness of good fortune throughout the world.

Poetry to appease the fever of a watch along the edge of the sea. Poetry to fire our watch in the delight of the sea.

And it is a dream at sea such as was never dreamt, and it is the Sea in us that will dream it:

The Sea, woven in us, to the last weaving of its tangled night, the Sea, in us weaving its great hours of light and its great trails of darkness—

All freedom, all renascence and all resipiscence, the Sea! the Sea! in its sea-flowing,

In the overflowing of its bubbles and the infused wisdom of its milk, ah! in the sacred ebullience of its vowels—sacred beings! sacred beings!—

The Sea itself all foam, like a Sibyl in flower on her iron chair . . .

4

Thus praised, O Sea, will you be wreathed with blameless praise.
Thus bidden, will you be guest of whose merit it is proper to say nothing.
And of the Sea itself it will not be question, but of its reign in the heart of man:
As it is well, in the plea to the Prince, to interpose ivory or jade
Between the suzerain face and the courtesan praise.
And I, bowing in your honor in a bow not too low,
Shall exhaust the reverence and balancing of the body;
And the smoke of pleasure once more will encircle the head of the fervent,
And the delight of the well-chosen word once more beget the grace of a smile . . .

And with such a greeting will you be greeted, O Sea, that it will be long remembered like a recreation of the heart.

5

. . . Now, it had been such a long time that I had nursed a taste for this poem, mingling in my daily talk all that alliance, afar, of a great flash of sea—as on the edge of the forest, between the leaves of black lacquer, the swift layer of blue and of rock-salt: vivid scale, among the meshes, of a great fish taken by the gills!

And who then could have surprised me in my secret purpose? guarded by smile and courtesy; speaking, speaking the tongue of an alien among men of my blood—in the corner perhaps of a Public Garden, or else by the grilles, pointed with gold, of some Chancellery; the face perhaps in profile and the gaze far off, between my phrases, on some bird singing its lay over the roof of the Harbormaster.

For it had been such a long time that I had nursed a taste for this poem, and with such a smile did I keep my devotion to it: all invaded, all invested, all menaced by the great poem, as by the milk of madrepores: at its flood, docile, as at the midnight quest, in a very slow heaving of the great waters of dream, when the pulsations of the open sea pull gently on the hawsers and on the cables.

And how it came to us to induce this poem is what we will have to tell. But is it not enough to take pleasure in it? And how good it was, O gods, that I took care of it before it was taken away from us . . . Go and see, child, at the turn of the street, how the Daughters of Halley, the beautiful celestial visitors in Vestal robes, caught in the night by the hook of glass, are prompt to escape at the turn of the ellipse.

Morganatic is the far-off Bride, and the alliance, clandestine! . . . The nuptial chant, O Sea, will be for you the chant: "My last song! my last song! which will be song of a man of the sea . . ." And if it is not this song, I ask you, what would testify in favor of the Sea—the Sea without stelae or porticos, without Aliscamps or Propylaeas; the Sea without stone dignitaries on its circular terraces, or ranks of beasts saddled with wings along the highways?

I have taken charge of the writing, I will honor the writing. As at the foundation of a great votive work, the man who has offered to prepare the text and the announcement; and was asked to by the Assembly of Donors, he alone having a vocation for it. And no one knew how he set to work: in one quarter, you will be told, of horse slaughterers or of smelters—at a time of popular uprising—between the bells of the curfew and the drums of a military dawn . . .

And already in the morning the Sea ceremonial and new smiles at him above the cornices. And She, such an Alien, mirrors herself in his page . . . For it was such a long time that he had nursed a taste for this poem; having for it such a vocation . . . And it was such a sweetness, one evening, to give his devotion to it; and to yield to it, such impatience. And with such a smile also did he join allegiance with it . . . "My last song! my last song! which will be a song of a man of the sea . . ."

6

And it is the Sea that came to us on the stone steps of the drama:

With her Princes, her Regents, her Messengers clothed in pomp and metal, her great Actors their eyes gouged out and her Prophets chained together, her women Magicians stamping on wooden clogs, their mouths full of black clots, and her tributes of Virgins plodding in the furrows of the hymn,

With her Shepherds, her Pirates, her Wet-nurses of infant kings, her old

Nomads in exile and her Princesses of elegy, her tall silent Widows under illustrious ashes, her great Usurpers of thrones and Founders of distant colonies, her Prebendaries and her Merchants, her great Concussionaries of provinces rich in tin, and her great traveling Sages mounted on rice-field buffaloes,

With all her lease of monsters and men, and all her breed of immortal fables, joining with her masses of slaves and helots her tall bastards of the Gods and her large daughters of Stallions—a crowd in haste rising on the tiers of History and all moving in a body towards the arena, with the first chill of the evening and the smell of seaweed,

Recitation marching towards the Author and towards the painted mouth of his mask.

*

So the Sea came to us in its great age and its great Hercynian folds—the whole sea, as a sea facing us, a single part and a single flank!

And to us came the Sea like a people towards us whose language is new, and like a language towards us whose phrasing is new, carrying to its bronze tables its supreme commands,

With great upheavals of humor and great swellings of language, with great reliefs of images and luminous slopes of shadow, running to its massive splendors of a very fine periodic style, and such, in its great fires of scales, and lightning flashes, as in the midst of heroic packs,

The Sea, moving, that makes its way on the gliding of its great errant muscles, the slimy Sea with the gliding motion of a pleura, and all running to the high flood of a sea, came towards us on its coils of a black python,

Very great thing moving towards the night and towards divine transgression . . .

*

And it was at sunset, in the first chills of the evening encumbered with viscera, when on the gold-fretted temples and in the Coliseums of old casting breached with light, the sacred spirit wakens in screech-owls' nests, amid the sudden animation of the ample parietal flora.

And as we ran to the promise of our dreams, on a very high slope of red earth loaded with offerings and horned beasts, and as we were trampling the red earth of sacrifice, adorned with vine leaves and spices, like the brow of a ram under the gold fringes and braids, we saw rising in the distance that other face of our dreams: the sacred thing at its level, the Sea, strange, there, watching its watch of a Stranger—irreconcilable, and singular, and forever unmatched—the erring Sea taken in the trap of its aberration.

Raising the arch of our arms in support of our "Aaah . . ." we gave this cry of man at the limit of the human; we had, on our head, this royal load of the offering: all the Sea smoking with our vows like a vat of black bile, like a great tub of entrails and offal in the paved courtyards of the Sacrificer!

We had, we had . . . Ah! say it again, is it really so? . . . We had—and it was such splendor of gall and black wine!—the Sea higher than our face, at the height of our soul; and in its nameless crudity at the height of our soul, its whole hide, raw, on the drum of the sky, as, against great deserted clay walls,

On a cross of four wooden stakes, a buffalo skin hangs, stretched out!

*

. . . And from higher, and higher seen, had we not held the Sea higher in our knowing,

Face washed with forgetfulness in the effacing of signs, stone freed for us of its relief and of its grain?—and from higher still and farther off, the Sea higher and more distant . . . inallusive and innocent of all figures, the tender luminous page without foil against the night of things? . . .

Oh! what great tree of light found here the source of its milk? We have not been fed on such a milk! We have not been named to such a rank! Daughters of mortal women were our ephemeral companions, threatened in their flesh . . . Dream, O dream aloud your dream of a man and an immortal! "Ah! let a Scribe approach and I will dictate to him . . ."

Would any Asiarch, responsible for a season of festivals and games, have ever dreamed such a dream of space and leisure? And that there was in us such a desire to live at that height, is not that, O gods! which qualified us? . . . Do not close, eyelid, until you have seized that pure instant of equity! "Ah! let some one approach and I will dictate to him . . ."

The sky, turning to a sea-gull blue, is restoring to us our presence, and over the assailed gulfs our millions of votive lamps are straying,—as when cinnabar is thrown into the fire to exalt man's vision.

*

For you will return to us, presence! with the first wind of the evening,

In your substance and in your flesh and in your weight of sea, O clay! in your color of sable stone and of dolmen, O Sea!—among begotten men and their countries of robur oaks, you, Sea of force and of furrows, Sea with the scent of female entrails and of phosphorus, in the great cracking whips of rape! Sea seized in the fire of your finest acts, O mind! . . . (When the Barbarians are at Court for a very brief stay, does union with the daughters of serfs exalt to such a height the tumult of the blood? . . .)

"Guide me, pleasure, on the ways of every sea; in the flurrying of every breeze where the instant is alerted, like a bird clothed in the clothing of wings . . . I go, I go a way of wings, where sadness itself is no more than wing. The fair land of birth has to be reconquered, the fair land of the King that he has not seen since childhood, and its defense is in my song. Command, O fifer, the action, and again this grace of a love which places in our hands only the swords of joy! . . ."

And who are you then, O Sages, to reprove us, O Sages? If the fortune of the sea nourishes again, in its season, a great poem beyond reason, will you refuse me access to it? Land of my seigniory, there may I enter, having no shame at my pleasure . . . "Ah! let a Scribe approach, and I will dictate to him . . ." And who, then, born of man, would stand without offense, beside my joy?

—Those who, by birth, hold their knowing above knowledge.

STROPHE

I

Tall Cities Flamed in the Sun
All Along Their Sea Front

1

Tall Cities flamed in the sun all along their sea front, their large stone buildings bathed in the golden salts of the open sea.

Port officers conferred like frontier guards: agreements on toll-gates and watering places; settlements of limits and regulations for rights of way.

We were waiting for Plenipotentiaries of the high sea. Ha! that the alliance be offered to us, at last! . . . And the crowd flocked towards the heads of the sea-walls in the white water,

To the edge of the most often used ramps, and as far as the rocky points, level with the sea, which are the sword and the spur in the great stone concepts of the design.

What deceitful star with horned beak had again blurred the numbers, and reversed the signs on the table of the waters?

In the lock basins of the Priests of Commerce, as in the fouled vats of the alchemist and the fuller,

A pale sky diluted the oblivion of earth and its fields of rye . . . White birds soiled the ridge of the high walls.

2

Frontier architecture. Harbor works on land and sea . . . We beseech you, mediating Sea, and you, Earth of Abel!

The prestations are accepted, the easements exchanged. The earth subject to forced labor in the judgment of the stone!

And, praised, the sea opened its blocks of green jasper. And, moving, the water washed the silent bases.

"Find your gold, Poet, for the ring of alliance; and your alloys for the bells, in the pilot lanes.

The sea-breeze is at every door and the sea at the end of every street, breeze and sea in our maxims and in the birth of our laws.

Rule laid down for the highest luxury: a woman's body—golden number!—and, for the City without ivories, your woman's name, Patrician!"

For we hold everything on hire, and it is enough to enmesh the hour in the yellow meshes of our sheltered waters . . .

The sea in medusa spasms led and led again its golden responses, in great luminous phrases and great pangs of green fire.

And the escutcheon still vacant for the dedications of the outer harbor, the men of memory voted for some winged beast;

But the male ring, in the muzzle of the pierheads, under the white feather trophy, dreamed, dreamed, amid the foam,

Of more distant relays where foam flies from other manes . . .

3

Elsewhere the story was less clear. Low-lying Cities prospered in ignorance of the sea, seated among their five hills and their iron deers;

Or going up, at a shepherd's pace, through the grass, with the litter mules and the publican's teams, went to people there, on the heights, a whole slope of fertile, tithable land.

But others, weary, leaned back against the stretch of water with their great walls of asylums and penitentiaries, the color of anise and of fennel, color of the groundsel of the poor.

And others, bleeding like girl mothers, their feet spotted with scales and their brows with lichen, descended to the mud flats of the port like women bearing refuse.

Harbor for beaching on props. Dump-carts on the borders of lagoons, on entablatures of marl and of black chalk.

We know these ends of paths, of alleys; these hauling-slips and these waste pits where the broken stairway spills its alphabet of stone. We have seen you, iron railing, and that line of rose tartar at the low-water mark of the sea,

There where the scavenger girls, before the eyes of children, remove, one evening, their monthly cloth.

Here the people's alcove with its litter of black clots. The incorruptible sea washes away its stains. And it is a bitch's lapping on the caries of the stone. There comes to the lines of suture a soft layer of small violet algae, like an otter's fur.

Higher up the square without curb, paved with dark gold and green night like a peahen of Colchis—the great black stone rose of the days following a riot, and the fountain with the copper beak where man bleeds like a cock.

4

You made your way, laughter of the sea, as far as these haunts of the landsman.

Far off, the shower, pierced with the rainbow's irises and with luminous sickles, laid open to itself the charity of the plains; wild boars rooted in the earth of the gold masks; old men attacked the orchards with sticks; and over the blue valleys peopled with barking, the brief horn of the crop-watcher joined in the evening with the conch of the fish-seller . . . Some men had a yellow bunting in a green wicker cage.

Ah! may a broader movement of things to their shore, of all things to their shore as into other hands, alienate from us at last the ancient Sorceress: the Earth, her tawny acorns, the heavy Circean braids, and the red evening moving in the pupils of tamed eyes!

An avid hour turned purple in the sea lavender. Stars awakened in the color of desert mint. And the shepherd's Sun, in its setting, under the hissing of bees, beautiful as a madman in temple ruins, went down to the yards towards the careening-beaches.

There, among ploughmen and sea blacksmiths, strangers victorious over enigmas on the highways, drank their fill of wine. There, before the night, the vulva smell of low waters began to rise. The shelter lights grew red in their iron baskets. The blind men sensed the crab of the tombs. And the Moon in the quarter of the black pythonesses

Grew intoxicated on sour flutes and tin clamor: "Torment of men, fire of the evening! A hundred mute gods on their stone tablets! But the sea for ever behind your family tables, and all this seaweed perfume of woman, less insipid than the bread of priests. . . . Your heart of a man, O passer-by, will camp tonight with the harbor men, like a cauldron of red flames on the foreign prow."

Warning to the Master of stars and navigation.

II

From the Master of Stars and Navigation . . .

From the Master of stars and navigation:

"They called me the Dark One, and my words were of the sea.

The Year I speak of is the greatest Year; the Sea where I question is the greatest Sea.

Reverence to your shore, madness, O major Sea of desire . . .

The earthly condition is miserable, but my ownership on the seas is immense, and my profit incalculable on the tables beyond the seas.

An evening sown with luminous species

Holds us on the edge of great Waters as on the edge of her cave the Eater of mallows,

She whom the old Pilots in robes of white skin

And their great men of destiny, bearers of armor and of writings, at the approach to the black honored with white domes, are accustomed to salute with a pious ovation.

Shall I follow you, Accountants! and you Masters of the number!

Divinities more furtive and villainous than piracy at sea before the dawn?

Sea gamblers engage with success

In distant speculations: innumerable headings, open to the lighting of vertical lines . . .

More than the Year called heliacal in its thousands and millions

Of millenniums, open, the total Sea encompasses me. The infamous abyss is delight to me, and immersion, divine.

And the wandering star of no allegiance travels in the heights of the green Century,

And my prerogative on the seas is to dream for you this dream of the real . . . They called me the Dark One and I dwelt in radiance."

*

"Secret of the world, go forward! And may the hour come when the helm

At last is taken from our hands! . . . I saw slipping through the holy oil the large lustrous obols of the celestial clockwork,

Great welcoming hands open for me the ways of the insatiable dream,

And I had no fear of my vision, but taking my ease in the seizure, I keep my eyes open to the immense favor, and in adulation.

Threshold of knowledge! doorsteps of glory! . . . Fumes of a wine that saw me born and was not pressed here.

The sea itself like a sudden ovation! Conciliator, O Sea, and sole intercessor! . . . A bird's cry on the reefs, the wind in course to its function,

And the shadow of a sail passes at the borders of the dream . . .

I say that a star breaks its chain in the stables of Heaven. And the star of no allegiance travels in the heights of the green Century . . . They called me the Dark One and my words were of the sea."

*

"Reverence to your speech, Pilot. This is not for the eye of the flesh,

Nor for the white eye lashed with red that is painted on the gunwale of vessels. My chance is in the adulation of evening and in the argus-blue hour of intoxication where flows the prophetic breath, like the flame of green fire among the flora of the reef.

O gods! no need of aromas or essences in the iron braziers, on the points of promontories,

To see pass, before the day, and under its loosened veils, at the pace of her femininity, the great Delian dawn in progress over the waters . . .

—All things spoken at evening and in the adulation of evening,

And you who know, increate Dream, and I, created, who know not, what do we do, on these shores, but spread together our nets for the night?

And the Women who bathe in night, at the ends of islands honored with white domes,

Their tall urns encircled with a bare arm, what do they do, O pious ones, more than we do? . . . They called me the Dark One and I dwelt in radiance."

III

The Tragediennes Came . . .

The Tragediennes came, descending from the quarries. They raised their arms high in honor of the Sea: "Ah! we had augured better of man's stature on the stone!

Incorruptible Sea judging us! . . . Ah! we had presumed too much of man under the mask! And we who mime man in the spice of the crowd, could we not hold memory of that highest language on the shores?

Our texts are trampled at the gates of the City—the wine gate, the grain gate—. Town girls drag in the gutter our wide wigs of black horsehair, our heavy damaged feathers, and the horses' hoofs are caught in the great theater masks.

O Specters, measure your brows of monkeys and iguanas in the immense oval of our helmets, like the parasite creature in the chamber of the conch . . . Old lionesses in the desert lie heavily on the stone borders of the stage. And the golden sandal of the great Tragedians shines in the urine pits of the arena

With the patrician star and the green keys of the setting sun."

*
* *

"But again we raise our arms high in honor of the Sea. In the saffroned armpit all the spices and salts of the earth!—high relief of the flesh, modeled like a groin, and again this offering of human clay where the expected face of the god is taking shape.

At the hemicycle of the City, where the sea is the stage, the bent bow of the crowd still holds us on its string. And you who dance the crowd's dance, lofty word of our fathers, O tribal Sea on your heath, will you be for us a sea without response and a dream more distant than a Sarmatian's dream?

The wheel of drama turns on the millstone of the Waters, crushing the black violet and the hellebore in the blood-soaked furrows of evening. Each wave raises towards us its acolyte's mask. And we, raising our illustrious arms, and turning again towards the Sea, at our arm-pit feeding the blood-stained muzzles of evening,

In the midst of the crowd, towards the Sea, we move as a crowd, with that very broad movement which our wide hips of country women borrow from every ocean swell—ah! more earthy than the plebs and the wheat of Kings!

And our ankles also are painted with saffron, our palms painted with murex in honor of the Sea!"

*
* *

The Tragediennes have come, descending the small streets. They have mingled with the people of the port, in their stage dress. Have made their way to the edge of the sea. And their broad hips of country women settle into the crowd. "Behold our arms, behold our hands! our palms painted like mouths, and our wounds feigned for the drama!"

They joined with the events of the day their large fluid pupils and their fabulous eyelids in the forms of shuttles. At the fork of fingers the empty sockets of the great mask gaping with dark holes like the stencil of the cryptographer. "Ah! we had expected too much of the mask and the written word!"

They descended, with their male voices, the echoing stairs of the harbor. Bringing to the edge of the sea their reflection of great walls and their whiteness of ceruse. And from treading the star-studded stone of the stairways and breakwaters, they recovered the gait of old sway-backed lionesses leaving their dens . . .

"Ah! we had augured better of man's stature on the stone. And at last we are walking towards you, legendary Sea of our fathers! Behold our bodies, behold our mouths; our broad foreheads with the double lobe of heifers, and our knees modeled in the form of medals, from a very wide module. Will you accept, exemplary Sea, our flanks scored with stretchmarks by the ripenings of the drama? Behold our breasts of Gorgons, our hearts of she-wolves under the frieze cloaks, and our black teats for the crowd, nursing a people of child kings. Or do we, raising the theatrical frieze, need to produce on the sacred shield of the belly the hairy mask of sex,

As in the fist of the hero, by its tuft of black hair against the haggard sword, the severed head of a woman—Stranger or Magician?"

*

* *

"Yes, it was a long time of waiting and dryness, when death watched for us at every fall of the writing. And boredom was so great in us, among our painted scenes, nausea in us so great, behind our masks, at all the celebrated works! . . .

Our stone circles have seen the step of man diminish on the stage. And certainly our tables of golden wood were adorned with all the fruits of the century, and our front-stage consoles with all the wines of Maecenas. But the divine lips strayed to cups, and the Sea in long draughts withdrew from the dreams of the Poet.

Will the Sea of violet salt steal from us the haughty daughters of glory? . . . Where is our text, where is our rule? . . . And to provide against the charges of the theater, in which courts of Despots shall we have to seek for great patrons and hosts?

Always there was, behind the crowd on the shore, this pure grievance of another dream—this greater dream of another art, this great dream of another work, and this rising, always, of the greatest mask at the horizon of men, O living Sea of the greatest text! . . . You spoke to us of another wine of men, and over our debased texts there was suddenly that reluctance of the lips which all satiety creates,

And we know now what took the life from us, in the middle of our strophe."

*

* *

"Ebb-tide, we call on you! strange sea swell, we shall watch your errant course round the world. And if, freer, we must make ourselves fresher for the welcome, we strip off, in sight of the sea, all equipment and all memory.

O Sea nourisher of the greatest art, we offer You our bodies washed in the strong wines of drama and of the crowd. We lay down, in sight of the sea, as on the approaches to the temples, our trappings of the stage and our accouterments for the arena. And like the daughters of fullers in the great triennial festivities—or the women who stir with the stick the mother color in tanks, and those, naked and red to the groin, who press grapes in the vats—expose on the public way their utensils of a poor wood, we raise to honor the worn instruments of our office.

Our masks and our thyrsi we lay down, our tiaras and scepters also, and our long flutes of black wood like the rods of magicians—our arms also and our quivers, our coats of mail, our tunics, and our fleeces of the very great roles; our fine helmets crested with pink plumes and our head-dresses of Barbarian camps twin-horned in metal, our massive bucklers breasted like goddesses, we lay them down, we lay down! . . . For you, foreign Sea, our very great ceremonial combs, like weavers' tools, and our mirrors of beaten silver like the small cymbals of the woman Initiate; our great shoulder jewels in the shape of stag-beetles, our great open-work clasps and our nuptial fibulae.

Our veils also we lay down, our frieze cloaks painted with the blood of murders, our silks tinted with wine of the Courts; and our staves also of beggar-women, and our crooks of suppliants—with the lamp and the spinning wheel of the widows, and the clepsydra of our guards, and the horn lantern of the watch; the oryx's skull rigged as a lute, and our great eagles worked in gold and other trophies of the throne and alcove—with the cup and votive urn, the ewer and copper basin for the guest's ablutions, and the Stranger's refreshment, the flagons and phials of the poison, the painted caskets of the Enchantress and the gifts of the Emissary, the golden cases for the message and the papers of the Prince in disguise—with the oar from the shipwreck, the black sail of the portent and the torches of sacrifice; with also the royal insignia, and the tall fans of triumph, and the red leather trumpets of our women Messengers . . . the whole decaying apparatus of drama and fable, we lay down! we lay down! . . .

But we keep, O promised Sea! with our clogs of hard wood, our golden rings in bunches on our wrists of lovers, for the scansion of future works, very great works to come, in their new pulsation and their incitement from elsewhere."

*
* *

"Destitution! Destitution! . . . We beg that in sight of the sea promise shall be made to us of new works: of strong and very beautiful works, which are all strength and will and which are all beauty—great seditious works, great licentious works, open to every audacity of man, and which will recreate for us the desire to live the part of man, in his own measure, at the greatest stride of man on the stone.

Very great works and such, in the arena, that men will no longer know their species or their race . . . Ah! may a lofty style again surprise us, in our wasting years, which will come to us from the sea and farther than the sea, ah! may a larger meter chain us to that greater narration of things throughout the world, behind all things of this world, and may a larger breath rise up in us which will be to us like the sea itself and its great breath of a stranger!

Of a greater meter at our frontiers, there is nothing known. Teach us, Power! the major verse of the greatest order, give us the tone of the greatest art, exemplary Sea of the greatest text! teach us the major mode, and may the rhythm at last be given us which, on the red granite of drama, will open to us the hour of which we are enamored! . . . To the movement of the princely waters who will again tie for us the great phrase taken from the people?

Our hips, that every sea swell teaches, are already roused and related to the distant movement of the crowd. Let us again be summoned on the stone, at our pace of Tragediennes! Let us again be oriented towards the sea, on the great arc of bare stone whose chord is the stage, and let there be placed in our hands, for the greatness of man on the stage, some of those great texts of which we spoke: sown with lightning flashes and hailed with storms, as burned with sea nettles and irritant medusae, where speed with the fires of the open sea great confessions of dreams and bold ventures of the soul. There hisses the hydra head of pleasure; there shines the very spark of woe, like the violet salt of the sea in the green flames of burning wrecks . . . Grant that we may read you, promises! on freer thresholds, and the great phrases of Tragedy, in the sacred gold of evening, will surprise us again above the heads of the crowd,

As beyond the Wall of stone, on the high spreading page of sky and sea, those long convoys of ships under sail which suddenly round the point of the Capes, during the unfolding of the drama on the stage . . ."

*
* *

"Ah! our cry was that of Lovers! But ourselves, Serving-women, who then will visit us in our stone chambers, between the menial lamp and the iron tripod of the depilator? Where is our text? where our rule? And who is the Master who will raise us from our fall? Where is the One—how we long to see him—who will know how to seize us, and raise us still murmuring, at the cross-roads of drama, like strong boughs at the mouths of sanctuaries?

Ah! may He come—will it be from the sea or from the Islands?—who will keep us under his rod! May he seize us, living women, or we will seize him! . . . A man new in his bearing, indifferent to his power and unconcerned with his birth: his eyes still burning from the scarlet flies of his night . . . May he gather under his reins this very large scattered course of wandering things in our age!

By that secret spasm of an eagle in our flanks, we shall know the despotic approach—as at the ruffling of a breeze over the waters, secret sulkiness of the genius scenting far off the trail of his gods . . . A new text, the Sea

Lies open on its great stone books. And we had not overrated the chances of the written word! . . . Listen, man of the gods, to the step of the Century marching towards the arena.—We, tall saffroned girls in the blood-stained councils of evening, dyed with the fires of evening even to the grain of our nails, we will raise higher our illustrious arms towards the Sea! . . .

We solicit new favor for the renovation of the drama and the greatness of man on the stone."

IV

The Patrician Women Also Are on the Terraces . . .

The Patrician Women also are on the terraces, their arms laden with black reeds:

"Our books read, our dreams closed, was that all there was? Where then is the fortune, where the issue? Where did it come to fail us, and which is the threshold that we did not cross?

Nobility, you lied; birth, you betrayed! O laughter, golden gerfalcon over our scorched gardens! . . . The wind raises in the Deer Parks the dead feather of a great name.

The rose one evening was without perfume, the wheel legible in the fresh cracks of the curbstone, and sadness opened its mouth in the mouth of the marbles. (The last to sing before our golden trellises, the Black who bleeds our lion cubs and will, this evening, give flight to our coveys of Asia.)

But the Sea was there, that no one named to us. And such great swells came to rest on the shelves of our cedars! . . . Could it be, could it be—with all the age of the sea in our women's eyes, with all the sunlit sea mirrored in our silks of the evening

And the whole confession of the sea in the most secret intimacy of our beings—could it be, O prudence! that they thought to keep us so long behind the yews and the torches of the Court and those sculptured panelings of cedar or thuja, among the burning leaves? . . .

One evening of strange rumors on the confines of our feasts, when honor had deserted the most beloved brows, we went out alone on that side of the evening and the terraces where one hears the sea rise on our stone confines.

Walking towards this very large area of oblivion, as below our parks towards the stone watering-trough and the paved border of the ponds where one bribes the Stable-master, we looked for the footpaths and the way out.

And there we were suddenly on that side of the evening and the earth where one hears the sea rise on its confines of sea . . ."

*

"With our dazzling stones and our night jewels, alone and half naked in our festival garments, we advanced to the white cornices above the sea. There, creatures of the earth, stretching

The extreme vine of our dreams to that sensitive point of rupture, we leaned our elbows on the dark marble of the sea, as on those tables of black lava set in copper where signs are oriented.

On the threshold of so great an Order where the Blind One officiates, we veiled our faces with the dream of our fathers. And as one also remembers a country of the future,

We remembered the natal place where we were not born, we remembered the royal place where we have no seat,

And it is since that time that we entered the festivals, our brows as though crowned with black pine-cones."

*

"Be one with us, O Mother of portents, even in our nuptial linens! Implacable Sea under the veil, O sea teacher of women in labor, on their lofty beds of lovers or wives! . . . The enmity rooted between us

Will not keep us from loving. Let the cattle give birth to monsters at the sight of your mask! we are of another caste, and of those who converse with the standing stones of drama: we can contemplate horror and violence without impregnating our daughters with ugliness.

Apprehensive, we love you for being this Camp of Kings where, capped with gold, run the white bitches of misfortune. Avid, we envy you this field of black poppies where forked lightning anchors. And we are moved towards you with a passion without shame, and by your act, in our dreams, we conceive.

Now you are no longer for us a mural figure or a temple embroidery, but in the crowd of your leaf, as in the crowd of your people, a very great rose of alliance and a very great hierarchical tree—like a great tree of expiation at the meeting of invasion roads,

Where the dead child hangs swaying among golden gourds and stumps of swords, of scepters, among effigies of black clay, and braids of hair plaited with straw, and great forks of red coral mingling the tribute offering with the regal spoils.

Others have seen your noonday face, where the terrible majesty of the Ancestor suddenly shines. And the warrior who is about to die covers himself in dreams with your armor, his mouth full of black grapes. And your sea radiance is in the sword's silk and the blindness of daylight,

And your sea savor is in the bread of consecration, and in the bodies of women who are consecrated. "You will open to me your dynastic tables," says the hero in quest of legitimacy. And the afflicted one who embarks on the sea: "There will I take my titles of nationality."

Laudable also is your face of a

Stranger, in the first milk of day—icy morning of green mother of pearl—when on the coastal roads where flow the migrations of Kings, some turn of history delivers us, between two Capes, to that mute confrontation of free waters.

(Rupture! rupture at last of the terrestrial eye! and the word spoken, between two Capes, on the retribution of pearls, and on our tragic embarkations in robes of woven silver . . . Vessels pass, in mid-sky, a whole *élite* of great marbles, high-winged, and their followers of black bronze;

Pass their burden of gold plate, with the hallmark of our fathers, and their harvest of specie, bearing the sign of the tunny or of the Wagoner.)"

*

"Thus from the land and from the shores, thus accomplices and won over, we yield . . . And if we must carry farther the offense of being born, let us find, through the crowd, an opening towards the port and the paths of unruled sea.

This evening we shall consort with the ancient salt of drama, the sea which changes dialect at all the gates of Empires, and that sea also which keeps vigil at other gates, the very one in us which keeps vigil and holds us in wonder!

Honor and Sea! schism of the Great, radiant rift athwart the Century—is that your claw again at our flanks? We have read you, cipher of the gods! We will follow you, royal course! O triple row of foam in flower and that smoke of a consecration over the waters,

As on the terrace of the Kings, on the peninsular causeways painted in great white lines with the magic signs, the triple row of aloes in bloom and the explosion, high on their stems, of their centenary blossoms in the solemn opening out of the night! . . ."

V

Language Which Was the Poetess . . .

Language which was the Poetess:

"Bitterness, O favor! Where now burns the aromatic herb? . . . The poppy seed buried, we turn at last towards you, sleepless Sea of the living. And you to us are something sleepless and grave, as is incest under the veil. And we say, we have seen it, the Sea for women more beautiful than adversity. And now we know only you that are great and worthy of praise,

O Sea which swells in our dreams as in endless disparagement and in sacred malignancy, O you who weigh on our great childhood walls and our terraces like an obscene tumor and like a divine malady!

The ulcer is on our side like a seal of franchise, love on the lips of the wound like the blood of the gods. Love! love of the god equal to invective, the great talons raking our woman's flesh, and the fleeing swarms of the spirit on the continuity of the waters . . . You will gnaw, sweetness,

Even into that prudery of the soul which is born in the curves of the neck and the inverted arc of the mouth—that malady which grows in the heart of women like a fire of aloes, or like the satiety of the rich man among his marbles and his murrhine vases.

An hour rises in us that we had not foreseen. It is too much to wait on our beds for the upsetting of the domestic torches. Our birth is of this evening, and of this evening our faith. A taste of cedar and olibanum still exalts our rank in the favor of the Cities, but the savor of the sea is on our lips,

And from a smell of the sea in our linen, and in our beds, in the deepest intimacy of night, date for us the blame and suspicion cast on all the vine arbors of the earth.

Good fortune to your steps, divinities of the threshold and the alcove! Dressers and Hairdressers, invisible Guardians, O you who took rank behind us in the public ceremonies, raising to the fires of the sea your large mirrors filled with the specter of the City,

Where were you, this evening, when we severed our ties with the stable of happiness?

But you who are there, divine hosts of the roof and the terraces, Lords! Lords! masters of the whip! O Masters to teach the dance of men before the Great, and masters forever to teach the step of the possessed—O you who hold high the cry of women in the night,

See to it that one evening we remember all those proud and real things which were consumed there, and which came to us from the sea, and which came to us from elsewhere,

Among all illicit things and those which pass understanding . . ."

VI

And This Girl Prophet Among the Priests . . .

And this girl prophet among the Priests:

"Prophecies! prophecies! Lips wandering over the sea, and all the things, under the foam, enchained by the newborn phrase which has no end . . .

The girls bound at the foot of the Capes take the message there. Let them be gagged in our midst: they will speak more clearly for the god they relay . . . Girls bound at the end of Capes as to the poles of chariots . . .

And impatience is over the waters for the word which tarries in our mouths. And the Sea washes on the stone our eyes burning with salt. And on the asexual stone open the eyes of an Alien Woman . . ."

*

". . . Ah! is there nothing but this blossoming of happy bubbles which sing the eager hour and sing the blind hour? And is this sea still a sea, which moves in us its great shoals of sand, and speaks to us of other sands?

More accomplices on the waters, more accomplices under the waters than the Poet meets in his dreams! . . . Solitude, O abundance! who now will release for us our invisible Sisters captive under the foam?—*mêlée* of hives and umbels, wheeling of resting wings and a hundred breakings of wrenched wings,

Ah! so many girls in irons, ah! so many girls under the curb, and in the winepress—tall seditious girls, tall acrimonious girls, drunk on a wine of green reeds! . . ."

*

". . . All this your sons will remember, their daughters and their sons will remember, and that a new race far off on the sand doubled our steps of infallible Virgins.

Prophecies! prophecies! the hooded eagle of the Century is whetted on the emery of the Capes. Dark beggars' sacks hang heavy low in the wild sky. And the rain, on the islands lighted with pale gold, suddenly pours the white oats of the message.

But what would you fear from the message? fear from a breath on the waters, and from this finger of pale sulphur, and from this pure sowing of small dark birds which are scattered in our faces, like ingredients of a dream and the black salt of a portent? (Procellarian is the name, pelagic the species, and the flight erratic like that of nocturnal moths.)"

*

". . . There are, there are things to say in favor of our age. There is, in the fracture of things, a singular pungency, as on the broken end of the blade that taste of dry clay and ironware which will always tempt the lips of the highest born.

"I hunger, I hunger with you a hunger for unfamiliar things": cry of the sea bird at its highest pairing! And things lose their meaning on the land open to the sea . . . For us the Continent of the sea, not the nuptial land with its perfume of fenugreek; for us the free space of the sea, not this earthly side of man, blinded by domestic stars.

And praise to those Women with us who, on the beaches soiled with seaweed, like abandoned lairs, and in the sacred stench rising from the vast waters—when the sand ipomoea turns to hyacinth red—and the sea again dons its color of holocaust—will have known how to stretch themselves on higher yards! . . ."

*

". . . Vivid canvas unfurled lights up in the depth of the sky which changes sails. And the murmuring in us is appeased under the iron comb. The sea rises in us, as in the deserted chambers of the great stone conch shells . . .

O Sea by which the eyes of women are grayer, sweetness and breath more than sea, sweetness and dream more than breath, and favor to our brows brought from so far away, there is in the continuity of things to come

Something like a holy saliva and like an eternal sap. And the sweetness is in the song, not in the elocution; is in the exhausting of the breath, not in the diction. And the felicity of the being responds to the felicity of the waters . . ."

*

". . . The rain, over the severe Ocean, sows its marsh marigolds: as often as the god's eyelid closes. The rain over the Ocean lights up: as much sky spreads in the trough of the rice swamps. Tall girls, bound alive, bend their heads, under the burden of gray cloud oranged with gold.

And at times the calm sea, color of greater age, is like that sea, mingled with dawn, which mirrors itself in the eyes of the newborn; is like that sea, adorned with gold, which queries itself in the wine.

Or else, clothed in gray pollen, and as though dusted with the powders of September, she is the chaste sea, going naked among the ashes of the spirit. And who then, to our ear, is still speaking of the true place? . . ."

*

". . . We listen, hailed in a low voice, to the thing in us very near and very distant—like that very pure whistling of the Etesian wind at the highest peak of the rigging. And the sweetness is in the waiting, not in the breath or the song. And these are things not very tellable, and by us alone half-perceived . . . Better that we be silent, our mouths refreshed with small shells.

O Voyagers over black waters in quest of sanctuaries, go forth and grow in stature, rather than build. The earth with loosened stones comes to its undoing at

the brink of those waters. And we, Servants, set free, go away, our feet vain, over very mobile sands.

Silken outcroppings of white sweetish clay, gnarled thicknesses of white sweetish marl, precede towards the land our steps of drowsy women. And with the palm of the bare foot on these nocturnal macerations—as with the blind man's hand in the night of snow-clad signs—we follow there this pure molded language: a pure relief of meningeal prints, sacred protuberances with the lobes of the embryo's infancy . . ."

*

". . . And the rains have passed, by no one questioned. Their long trains of portents have gone away, behind the dunes, to undo their harnessings. Men full of night desert the furrows. Heavy beasts yoked turn alone towards the sea.

And may we be rebuked, O Sea, if we also have not turned our heads! . . . The salt rain comes to us again from the high sea. And there is a light of green water over the land such as was seen four times in a year.

Children, who wear on your heads the largest leaves of water plants, you will also take us by the hand in this midnight of green water: the Girl Prophets, released, are going away with the Rains to thin out the rice fields . . ."

*

(And now! what did we wish to say, that we were not able to say?)

VII

One Evening Raised by Divine Hand . . .

One evening raised by divine hand to the sweetness of dawn between the Islands, our daughters thrice hail daughters of other shores:

"Our fires tonight! our fires tonight on all shores! . . . And our alliance!—the last evening!!! . . ."

*

"Our mothers with breasts of the Fates, on their cedar chairs, fear the hoofs of the drama in their gardens of spindle-shaped flowers—having loved with too much love, even to its ending in yellow wasps

Summer which loses its memory in the white rose gardens.

We, slimmer in the hips and with sharper brows, swimmers soon tied to the withers of the wave, offer to the sea swells to come a more ready shoulder.

Neither the asp nor the stiletto of widows rests in our light baskets . . . For us this whistling of the Century in progress and its streaming splendor

And its great cry of the sea as yet unheard!

The storm with the gentian eyes does not debase our dreams. And the unfurling of the drama itself, on our steps, will be for us only the seething of foam and the tongue of a beast at our bare ankles.

Curious, we watch for the first crack of the whip! The Sword which dances on the waters, as danced on the people's square, the Prince's daughter by the Prince admonished,

Holds nothing for us but a dazzling ardent dialectic,

As in the flaming heart of great family emeralds . . .

*

To him who dances the bibase in the seven halcyon days comes sickness, one evening, in the weak moment of the dance, and sudden disgust would overcome him,

Were it not for the entry of the massive chorus

Like the sea itself hammering the mound of its swell—a surge of idols tottering at the pace of horned masks.

Tomorrow, we shall don the high soles of the drama, and shall face, without jewels, the large euphorbias of the road; but this evening, our bare feet still in the sandals of childhood,

We go down to the last vale of childhood, towards the sea,

By bramble paths where old flakes of yellowing foam tremble, mingling with the feathers and down of old broodings.

Friendship! friendship to all those girls who once we were: with foam and wing and tearing of the wing over the waters, with the sparkling of salt, and that great laughter of immortal women on the brawling of the waters,

And ourselves, swimming within the immense robe

Of white feathers! . . . and all the immense green netting, and all the immense gold weaving, which weaves, under the waters, an age of amber and gold . . .

*

One evening color of squill and of field scabious, when the green turtle-dove of the cliffs raises at our frontiers its happy plaint of a water flute—the sea cineraria being no longer the leaf one fears and the bird of the high sea robbing us of its cry—

One evening warmer to our brows than our untied girdles, when the distant barking of the Fates goes to rest in the belly of the hills—Clelia the garden thrush being no longer the singer one fears and the sea being there which was with us from birth—

We have pronounced the hour more beautiful than when, in our mothers, were conceived the most beautiful daughters. Flesh this evening is without defect. And the ablution of heaven washes us, as though washing painted eyelids . . . Love, it is you! no fallacy!

Who did not love by day, will love this evening. And who is born to this evening, we shall hold him as accomplice for ever. Women call out in the evening. Doors open on the sea. And large solitary chambers glow, enfevered, from the torches of the setting sun.

Open, open to the sea-wind our jars of fragrant herbs! Fleecy plants thrive on the headlands and in the drifts of small shells. Blue monkeys, stuffed with prickly figs, come down the red rocks. And the man who cuts an offering bowl out of rock-crystal yields up his offering to the flaming sea.

High above, where someone calls, are the clear voices of women at our doors—the last evening!—and our gauze garments, on the beds, which the breeze visits. High above, the servant-maids go airing themselves, and our linen-women busying themselves with our lingerie for the night.

And the freshness of linen is on the tables, the silver of the last evening withdrawn from the travel chests . . . In our rooms open to the sea, evening plunges an idol's arm. And in the temples without rites where the sun of the dead piles its golden faggots, dusty mules stop at the arches of the courtyards.

*

. . . And this is the hour, O living women! when the sea-breeze yields its chance to the last breath of the land. The tree ringed like a slave opens its rustling frond. Our guests wander over the slopes looking for trails to the sea, women looking for lavender, and ourselves, washed in the evening's ablution . . . No threat on the brow of evening, except this great sea-sky with the whiteness of the snowy owl. Moon of mint in the East. Green star in the lower heaven, like the stallion which has tasted salt. And the man of the sea is in our dreams. Best of men, come and take! . . ."

VIII

Stranger, Whose Sail . . .

Stranger, whose sail has for so long moved along our coasts, (and at times, in the night, we hear the creaking of your pulleys),

Will you tell us what torment is yours which prompts you, one evening of great warmth, to set foot among us on the custom-ridden land?

*

"In bays of black marble streaked with white wings in the breeding season,

The sail was of salt, and light was the mark of the talon on the water. Then was so much sky a dream for us?

Scale, soft scale taken from the divine mask

And the smile far at sea, of the great sacred ills . . .

Freer than the feather which is cast from the wing,

Freer than love leaving with the departing evening,

You see your shadow, on the mature water, free at last of its age,

And you let the anchor make the law in the undersea eclogue.

A white feather on the black water, a white feather towards glory

Has done us suddenly this great hurt, of being so white and so strange, before evening . . .

Feathers drifting on the black water, spoils of the strongest,

Will they tell you, O Evening, who was fulfilled there?

The breeze blew from the highlands, with that taste of areca nut and dead hearths which for a long time travels.

The illustrious Ladies, on the capes, opened to the fires of the evening a nostril pierced with gold.

And gentle again was the sea in the steps of greatness.

Will the stone hand of destiny be offered us again? . . .

It is the criste-marine, on your beaches, which was ripening again

This taste of flesh, of all flesh the happiest,

And the earth crying out on its porous banks amid the avid brambles and live roses

Of the foam, was for us a light thing, a more costly thing

Than women's linen in dreams, than the soul's linen in dreams."

IX

Narrow Are the Vessels . . .

Lovers, O late-comers among the marbles and the bronzes, in the lengthening fires of evening,

Lovers who kept silent in the midst of alien crowds,

You too will testify tonight in honor of the Sea:

1

. . . Narrow are the vessels, narrow our couch.

Immense the expanse of waters, wider our empire

In the closed chambers of desire.

Summer enters, coming from the sea. To the sea only shall we say

What strangers we were at the festivities of the City, and what star rising from undersea festivities,

Hung one evening, over our couch, on the scent of the gods.

In vain the surrounding land traces for us its narrow confines. One same wave throughout the world, one same wave since Troy

Rolls its haunch towards us. On a far-off open sea this gust was long ago impressed . . .

And the clamor one evening was loud in the chambers: death itself, blowing its conchs, could not have been heard!

The vessels shall you love, O lovers, and the sea high in the chambers!

The land one evening mourns its gods, and man hunts rust-red badgers; cities wear down, women dream . . . May it always be at our door

That immense dawn called sea—*élite* of wings and levying of weapons; love and sea of the same bed, love and sea in the same bed—

and this dialogue again in the chambers:

2

1—

". . . Love, love, that holds so high the cry of my birth, how great a sea moving towards the Woman who loves! Vine trampled on all shores, blessing of foam in all flesh, and song of bubbles on the sands . . . Homage, homage to the divine Ardor!

You, avid man, unclothe me: master more calm here than on his deck the master of the ship. And so much clothing falls away, there is nothing of the woman that you have not greeted. Summer opens, which is fed by the sea. And my heart opens to you a woman fresher than green water: seed and sap of sweetness, acid mingled with milk, salt with vivid blood, and gold and iodine, and the flavor too of copper with its essence of bitterness—all the sea borne in me as in the maternal urn . . .

And on the shore of my body man born of the sea lies stretched out. May he refresh his face even at the spring beneath the sands; and rejoice on my soil, like the god tattooed with male fern . . . My love, are you thirsty? I am woman at your lips keener than thirst. And my face in your hands as in hands fresh from shipwreck, ah! may there be for you in the warm night freshness of almond and flavor of dawn, and first awareness of fruit on the foreign shore!

I dreamt, the other evening, of islands greener than any dream . . . And sailors landed on the shore in search of blue water; they saw—it was ebb-tide—the new-made bed of streaming sands: an arborescent sea had left there, as it sank, its pure capillary prints, like those of great tortured palms, or of tall enraptured girls laid down in tears among their loin-cloths and unbraided tresses.

And these are figures of a dream. But you, man of upright brow, inhabiting the reality of the dream, you drink right from the round mouth, and know its punic lining: flesh of pomegranate and heart of prickly pear, fig of Africa and fruit of Asia . . . Fruits of woman, O my love, are more than fruits of the sea: from me not painted nor adorned, receive an earnest of the Sea Summer . . ."

*

2—

". . . In the heart of man, solitude. Strange the man, shoreless, near the woman, herself a shore. And myself a sea at your orient, as if mingled with your golden sand, may I go once more and linger on your shore, in the slow unrolling of your coils of clay—woman who forms and unforms with the wave that engenders her . . .

And you, more chaste for being more naked, clothed by your hands alone, you are no Virgin raised from the depths, Victory of bronze or white stone recovered, with the amphora, in the great meshes laden with seaweed by the workers; but woman's flesh before my face, woman's warmth in my nostrils, and woman's whole radiance, her aroma, like the rose flame of fire between half-joined fingers.

And as salt is in the wheat, the sea in you in its essence, the thing in you which was of the sea, has given you that taste of a happy woman to whom I come . . . And your face is upturned, your mouth is fruit to be consumed, in the hull of the bark, in the night. Free my breath on your throat, and from everywhere the rising of seas of desire, as in the full tides of the closest moon, when the female land opens to the salacious, supple sea, adorned with bubbles even in its ponds, its maremmas, and the sea high in the grass makes the sound of a noria, the night bursts with sea-hatchings . . .

O my love who tastes of the sea, may others graze their eclogues far from the sea, in the depth of the sealed valleys—mint, melissa, and melilot, warmth of alyssum and marjoram—and there one talks of bee-keeping, another deals with lambing, and the felt-padded ewe kisses the earth at the foot of the walls dusted with black pollen. When the peaches are set, and the ties for the vine are sorted, then have I cut the knot of hemp which holds the hull on the ways, in its cradle of wood. And my love is on the seas! and my burning is on the seas! . . .

Narrow are the vessels, narrow the alliance; and narrower still your measure, O faithful body of the beloved . . . And what is this body itself, save image and form of the ship? nacelle and hull, and votive vessel, even to its median opening, formed in the shape of a hull, and fashioned on its curves, bending the double arch of ivory to the will of sea-born curves . . . The builders of hulls, in all ages, have had this way of binding the keel to the set of frames and planking . . .

Vessel, my fine vessel, that yields on its timbers, and bears the burden of a man's night, you are to me a vessel bearing roses. You break the chain of offerings on the water. And here we are, against death, on the black acanthus paths of the scarlet sea . . . Immense is the dawn called sea, immense the expanse of the waters, and on the earth turned to dream, on our purple confines, all the distant swell that rises and crowns itself with hyacinths like a people of lovers!

There is no higher usurpation than in the vessel of love."

3

1—

". . . My teeth are pure under your tongue. You weigh on my heart and govern my limbs. Master of the bed, O my love, like the Master of the ship. Gentle the helm at the touch of the Master, gentle the wave in his power. And it is another woman, within, who moans with the rigging . . . One same wave throughout the world, one same wave reaching to us, in the very great distance of the world and of its age . . .

And such a surge, from all sides, that rises and finds its way up into us . . .

Ah! do not be for me a master hard in his silence and in his absence: most skillful pilot, too thoughtful lover! Take, take from me more than your own giving. Loving, will you not also wish to be the beloved? . . . I am afraid, and anxiety dwells under my breast. Sometimes, the heart of man wanders far away, and beneath the arch of his eye there is, as within the high solitary arches, this great stretch of the Sea upright at the gates of the Desert . . .

O you, haunted like the sea, by distant major things, I have seen your joined eyebrows seeking beyond woman. Does the night through which you steer hold no island, no shore? Who then in you always becomes estranged and denies himself?—But no, you have smiled, it is you, you come to my face, with all that great clarity of shadow like a great destiny on the march over the waters (O sea suddenly struck with light between its great spaces of yellow and green clay, like broad seeded fields!). And I, lying on my right side, hear your nomad blood beating against my bare woman's breast.

You are here, my love, and I have no place save in you. The source of my being I will raise towards you, and to you will I open my woman's night, clearer than your man's night; and in me the grandeur of loving will perhaps teach you the grace of being loved. License then for the body's play! Offering, offering, and favor of being! For you night opens a woman: her body, her havens, her shore; and her primeval night where all memory lies. May love make of her its lair!

. . . Narrow is my head between your hands, narrow my brow encircled with iron. And my face to be consumed like fruit from beyond the seas: mango oval and yellow, flaming rose, which Asian runners over the stone of imperial highways carry to lay, one evening, before midnight, at the foot of a taciturn Throne . . . Your tongue is in my mouth like wildness of the sea, the taste of copper is in my mouth. And our food in the night is no food of darkness, nor our drink, in the night, water from a cistern.

You will tighten the grip of your hands on my lover's wrists, and my wrists will be, in your hands, like as the wrists of an athlete in their leather bands. You will bear my joined hands back behind my head; and we will also join our foreheads, as for the accomplishment of great things in the arena, of great things in the sight of the sea, and I myself will be your crowd in the arena, among the fauna of your gods.

Or free are my arms! . . . and my hands hold license among the harness of your muscles: over all the high relief of the back, over all the moving knot of the loins, a racing quadriga of your strength like the very musculature of the waters. I will praise you with my hands, O power! and you, nobility of a man's flank, wall of honor and pride which, stripped, still bears the mark of armor.

The falcon of desire strains on its leather leash. Love with joined eyebrows bends above its prey. And I have seen the change in your face, predator! as happens to the ravishers of offerings in the temples, when the god's anger descends on them . . . You, god, our passing guest, salacious Conger of desire, ascend in us again the course of the waters. The copper obol is on my tongue, the sea flames in the temples, and love thunders in the conchs like the Monarch in the Council-chambers.

Love, love, alien face! Who opens to you the sea-ways deep in us? Who takes the helm, and from what hands? . . . Hasten to the masks, O precarious gods! cover the exodus of the great myths! Summer, crossed with autumn, bursts in the over-heated sands its eggs of bronze marbled with gold where monsters and heroes grow. And the sea in the distance smells strongly of copper and the odor of the male body . . . Sea-alliance is our love, rising to the Gates of Red Salt!"

*

2—

". . . Lover, I will raise no roof for the Beloved. Summer hunts with the boarspear across the ploughed plains of the sea. Desire whistles above the aerie. And I, like the hawk of the shores reigning over its prey, have covered with my shadow all the radiance of your body. Celestial decree, that binds us! And the time is past, O proffered body, for raising in my hands the offering of your breasts. A place of lightning and of gold overwhelms us with its glory! Wages of embers, not of roses . . . And was ever a maritime province, beneath its roses, so expertly pillaged?

Your body, O royal flesh, matures the signs of the Sea's summer: flecked with moons and moondust, dotted with honey and dark wine colors, and filtered like sand through the sieves of gold washers—enameled with gold and caught in the nets of great luminous seines that drag in clear water. Royal flesh, and sealed with a divine seal! . . . From the nape of the neck to the arm-pit, to the hollow of the knees, and from the inner thigh to the ocher of the ankles, I will seek, brow lowered, the occult cipher of your birth, among the assembled symbols of your natal order—like those stellar numerations which rise, each evening, from the undersea tables and drift slowly westward to join in the panegyrics of the Sky.

Summer, burner of barks and of resins, mixes with the amber of woman the perfume of black pines. Tan of woman and glowing of amber are the scent and bite of July. Thus the gods, prey to an ailment which is not ours, turn to the gold of lacquer as though sheathed in women's skin. And you, robed in such a lichen, are naked no longer: flank adorned with gold, and thighs polished like the thighs of a hoplite . . . Praise to you, tall body veiled by its own radiance, stamped like gold fresh from the mint of the Kings! (And who has not dreamt of laying bare those great ingots of pale gold, wrapped in the softest doeskin, which voyage towards the Courts, in the ships' stores, under their bands of heavy hemp and their network of wide rush straps?)

Ah! like Her who has drunk the blood of a royal person! yellow of the yellow of a priestess, and rose of the rose of great jars! You were born marked by the divine Standard. And what other flesh scorched at the fire of vine branches on the terraces has ever borne higher witness? Burned with love, the nape of the neck, ardent the hair where the fiery season dwelt, and the arm-pit seized with fever like ashes of roses in clay bowls. . . . You are like the bread offered on the altar, and bear the ritual incision heightened with the red mark . . . You are the idol of virgin copper, in the form of a fish, that is smeared with honey from the rocks and the cliffs . . . You are the sea itself in its luster, when noon, explosive and violent, spills the oil of its lamps.

You are also the nubile soul and the impatience of rosy fire in the widening basins of the sand; you are the aroma, and the warmth, and the very favor of sand, its breath, in the shadow feasts of the flame. You smell of immortal dunes and all unassigned shores between land and sea, where the dream, pale poppy, trembles. You are the exclamation of salt, and the divination of salt, when the sea has withdrawn afar over its porous tables. You are the scale, and the green fire, and the snake of green fire, at the base of schists foliated with gold, there where the myrtle and the dwarf oak and the wax shrub of the beaches descend to the sea's fire seeking their freckles of red lichen . . .

O woman, and fever made woman! lips which have known your ascent, bear no fragrance of death. Living—and who more alive?—you smell of green water and the reef, you smell of virgins and seaweed, and your sides are laved in the favor of our days. You smell of the stone spangled with stars and of copper heated in the lubricity of the waters. You are the stone laureled with algae in the wake of the swell, and you know the underside of the tallest sea-fronds encrusted with limestone. You sway with the wild oats and the sand millet and the marsh grass of the flooded beaches; and your breath is in the exhalation of straw towards the sea, and you move with the migration of sand towards the sea . . .

Drunk, very drunk, regal heart, from harboring such a swell, and the flesh more sensitive than the tissues of the eyes . . . You follow the sea, ineluctable and strong, in its work. And you feel the incoercible pulse, and are open—bound, unbound—to the dilation of the waters; and the retractable sea keeps pulsing in you its rings, its pupils, and the day contracts, and the night enlarges, the immense eye that possesses you . . . Homage! homage to the complicity of the waters. There, no offense to your soul! Like the violent spirit of the god who takes possession of the unborn man in the woman, and tramples the woman in her linens and divided membranes, ah! like the sea itself, devourer of kelp and embryos, and who casts before the assembly of Judges and Mothers her great placentary pouches and her great folds of kelp, her very large leather aprons for midwives and Sacrificers, may it please the sacred pleasure to rejoin its victim, and may the Woman lying in her floral sheaths deliver to the sea's night the bruised flesh of a great labiate! No offense there to her soul . . .

Immersion? submission! May the sacred pleasure flow in you, its dwelling! And the jubilation is high in the flesh, and spur to the flesh is the joy of the flesh. I have seen glistening between your teeth the red poppy of the goddesses. Love at sea burns its vessels. And you take delight in the divine ardor, as do the agile gods seen through the clear water, where the shadows move, releasing their light girdles . . . Homage, homage to the divine diversity! One same wave throughout the world, one same wave our course . . . Narrow the measure, narrow the caesura, which breaks the woman's body at the middle like an ancient meter . . . You will grow, license! The lubricious sea exhorts us and the odor of its basins lingers in our bed . . . Red as the red sea-urchins are the chambers of pleasure."

4

1—

". . . Cries of passion in the arena, sighs of passion in the night are but cooings of a storm in flight over the waters. Doves of storm and cliffs, and a heart that breaks on the sand, how much sea there still is in the tearful joy of the Woman who loves! . . . You, the Oppressor, who trample us, like coveys of quail and floods of migratory wings, will you tell us who calls us together?

Sea mingled in my voice and sea blended always in me, love, love that speaks loudly on the breakers and the coral reefs, will you allow measure and grace to the body of a woman who loves too much? Cry of woman, vintage in the press—cry of woman, joyous and unharmed . . . extend, O Master, my torment; draw out, O Master, my delight! What tender prey harpooned was ever to her joy so chastised?

Woman am I and mortal, in all flesh deserted by Love. For us the cruel team racing over the waters. May it trample us under its hoofs, and batter us with its ram, and with the bronze-studded pole may it strike us down! . . . And the Woman holds her Lover like a tribe of brutes, and the Lover holds the Woman like a *mêlée* of stars. And my body opens without decency to the Stallion of the rite, like the sea itself to the assaults of the lightning.

O Sea raised against death! How much love is marching through the world to an encounter with your horde! One single wave on its lever! . . . And you the Master, who command, you know the use of our weapons. And love alone holds in suspense, holds on its threatening stem, the tall wave curving and sleek on its painted cobra's throat.

No flute of Asia, swelling the bulb of its gourd, would appease the dilated monster. But tongue to tongue, and breath to breath, panting, her face streaming and her eyes devoured with acid, she who alone sustains the ardent controversy, the Lover, erect in wrath, who recoils, who bends taut, and stands fast, utters her hissing of lover and priestess . . .

Will you strike, divine staff?—Favor of the monster, my reprieve! and more strident, the impatience! . . . Death with beveled head, love with faired head darts its very frequent tongue. Incessant is its name; innocence is its hour. Hear death living—its cry of a cicada . . .

You will strike, promise!—More prompt, O Master, your answer, and stronger your summons! Speak louder, despot! and assail me more assiduously: irritation is at its height. Search farther, royal Conger: so does lightning on the sea seek the ship for a sheath . . .

You have struck, divine lightning!—Who in me gives this very great cry of a woman unweaned? . . . O splendor! O sadness! and the very tall comb of immortality crowning the radiant foam! and all this glory which flares out, golden harrow! . . . Did I haunt there the forbidden, and the heart of fable?

You, god, who were there, my guest, keep alive in me the helix of your rape. And may we also be ravished by this very long cry of the soul—not cried aloud! . . . Death, dazzling and vain, goes, with the step of mimes, to honor other beds. And the alien Sea, seeded with foam, engenders far off on other shores its parade chargers . . .

These tears, my Love, were not tears of a mortal woman."

*

2—

". . . Vessel which opens on its keel, illumined with embers and with gold, flaming brazier of the shipwreck! O splendor, O sadness! To haunt the Being, and so prompt! The sea is not more eager to consume its god . . .

Favor for Her who was there, and so briefly was there—ah! like One who drank blood from the royal cups and who no longer knows her caste nor her rank, but whose dream still remembers: "I frequented death, dazzling and vain, I conversed as an equal with the faceless lightning: and I, who know of the sea more than the living know, know also the ancient evil in its glade of yellow fire. He who dreams of the naked sword resting in clear waters, has not banished from the tale the torches and the tears . . ."

Tears of the loved one, O ill-loved one, do not have their source in the lover. Enmity to the jealous god who harvests your vine in my arms! Alien the hand which presses the grape between our faces. You, the undivided one, betrayed . . . Transgression, transgression, O sadness! To haunt the Being is but an act of a mime. Has someone then spoken? He could not be heard. The uninhabitable is our site, and intrusion yields no profit. But the pride of living is in the reaching, not in the using or having.

. . . You will rise again, Desire! And you will tell us your other name. O passion, royal highway, where the drunken King, escorted by the Blind, rises from the dust again! Desire, desire, who go before us and assist us, is that your only name and is there no other? . . . O you who cause the sand to cry far off on invisible thresholds, and make visible on the waters the approach of the message, O you, the Precursor and you the Annunciator, yours is the widest search, and your ways are numberless. You recover your breath before me. And always offering your weapon, will you always offer me the woman as arrow for the bow?

*

Tornadoes in the wake of desire, and lightning from all sides scattering its portents! The suction of the strong god is on the tumefied surface of the waters. The sea with its lophius-mask no longer weds the gloomy depth of things. Desire, O Master, live your work! . . . And the craggy sea of the dream, with great shafts of black glass, like vitrified lava, yields to the chisel its cubes, its trihedrals!

Go down, sculptor, great of heart—for the work is great—among your daughters, your laborers, and all your host of quarriers. O Dream, look again on your work: not the shield of the goldsmith, nor the mirror of chased silver overrun with the ignominy of roses (the leopard in the vineyard, the virgin on the bull's back, and the dolphin crowned with vine branches of foam),

But of a single mass and of a single block of jet, shiny and black, like a load of iron links in the packed holds of ships, all this powerful plexus of forces and of alliances: the sea, its ringbolts, its sphincters, and its millions of mouths closed on the ring of desire—or else the sea out of its bonds, in its great robe of a black mare slashed with wounds: fresh and lubricious openings!

. . . My love, I have better to say, and the gods have passed: of one surface and of one stretch, on the back of the swell, and on its long smooth tables of graphite, in the far appeasement of the most beautiful fields of gray poppies, I saw of a sudden the immovable sea, color of sediment: the sea far off like a Sudan dreaming of its black queens with their foreheads punctuated with blue . . .

*

. . . O woman, high in her flood as if taken in her course! I will rise again in arms in the night of your body, and will be streaming again with your sea years.

Close bound again the soul, at the incision of the body! And you, singing and stammering on your thorny bank, Sibyl open on her rock like the Erythrean virgin—great hydra of force and tenderness who disgorges her god—you will again frequent the truth of the dream: that other sea, most vast and nearby, that no one teaches or names.

Run your course, transient god. We are your relays! One same wave throughout the world, one same wave since Troy . . . The swell rises and is made woman. The sea with the belly of a loving woman kneads untiringly its prey. And love causes the singing, and the sea the rocking, of the cedar bed on its boards, of the curved hull on its joints. Our bed rich with offerings and with the burden of our works . . .

Virgin nailed to my prow, ah! like her who is immolated, you are the libation of the wine at the cutwater of the bow, you are the offering of the high seas to the dead who rock the living: the loose chain of red roses which opens over the waters after the rites of farewell—and the vessels of the trader will cut through the fragrant line in the night.

Desire, O Prince under the mask, you told us your other name! . . . And you the Loved One, again you whistle for your God your whistle of an osprey. And you, the Loved One, you will again arch yourself on your breath for the delivering of the cry—until that very soft utterance, guard it, and that lowest vowel that enlists the god . . . Submission, submission! . . . Submissive again to the question!

And who then has roused you again to violence, rearing on your wings, like the female eagle on its faggot of thorns. talon pressed against the flank of the Questioner? . . . O most powerful embattled briar backed against the rock, you hold higher than the sea your invective against death. Let love and the sea be heard! Birth and death in the same slings! . . . I have unleased the lightning, and its quest is not in vain. You will strike, divine lightning! . . . To haunt the Being is not a delusion. And the Woman who loves is no mime. Forked tree of the rape which the lightning ascends! . . .

—Thus She who has a name strikes at noon the dazzling heart of the waters: Ishtar, splendid and naked, spurred with lightning bolts and green eagles, in the great green gauzes of her driftwood fire . . . O splendor, not sadness! Love which triumphs and does not retreat! and the heart at last free from death! . . . You have given me this very great cry of a woman which lasts over the waters."

5

1—

". . . Laid at your side, like the oar in the bottom of the boat; rolled at your side, like the sail with the yard, lashed at the foot of the mast . . . A million bubbles more than happy in the wake and beneath the keel . . . And the sea itself, our dream, like a single vast umbel . . . And its million of flower heads and florets in course of dissemination . . .

Survival, O wisdom! Coolness of receding storm, bruised eyelids, with the blue of the storm . . . Open your palm, happiness of being . . . And who was there, of whom nothing remained but goodness? In me a step recedes which is not of a mortal. Far away voyage travelers whom we have not hailed. Pitch the tent impregnated with gold, O pure shadow of afterglow . . .

And the great silent wing which was thus, for so long a time, at our stern, still directs in the dream, still directs on the waters, our bodies which have so greatly loved each other, our hearts which have been so deeply moved . . . Afar, the course of the one last wave, tossing higher the offering of its bridle bit . . . I love you—you are here—and all the immense joy of being which here was consummated.

Go more gently, O course of things to their end. Death sails in death and has no care for the living. The salty night bears us in its flanks. And we loosen the clasp of our arms to listen to the sea without shores or reefs reigning in us. Passion very strong and very docile. A thousand favorable eyelids . . .

And the Woman who loves fans her eyelashes in all this very great calm. The level sea surrounds me and opens for me the fronds of its palms. I hear beating in the blood the steady, nourishing sap—O dream again that I nurse! And my lip is salty with the salt of my birth . . . You are here, my love, and I have no place save in you.

Smile of being in your breath, as in the shelter of the ship's canvas. The breeze is in the awning . . . May I be for you sweetness allied and tender grace on the waters: silence and vigil in your vigil and fluttering in the shadow of your lashes. For you my woman's brow and the perfume of the spouse at the line of the brow; for me this very strong beating of the blood in the medusa of man's heart.

And my left breast is in your hand, the seal of empire is seized! . . . Close your palm, joy of being . . . The hand which reigns on my hip governs afar the face of an empire, and the goodness of loving extends to all its provinces. May the peace of the waters be with us! and the opening, afar, between snow and sand, of a great coastal kingdom which bathes its white beasts in the waves.

And what am I, in the depth of clear waters, but the grave ease of a palm, which rocks itself, a sea-fan? I hear living in the night the great nameless thing . . . And the thorn of fear is absent from my flesh. The stone of the sill is along the sill, and the sea beyond the stone of the sill. Depth, heretical and vain, reprieved! Cause gained, sea conciliated. And the favor is shared far off, love is avid of its possessions.

You who have saved me from death, be praised, scatheless gods, for all this fulfillment which was ours, and all this great labor of love which you have traced in me, and all this very great cry of the sea which you have cried in me. Death which changes its tunic goes far away to nourish its host of believers. The sea seeded with foam assembles for us its parade chargers. And you whom I love are here. My heart, my body free of death, take them in your watch and care . . .

*

Blinds down and fires out, the house of timber sails like a trireme, and under the roof of light wood the rafters hold their alignment like a row of oars leveled for the flight. Fleeing, fleeing, with the flight of our ivory laths . . . The breeze is fresh in the blinds, and speaks a name fresher than Anchises; and the house breathes in its walls of straw . . . O vagrant soul, returning quest, tell us the road you follow, and what happy trireme you too are launching towards the dawn.

Who then in us voyages, who has no vessels on the sea? To life will there be no end? May no one die till he has loved!

We who cross the seas on our bed without oars or rigging, know that it has no end, this course of reversible things. Love and the sea and the sea lanes . . . The low-hung moon fills the lamps, the salt-flats. I have seen, slipping through our shutters, her sharp blade of an oyster-knife . . . Or is it the star Belus which nests in the palms, and cools the summer night with its coveys of blue icicles? Barefooted then on the wooden galleries and the slabs before the threshold . . . I have seen the first night open out and all its blue of true pearl.

The land and its black does descend to the low-tide marks of the sea. And the sea, with bare feet, withdraws over the sands. The continents edged with gold voyage in their haloes. The enlarged islands yield to the medal collection of the shores their great planed coins of polished wood, or of leather; and the half-opened pods, in the shape of hulls, which have emptied their cells, their basins, expose their partitions, white and dry, like rowers' benches. Floating seeds bury themselves where they come to rest. And from them grow trees for the cabinet-maker's art.

O dwelling, O branchiae between the sea of things and me . . . What is all this unknowable world where we love, among the submerged swells, as if on the late-flowering crests of flooded forests? . . . Tonight, the star is double and swells on the waters. Very large streaming planets rise from the sea like live swords without guard or hilt; and the sea flings back to us the blade of the gladiator. Companies without arms deploy in the stone gardens, as at the breaking up of great interracial celebrations where the happy conquerors, marriers of races on the beaches, took their pleasure.

It will rain before daylight. Night tears its bandlets. And on the rain-pecked sands no man will decipher the writing. The stone threshold is covered with pale arborescences, with omens. The deified beasts awaken in their urns. The horoscopes are drawn. Sea conciliated, cause gained. And the sea mists besiege the mouths of the cisterns, and on the ancient masonry bound with sea sand spread the stains of the divine infection. And tall white stones, their back to the wall, are licked by goats. Gone is the pain on its migrations. And I love; and you are here. There is no security as great as in the vessel of love.

. . . Now comes the breeze before the rain! Listen to the fall, on the roof, of these little palm nuts. We will gather them under our eaves, to be the ornament of the day, and I will show you how, shod with horn or ivory, set with claws and shells, they are turbaned in the style of the Indies . . . The sea-breeze is on the cays. The palm wine is in the palms. What other soul, suddenly, beats its wings captive in our straw hangings battened with rush, as are the sails, we are told, of the tall Asiatic ships?

. . . It is raining on the terraces and the channeled roofs: tiles take the color of horn and of nutmeg, color of sonorous stones for light drums and dulcimers. The earthen jar is under the eaves, and its haunch is happy. The sea shower falls on the tiles and on the threshold stone; falls in the outer basins and the varnished earthen vessels with Nubian women's lips. There, the Loved One will wash herself of her night of love; will wash her hips, and then her breasts and her face, will wash her thighs to the groin and to the fold of the groin. The star also will be washed there, the last to come and late weaned.

. . . It has rained, it is day. Moon color of alum. And the sky in the east takes on the color of a teal. Welcome to all grace! The Summer dawn is, on the sea, the first step of the Loved One naked, out of her linen dropped in circle around her. Issue of the sea, and by women, the woman's body born of woman . . . And she who for the night had kept her pearls born of the sea, will again ally herself with the century of coral . . . And perhaps it has not rained: so sweet, O rain, was your approach . . . And who would not doubt it, were it not for this delicate tracing of signs on the sands, like delicate bruises on the flanks of your mothers?

*

Morning washed like the spouse. And color restored to the world: mediator and propitiator! The sea is there, that is no longer dream. And may it be given an ovation! as to the sea of noon itself, which bathes her lion cubs behind the pepper plants in flower . . . I know that a multitude of small medusae, in the shape of ovaries, of matrices, already fills the night of coves brought to light. And the sea grape is visited by small nocturnal rodents. Very tall fragrant trees turn in grace towards the sea. And all beasts covered with parasites, curry themselves against bars of the lagoons. And the sea rolls up to us its round dolls of white coral. The seekers of ambergris, on their ambling horses, alone scour the very long renewed beaches. The gatherers of quail bend towards the grottoes and in the hollows of the coast.

And here is gathered also, for the approaches of temples and for places of refuge, that little dry seaweed for bedding called posidony. And the women who sort lentils, capped with long visors of leaves, seat themselves at tables on the stone tiers and on the jutting rocks in the shape of counters. At the points of the islands are the terns which mix with the oyster-catchers. And the magnetic needle of happiness holds straight on the submerged sands its heavy arrow of massive gold. A blue fish, of a goldsmith's blue, which veers towards the green of malachite loved by the great Nomads, cruises alone, in clear water, like a votive vessel . . .

Welcome! welcome! to all our guests —O Kinsmen! . . . May the same palm be extended to all! And you whom I love are here. The peace of the waters be with us! . . . and sleep also, that for the Woman who loves, lays itself open to the censure of broad daylight . . .

There is no security so great as in the sleep of the Woman who loves . . .

*

2—

". . . Solitude, O heart of a man! Does She who falls asleep on my left shoulder know all the depth of the dream's abyss? Solitude and shadows at the high noon of man . . . But also secret spring for the Loved One: like the spring under the sea where stirs that mist of sand and gold . . .

You shall withdraw, desire, so I may know also the woman's brow bared to me. Sweet the woman to the man's nostrils, and sweet in the talons of the mind . . . O vagrant soul, returning guest, shall you tell us the shore that you follow, and if you need, favor, this flexible neck of a woman to make your way to us?

She who breathes in my breath and sighs at my face this very pure and childlike sigh, opens before me the wake of her grace, and from her so docile lip to her brow of a deva, more naked than woman, offers her unknown face like the other side of satellite moons.

O of all faces sweet to see, the sweetest watched over . . . In the pure oval of sweetness where so much grace keeps countenance, what other grace, more distant, tells us of woman more than Woman? And by Whose mercy do we receive of woman this favor of loving?

Savor of virgin in the lover, favor of lover in the woman, and you, perfume of spouse at the line of the brow, O woman taken in her aroma, woman taken in her essence, lips that have known your scent bear no fragrance of death . . . More incorruptible, O grace, than is the rose captive in the lamp.

And due to you, gold lights up in the fruit, and the immortal flesh tells us its heart of rosy saffron; and due to you, the nocturnal water keeps presence and savor of soul, as in the white inner tissues, without stain, of the great pharaoh palms, at the very pure, very silk place of their detachment.

*

. . . O you who, in sleep, go repudiating your mortal part,

You are to me promise in the Orient that will be redeemed at sea, and you are to me the strangeness in the sail and the vellum of the dream, and you swing with the yard on the great arc of the sky color of rosy red mullet. Or better, you are the sail itself, its office, and, of the sail, the pure idea—very chaste speculation of the spirit on the area of sail and the sail design . . .

You are to me the approach of morning and to me the newness of day, you are to me freshness of the sea and freshness of dawn beneath the milk of Aquarius, when the first rosy mist is reflected in the water mirror of the sands, and the green star of morning, titulary Princess of day, descends with bare feet the green terraces of the sky to give alms to childhood at the curled brow of waters . . .

You are to me the transparent waters of awakening and premonition of the dream, you are the invisible itself in the spring, at the place of its emission, like the invisible itself in the flame, its essence, at the place very pure and safe, where the frail heart of the flame is a ring of sweetness . . .

You are an eater of petals and are flesh of the beach amaryllis, you have tasted salt in the palms of the Lover and have fed him the rice of your rice fields. You are the innocence of fruit in a strange land; the grain gathered on Barbarian soil; the seed sown on the deserted coast for the voyage of return . . .

O woman taken in her course, and who follow between my arms like the night through the springs, who then in me descends the flood of your weakness? Are you to me the river, are you to me the sea? or indeed the river in the sea? Are you to me the voyaging sea itself, which no one entering twice has ever twice found the same? . . .

Happy the curve inscribed in the pure delight of the woman who loves.

*

. . . She who flows over my left shoulder and fills the haven of my arm, sheaf fragrant and free, not bound (and very silken to my touch was the story of those happy temples),

She who rests on her right hip, her closed face against me (and so tall vases voyage in their cradles of very tender wood and on their saddles of white felt),

She who stirs in the dream against the rising of shadows (and I have raised the awning against the sea spray and the night dew, and the sail is set towards the clearest waters),

She, sweeter than sweetness in the heart of the man without alliance, to me is a load, O woman, lighter than a load of spices, of aromatics—very precious seed and incorruptible freight in the vessel of my arms . . .

*

Go more softly, O step on my roof, like a woman's bare feet on the deck. The sky at sea gives its milk, and it is again the sweetness of a dawn under the milk of Aquarius.

I watch along and I am troubled: carrier of woman and of woman's honey, like a vessel carrier of African wheat or wine from Baetica. And it is still vigil in the East, the hour porous to our thought.

The teredo of death is in the wood of the bed, is in the keel of the boat. But love knocks more loudly on the paneling of dreams. And I hear the night torn on the cutwater of a prow.

As the June sea breathes in the chambers—and She who loves moves her lashes under the flail of dream—behold the sea itself in flower under the first shower of the day.

I know, I saw: mixed with grasses and holy oils, between its great black dilated mallows and its sparkling patches raised from the abyss, swaying, pressing the happy mass of its fronds,

And of a single luxuriant swell, as of a single stamping tread of women treaders of wine, soon trampled, all the sea trampled in vain, and which falls and rises, very slow lactation, at the very breast of Being, its constancy . . .

The wind in the East is on the new water, wrinkling of newborn flesh. The low-hung moon over the dunes pursues afar the white otters of childhood. The night keeps its woman's hands in our hands . . .

She who still sleeps in daylight, the sea's night is on her face, mirror of a faceless dawn. And I watch on her shore, gnawed by a star of sweetness . . . I shall have for her who does not hear

words that of man are not words.

*

. . . O Voyager coming to me from your woman's night, and who awakens in profane hands, like the daughter of an immortal raised by the shoulders out of the mother foam, who else are you for me in day, and all this darkening of the Being, under its bark?

You were being born, I was watching . . . You sleeping one lying under the burden of your arms and under the shield of your breasts, you smiled, guarded from evil, entrusted to my hands, like a daughter of high birth who is sent across the sea—and now you awaken, forehead marked with a sacred frown; and what further presage opens up to you its route of mauve wild saffron?

Rest, O troubled heart. There is no threat nor peril. On your weakness have I founded, and on your grace, composed. The sovereignty of loving exerts itself at last against doubt and quibbling. And are you not of those to whom the sea voice has made itself heard? "May no woman find her fear reflected in the mirror of my waters!"

Outside, the sky breathes through its salt-crystaled gills. The summer night takes in its sails and calls home its boats rigged with wings. The moon finds appeasement in the wine of mallows. And the servant lying back on her rush mat welcomes at the end of the gulf the great celestial figurations on the way to immersion.

Dawn is on the step of the forges; distant the town and all its people with dark-circled eyes like the dead. The vessels swing at anchor. The guards have released the chains of the outer harbor. And the horn lanterns go out in the taverns.

You will be well received, O first visiting swell that loves the hulls in the basins, and the masts, deep in the port, like arrows in a quiver. Those who have died a violent death go down the estuaries with the water hyacinths. Childhood and its yellow dogs desert the families. And far in the distance the sea of Jason feeds its carnivorous plants . . .

Love, O grave regained under the censure of full daylight . . . Do not rob me, light! of that favor of love in all things, as of the wind in the sail . . . Narrow are the vessels, narrow our couch. And from having so long, in the night, bent the arch of tenderness, shall we keep against the day that curve of body and of shoulder that is slow to come undone,

as happens to those who for a long time within the faithful curve of a narrow hull have lain? . . ."

6

1—

". . . A little before daybreak and the swords of day, when the sea-dew covers the marbles and the bronzes, and the distant barking from the camps shakes the petals from roses in the city, I saw you, you were lying awake, and I feigned sleep.

Who then in you always becomes estranged, with the daylight? And your abode, where is it? . . . Will you go tomorrow on the alien sea without me? Who then is your host, far from me? Or what silent Pilot mounts alone to your deck, from that seaward side whence no one boards?

You whom I have seen reaching far beyond my haunch, like a watcher bent on the brim of the cliffs, you do not know, you have not seen, your face of a peregrine eagle. Will the bird carved in your face, pierce the mask of the lover?

Who then are you, new Master? Towards what reaching, where I have no part? and on what border of the soul raising yourself like some barbarian prince on his mass of saddlery; or like that other, among the women, scenting the acidity of weapons?

How can one love, love with a woman's love, him for whom no one can do anything? And of love what does he know, who can only watch, in the miracle of the forehead, this sole happiness of woman he is creating? . . .

Here is the truth. The wind rises. And the strigil of the athlete already curries the coursing waters. The Sea in arms always commands! . . . Is there no love so great that it does not yearn for action?—love, love, which is so great only at the time of its desertion . . .

The eagles this night were not with the armies. A quivering of arms beneath the sand and the stone of the doorsill . . . And always, at your door, the same neighing wave, with the same gesture offering, by its two shafts held high, the same specter of the arrogant bit.

From the sea too, did you know? there comes to us at times this great terror of being alive. And anguish then is in the woman's breast like the horned viper of the sands. Curlews of the heart, fears of the Woman who loves, there is no peril greater than in the sleep of the Woman who loves.

He who, in the night, crosses the dune of my body and goes off, bare-headed, towards the terraces to question Mars ruddy and strong as a ship's running lights on the sea, I say he has of woman neither the usage nor the care . . .

*

. . . Solitude, O heart of a man! will the high sea borne in you feed more than dream? The alabaster night opens its urns to sadness, and through closed chambers of your heart I have seen lamps moving without their guardians.

Where you are? says the dream. And you have no answer: bent over your pain like a navarch's son, deprived of vessels, who has built in view of the sea on the deserted coast—and his bed looks out, all bays opened, on the expanse of the waters.

Where are you? says the dream. And you live far off, you see far off that line which moves and cries madness: the sea, far off, an uneven soul, like an army without a master encumbered with soothsayers . . . And what do I still know of the routes that lead to you?

Do not be to me a Master harsh in his silence and in his absence. O loving face, far from the threshold . . . Where do you fight so far away that I am not there? For what cause that is not mine? And what are your arms whose face I have not washed?

I am afraid, and you are not here. The wife is alone and threatened, the Woman who loves is scorned. Where are your emissaries, your guards? Will the deserted wife also be betrayed? . . . Who holds the siege by the sea? The intrigue is on the seafront. You have secret speech with the enemy. And who, then, introduces the Stranger in the square?—The Sea is there, which gives no name. And makes the round of the house. The investment nears its end. The crowd is in the chambers. The wife is no longer guarded from promiscuity . . . And these are not, on our doorsill, the steps of aged nurse or grandmother, but the Sorceress has been brought in. She who is let in through the kitchens and the quarters of the women oyster-shellers. May she open her veins in the chamber and not approach your bed! Sea adulteress and sorceress, who opens her green skirts here for you, and offers me her green potions to drink. And like two accomplices we bathe in the green eyes of the Thessalian woman—threat and shame for the Woman who loves.

Beneficent gods, terrestrial gods! Will you not take the side of the Woman who loves against the sea? . . . And you, heart of a man who is not cruel, may Heaven also absolve you of your force!

*

. . . You whom I have seen asleep in my woman's warmth, like a nomad rolled tightly in his woolen rug, may you remember, O my lover, all those chambers open on the sea where we have loved.

Our beds undone, our hearts laid bare, think of all that beating of storms and of high seas which was our very blood, in search of the avowal; of all those burnt-out stars that we carried out to the sea before daylight, walking barefooted among the myrtles like ritual murderers with the bloody hands of sacred bards; of so many wasted moons that we threw from the top of the capes into flights of predatory gulls.

Loving also is action! I call death to witness, to whom alone love is an offense. And our foreheads are adorned with the red salt of the living! My love, do not go away towards the cities, where old men weave the straw of crowns. Neither glory nor power is well founded save at the height of man's power. And love in the desert consumes more purple than was used to clothe the fall of Empires.

Neither go far from me on the uncertain sea. There is no sea, nor hour, nor action, where woman cannot live, your servant. And the woman is in the man, and in the man is the sea, and love sails far from death on all the seas. But what do we know of the forces that unite us? . . . Hear my wing beat, captive, in your wing—appeal to the male osprey from his unweaned companion!

I am afraid, and I was cold. Be with me against the night of the cold—as on the mound of the Kings, facing the sea, and for the rite of the solstice, the red star fastened by the priest to its post of black perforated stone . . . Hold me tighter against doubt and the ebb-tide of death. Look at me, Powerful One! at this princely part of the brow, between the eyes, where with a very vivid brush is affixed the vermilion red of the sacred sign.

Captured the god! And fealty sworn! . . . Do not withdraw. Be there! May no one in you dream or become a stranger! And she who, lying on her right side, kept vigil of a mortal, will again raise herself at man's side for that great laughter of the immortals which binds us both to the dissipation of the waters . . . And my prayer then to the mute gods: may one same width of sea, to one same width of dream, unite us, one day, in the same death!

There is no action greater, nor prouder, than in the vessel of love."

*

2—

". . . Weapons broken in the heart of dawn—O splendor! O sadness!—and the sea afar ineligible . . . A man has seen vases of gold in the hands of the poor. And I wandered in the same dream, following the narrow human shore.

Neither traitor, nor perjuror. Have no fear. Vessel bearing woman is not vessel which man abandons. And my prayer to the gods of the sea: keep, O gods, the very chaste sword of a man's heart always crossed with woman.

My love, our race is strong. And the sea between us traces no frontier . . . We will go forth on the strong-smelling sea, the obol of copper between our teeth. Love is on the sea, where the vineyards are greenest; and the gods run to the green grapes, and bulls with green eyes bearing on their backs the most beautiful girls on the earth.

There I shall wash my nomad's linen, and this too populous heart of man. And there may the hours be such that we would beg them to voyage with us: like daughters of great houses when they embark without servants—ease of manners and very high tone, honor and fever of the soul!

Lovers, we are not men of the plough nor harvest hands. For us the high free wave that no one harnesses or compels. And for us, on the new water, all the novelty of living, and all the great freshness of being . . . O gods, who in the night see our faces uncovered, you have not seen painted faces or masks!

*

When we will have raised our laths of thin wood, an entire century of the drama will have spread its new hangings. Someone at last has made himself heard! What whinnying of a white stallion has caused this tremor of a loving woman to course, with the breeze, over the robe of the waters?

We shall go down to the half-closed bays where in the morning they wash the young animals in heat, still all sticky from the first flow of vaginal sap. And we shall swim again abreast, before raising anchor, on those shoals of clear water, checkered with azure and gold, where our shadows come together in the same breadth of dream.

The wind is rising. Hasten. The sail flaps along the mast. Honor is in the canvas; and impatience on the waters like fever in the blood. The breeze leads to the blue of the open sea its snakes of green water. And the pilot reads his course between the great patches of mauve night, color of eye shadows and bruises.

. . . Loved ones, I have dreamed so much of the sea on all our lovers' beds! and for so long a time the Intruder has, on our sills, trailed her robe of a Stranger, like the hem of a skirt under the doors . . . Ah! may one single wave throughout the world, the same wave, gather you all, companions and girls of all ranks, living and dead of every blood!

*

. . . And the sea comes to us from all sides, at the height of a man, pushing, raising the serried swarm of young waves, like a thousand brides' heads . . . Roses, says the legend, roses that caught fire in the hands of the Ravisher, will you envy me Her who passes with me through the door of quicklime, on the stairs of the port?

Of the best of our grain, of the best of our fruit, this flesh, O woman, was made. The black salts of the earth still powder her sealed lashes. Spirits of lavender, waters of citron rind will reveal more, on the sea, of her soul of green salt. And love on the deck dons sandals of red leather . . . "Ayah, the ship's goat, will give you her milk . . . The monkey has carried your pearls into the rigging . . ."

—Mortal? Ah! more greatly loved for being in peril! . . . You do not know, you do not know, O Fates, for the most secret heart of a man, the great price of that first line on the noblest part of a woman's calm brow. "Keep," said the man in the tale, "keep, O non-mortal Nymph, your offer of immortality. Your island is not mine where the tree sheds no leaves; neither does your couch move me, where man does not face his destiny."

Rather the couch of humans, honored by death! . . . I will exhaust the road of mortal man—perils of the sea and misfortunes—and will guard from the evil thorn Her who takes shelter under my sail. Perishable hands, sacred hands! you renew for me the dignity of conquering. Loving, I go where death goes, adventurous and vain. O free laughter of the Lovers, and the arrogance of ardent living, as on the sea, unseizable and brief, that great tremor of honor where skims the sail under its reefs! . . .

*

. . . Fine weather at sea, two pure lines on the very pure brow; and great blessing of the loving Woman over the waters. She whose heart feeds the innocence of the day, and brings to the indigent her bowl of sweetness; she who carries her love like lamps forgotten in full daylight; she who has spoken the truth in me, and who will ransom me from men of Barbary, that one, stronger than sweetness, has said to me more of woman than of woman is known. And the sea holds in us high caste of living beings.

Narrow are the vessels, narrow our couch. And through you, loving heart, all the closeness of loving, and through you, unquiet heart, all that which is beyond loving. Listen to the whistling, louder than the sea, of the horde of migrating wings. And you, new force, passion higher than loving, what other sea do you open before us, where vessels are of no use? (Thus I saw one day, between the islands, the fervent migration of bees, crossing the course of the ship, fasten for one instant in the high rigging the fierce swarm of a very numerous soul in search of its habitation . . .)

Terrible and secret Lovers, O silent Lovers, O you whom no sleep defiles, may the Sea have you in its power! . . . The world runs on to its renewing of foundations—sages torn under the prow, seed of lightning on every crest, and all the joyous disorder of the non-fallible drama. For us the inveterate sea of the dream, called real, and its great imperial highways bearing afar the alliance, and its great laws of irreverence bearing afar revelation; for us, O very prodigal face, the immense hive of the future, richer in cells than the Desert's cliffs studded with idols. And our waiting is no longer vain, and the offering is woman! . . .

Lovers! Lovers! where are our peers? We go forward, facing the night, with a star on our shoulder like the gerfalcon of the Kings! Behind us all this wake which grows and still draws milk at our poop, memory in flight and sacred way. And turning again towards the receding land and towards its multitude of balusters, we cry to it, O land, our lack of faith in its custom and in its ease; and of the sea we say that it leaves no powder nor ashes in the hands of the user.

With no office are we charged, being accredited by no one—neither princes nor legates of Empire, at the point of peninsulas, to attend the Royal Star in its setting at sea; but alone and free, without bail or bond, and having no part in the testimony . . . A golden trireme rows, each evening, towards that chasm of splendor where all the wreckage of history and the painted pottery of dead ages are thrown to oblivion. The gods go naked to their works. The sea of unnumbered torches raises for us a new splendor, like the scales of a black fish.

Lovers! Lovers! Who knows our course? . . . In the City they will say: "Let search be made for them! They go astray! And their absence wrongs us." But we: Where then is the abuse? The gods go blinded on the black water. Happy those who stray at sea! And of the Sea also may it be said: happy she who has strayed! . . . One same wave throughout the world, one same wave among us, raising, rolling the hydra enamored of its force . . . And from the divine heel, that very strong pulsation, which rules everywhere . . . Love and sea of the same bed, love and sea in the same bed . . .

Homage, homage to the divine veracity! And long memory on the sea for a nation of Lovers in arms!"

7

Comes winter, the sea hunting, night ascends the estuaries, the votive ships sway in the arches of the sanctuaries. Horsemen in the East have appeared, their horses color of wolf's hair. Carts loaded with bitter kelp mount slowly to the fields. And the grounded vessels are visited by small sea otters. The strangers come from the sea will be subjected to census.

My love, I have seen the sea barring your eyes like the eyes of the Egyptian woman. And the pleasure barks are pulled under the porches, by the alleys bordered with conchs, with whelks; and the damaged terraces are invaded by a late-blooming mass of small sand lilies. The storm gathers its black robes and the sky drags its anchors. The high dwellings on the headlands are stayed up with the beams. The cages of dwarf birds are brought indoors.

*

Comes winter, the sea straying, earth shows its knee bones. Pitch and tar are burned in the iron basins. It is time, O Cities, to adorn the gates of Cybele with the figure of the ship. And the time has also come to honor the iron on the two-horned anvil. The sea is in the sky of men and in the migration of roofs. Ropemakers walk backward in the harbor moats, and pilots without ships rest on their elbows in the taverns, geographers inquire about the coastal routes. Will the Magistrates in charge of foreigners tell you the hiding place of the Lovers?

Once again, O dream, speak the truth. Deliveries of driftwood pass the gates of the city. The Masters of the houses lay in supplies of salt. The daughters of great houses change their linen before the hearth, and the yellow flame beats its wings like a sea bird of prey in an iron cage. In the chambers they burn, on shovels, the hollow shreds of a dried bark. And the sea traffic pours its specie in the courtyards of family banks, the yoked beasts sniff the bronze of fountains—jingling of alloys in the chambers, abaci and counting boards behind the latticed doors—and here is a foreign currency in the shape again of a small boat, or of a woman's shoe . . . By the testimony of coins history and chronicles are clarified.

*

Comes winter, the flies dead, great green fabrics with red designs are lifted from theater trunks. Women who dress the dead are among the *figurantes* engaged in theaters. And the sea smelling of latrines, still inhabits the angle of old walls. The crowd marches, mixed with bone, in the clamor again of the conchs of September . . . My love, what other sea in us is immersed and closes its hellebore rose? Will the yellow stains of summer be erased from the women's brows? Here the depth of things rises to the light: drums of the blind in the alleys and powder on the walls skirted by the poor man. The crowd is vain, and the hour vain, where go the men without vessels.

O dream again, speak the truth. Comes winter, the stars are strong, the City shines with all its fires. Night is the passion of men. Voices are raised in the depths of the courtyards. The asp of the lamps is in the chambers, the torch avid in its ring of iron. And the women are painted for the night with the pale red of coral. Bemused their eyes, barred by the sea. And those of them who open themselves, in the chambers, between their golden knees, raise to the night a very soft plaint, memory and sea of the long summer— On the closed doors of the Lovers nail the image of the Ship!

*

. . . One same wave throughout the world, one same wave throughout the City . . . Lovers, the sea follows us! Death is not. The gods hail us in the port. And from under our beds we pull our largest family masks.

CHORUS

Sea of Baal, Sea of Mammon . . .

1

"Sea of Baal, Sea of Mammon—Sea of every age and every name,

O Sea without age or reason, O Sea without haste or season,

Sea of Baal and of Dagon—first face of our dreams,

O Sea promise of forever and the One who exceeds every promise,

Sea anterior to our song—Sea ignorance of the future,

O Sea memory of the longest day, as though endowed with madness,

Lofty vision directed over the expanse of things and over the course of Being, its measure! . . .

*

We invoke you, Wisdom, and involve you in our oaths,

O great in separation and difference, O great of great caste and high of high rank,

To yourself your race, your country, and your law; to yourself your people, your *élite,* and your masses,

Sea without regency or guardianship, Sea without arbiter or council, and without quarrel of investiture:

Invested from birth, imbued with your prerogative; established in your titles and your regalian rights,

And seated at ease in your imperial robes, to hold discourse, far and wide, on the ways of greatness, and to dispense, far and wide,

Your great rules of being, as favors of empire and domanial graces.

*

Were we sleeping, and yourself, Presence, when was dreamed for us such unreason?

We approach you, Table of the Great, our hearts wrung with human narrowness.

Must we cry out? must we create?—Who creates us in that instant? And against death itself is there nothing else but creating?

We select you, Site of the Great, O singular vicinity! Circus of honor and growth, field of acclamation!

And what now, we beg you, is this

alliance without return and this audience without recourse?

Better to burn, on the shores round you, a hundred leprous Kings with gold crowns,

Mass of honor and indigence and pride of men without appeal.

*

Free rein to your glory, Power! O Pre-established and Suzerain! . . . Immense is the district, plenary the jurisdiction;

And it is enough for us, within your province, to beg for usage and franchise,

O Sea without guards or enclosures, O Sea without vines or crops, over which falls the crimson shadow of the Great!

Seated on your stone confines like dogs with monkey heads, gods crossed with clay and sadness,

On all the gullied slopes, on all the sun-scorched slopes the color of faeces burnt white,

We dreamt of you, ultimate Session! and for you we had this dream of a higher instance:

The assembly, in long folds, of the highest summits of the earth, like a sacred amphictyony of the greatest Sages established—the whole earth, in silence, and in its ceremonial robes, which takes its seats and holds session in the hemicycle of white stone . . ."

2

With those who, departing, leave their sandals on the sand, with those who, silent, open their way to a dream from which there is no return,

We proceed one day towards you, in our festival clothes, Sea innocence of the Solstice, Sea unconcern of the welcome, and soon we no longer know where our steps will cease . . .

Or is it you, smoke of the threshold, who of yourself rise in us as the sacred spirit of the wine in the vessels of violet wood, at the season of the reddening stars?

We besiege you, Splendor! and we shall be your parasites, hive of the gods, O thousand, thousand chambers of the foam where transgression is accomplished.—Be with us, laughter of Cumes and last cry of the Ephesian! . . .

Thus the Conqueror, under his war plume, at the last gates of the Sanctuary: "I will live in the forbidden rooms and will stroll in them . . ." Bitumen of the dead, you are not the nourishment for such places!

And you will be with us against the night of men, glorious lava on our threshold, O Sea opened to the triple drama: Sea of the trance and the transgression; Sea of the feast and the radiance; and Sea also of action!

*

Sea of the trance and the transgression —behold:

We cross at last the royal green of the threshold; and doing more than dream of you, we walk in you, divine fable! . . . In the clearings under the sea radiates the faceless star; the soul more than the mind moves swiftly there. And you are grace to us from far away. In you moving, we move, rejoicing in the offense and the transgression, O Sea of the ineffable welcome and total Sea of delight!

We have not bitten into the green lemon of Africa, and we have not frequented the clear fossil amber and its captive wings of day-flies; but there we live, and unclothed, where the flesh itself is no longer flesh and the fire itself is no longer flame—in the radiant sap and the very precious seed: in all this green of green dawn, like a single vast leaf infused with dawn and luminous . . .

Unity regained! presence recovered! O Sea, shining instance and flesh of great lunations. It is light made substance for us, and the clearest part of Being brought to light, as in the sliding of the sword out of its sheath of green silk: Being, surprised in its essence, and the god himself, consumed in his holiest species, in the depths of the sacred palm groves. Visitation of the Prince to the stations of his glory! May the Host at last be seated with the guests! . . .

And the alliance is consummated, the collusion perfect. And behold us amid the people of your glory as the splinter is in the heart of the vision. Should we cry out? should we sing praises? Who then loses us in this instant—or who wins us? . . . Blind, we sing praises. And pray to you, Death visited by the immortal Graces. May our phrases, in the song, graced by the movement of the lips, signify more, O gods, than is permitted the dream to feign.

There are, there are, in a place of foam and green water, as in the clearings aflame of Mathematics, truths more restive at our approach than the necks of fabled beasts. And suddenly there we lose footing. Is it you, memory, and Sea still in your image? You go again and give your name, and sea still we name you, who have a name no longer . . . And we might still dream you, but for so short a time still, name you . . .

*

Sea of the feast and the radiance—behold:

God the Undivided governs his provinces. And the Sea rejoicing enters the amber fields of love . . . Eater of mallows, of marvels, O Sea eater of golden poppies in prairies glorious with an eternal Orient! Washer of gold in the diligent sands, and Sybil diluted in the white clays of the gulf! . . . It is you, as you move ahead and bring honor to yourself, O washer of tombs at all points of the earth, O bearer of torches at all gates of the arena!

The old chewers of ashes and barks rise up, their teeth blackened, to greet you before the day. And we who are there, have seen, between the palms, the dawn enriched by the work of your night. And you, yourself, in the morning, lacquered with black, like the forbidden virgin in whom grows the god. But at noon, incensed with gold, like the caparisoned mount of the god, whom no one mounts nor harnesses—the heavy, cadenced beast under its royal housing, set with jewels and heightened with silver, which rocks in the fires of day its high relief of striking images and its large plaques clasped with sacred jewels;

Or saddled with watch-towers, and under its large amulets of war hooked with old copper, the rugged beast arched between its shields of honor, which carried, hanging to its harness hooks, like a mass of entrails and seaweed, the rich load of mail, links and bronze swivels of its coat of armor, and its beautiful war irons, tallowed by wear, under the expanding flaps of its large leather aprons;

Or better still, and among us, the gentle beast naked in its color of asphalt, and painted with great motifs of fresh clay and frank ocher, bearer only of the scepter with the red jewel and the black baetyl; and votive and massive and heavy in the mire of the crowd, which dances, alone, and weighs, for its god, in the unmolested crowd . . .

*

And also Sea of action—behold:

There we look for our lances, our militia, and that quickening of the heart which forces us to the exploit . . . Tireless Sea of the ebb, infallible Sea of the flow! O Sea violence of the Barbarian and Sea tumult of a great Order, incessant Sea under armor, O more active and strong than at the rapture of love, O free and proud in your mating! may our cry answer your exultation, aggressive Sea of our Marches, and you will be for us athletic Sea of the Arena!

For your pleasure is in the mass and in divine propensity, but your delight is at the extreme point of the reef, in the frequency of the lightning and frequenting of the sword. And you have been seen, Sea of violence, Sea drunk with sea, in the midst of your large roses of bitumen and your luminous flowings of naphtha, rolling to the mouths of your night, like holy millstones marked with the impure hexagram, the heavy stones, washed with gold, of your giant turtles,

And yourself moving in your ordering of scales and your vast mortises, Sea incessant under armor and Sea very agile —O massive, O total—shining and curved on your mass, and as though tumefied with pride, and all hammered with the high surf of your war-fauna, you Sea of heavy foundation, and Sea, upheaval of the highest Order—O triumph, O plenitude—on one flood borne! swelling and raising to the height of your gold, like the guardian shield, Ancila, on its bronze slab . . .

The citadels dismantled at the sound of war flutes do not fill so vast a place for the resurrection of the dead! In the lights of iodine and black salt of the mediatory dream, the terrible ring of the Dreamer encloses the instant of an immortal terror: the huge courtyard paved with iron at forbidden sites, and the face, suddenly, of the revealed world of which we shall no more read the hidden side . . . And the Poet himself, in this redoubtable quest, and the Poet himself, what becomes of him, in such a storm of light?—Taken, his arms in his hands, will they tell you this evening.

3

. . . Prolific the image, and the meter, prodigal. But the hour comes also to lead back the Chorus into the circuit of the strophe.

Gratitude of the Chorus, in the rhythm of the lofty Ode. And the recitation resumed in honor of the Sea,

The Reciter again faces the expanse of the Waters. He sees, in its immensity, the Sea of a thousand creases,

Like the infinitely pleated tunic of the god in the hands of women of the sanctuary,

Or, on the slopes of poor grass, in the hands of daughters of fishermen, the ample sea net of the community.

And mesh to mesh is repeated the immense web of poetry—the Sea itself, on its page, like a sacred recitative:

*

". . . Sea of Baal, Sea of Mammon, Sea of every age and every name; O Sea of otherwhere and of all time, O Sea promise of the longest day, and She who passes all promise, being the promise of a Stranger; endless Sea of the recitation, O Sea nameless prolixity!

In you, moving, we move, and we pronounce you the unnamable Sea: mutable and movable in her moltings, immutable and immovable in her mass; diversity in the principle and parity of Being, truth in the lie and betrayal in the message; all presence and all absence, all patience and all refusal—absence, presence; order and madness—license! . . .

O Sea, lasting fulguration, face struck by the singular radiance! Mirror offered to the Outer-dream, and Sea opened to the Outer-sea, like the unpaired Cymbal in the distance paired! Wound opened in the terrestrial side for the sacred intrusion, rending of our night and resplendence of the other—threshold stone washed with love and terrible place of desecration!

(Imminence, O peril! conflagration borne afar as into the deserts of insubmission; and passion borne afar as towards the unsought spouses of another bed . . . Country of the Great, hour of the Great—the next to last, and then the last, and this one here, infinitely durable under the flash!)

O multiple and contrary! O plenary Sea of alliance and of discord! You measure and you beyond measure, you violence and you mansuetude; purity in impurity and in obscenity—anarchic and legal, illicit and allied, madness! and what, O what, O what else, unforeseeable?

The incorporeal and very real, imprescriptible; the irrecusable and undeniable and unappropriable; uninhabitable, frequentable; immemorial and memorable —and what, O what, O what else, unqualifiable? The unseizable and inalienable, the irreproachable irreprovable and also this one here: Sea innocence of the Solstice, O Sea like the wine of Kings! . . .

Ah! She who for us was always there and for us will always be there, honored by the shore and on the shore revered: conciliatrix and mediatrix, instructress of our laws—Sea of the Maecenas and the beggar, of the emissary and the merchant. And She also whom we know well: assisted by our court offices, seated between our priests and our judges who give their rules in distichs—and She also, who is questioned by the founders of maritime leagues, the great federators of pacific peoples and conductors of young men towards their brides of other shores,

The very Sea which is seen in their dreams by the men in garrison on the frontiers, and the sculptors of signs on the Empire boundary stones; the bonders of merchandise at the gates of the desert and purveyors of currency in shell money; the regicide in flight on the sands and the extradited man who is led back along the snow roads; and the keepers of slaves in mines resting against their watchdogs, the goatherds rolled in their leather rags and the cowherd carrier of salt among his circling beasts; the ones who go to harvest acorns under the prophetic oaks, those who live in the forests for cooperage work, and the seekers after kneed wood for the building of ships' stems; tall blind men at our gates in the season of dry leaves, and the potters, in the courtyards, who paint the waves in black curls on the clay of cups, the assemblers of veils for temples and the cutters of sea-canvas under the ramparts of cities; and you also, behind your bronze doors, nocturnal commentators of the oldest texts in the world, and the annalist, under his lamp, giving ear to the distant rumor of peoples and their immortal tongues, like the Barker of the dead on the edge of funeral ditches: travelers to a high country provided with official letters, those who travel in a litter among the rolling waves of the harvests or the stone-paved forests of the mad King; and the bearers of a red pearl in the night, who wander with October on the great high roads resounding with history of arms; captains in chains amidst the crowd of the Triumph, magistrates elected on street corners in the evenings of riots and mob-leaders raised over the great squares at high noon; the heroine embracing the lover's torso as the altar of the shipwrecked, and the hero chained far away by the bed of the Sorceress, and the stranger among our roses who is put to sleep by the sea sound in the bee garden of the hostess—and it is noon—a light wind—the philosopher dozing in his vessel of clay, the judge on his stone entablature formed like a prow, and the pontiffs on their boat-shaped seats . . ."

*

Ineffable, O promise! Towards you fever and torment!

Nations pull on their chains at your very name, O sea, beasts pull on their rope at your very smell of sea pastures and bitter weeds, and the man apprehended by death inquires again, on his bed, about the rising of the tide, the horseman lost in the fields turns again, on his saddle, in quest of your whereabouts, and in the sky, also, the clouds, daughters of your bed, gather in your wake.

Go and unseal the closed stone of the fountains, at a place where the springs take counsel on the choice of their road towards the sea. Cut also the tie, the foundation, and the tap-root! Too many rocks halted, too many tall trees tied, drunk on gravitation, are still immobilized in their orientation towards the sea, like cattle being milked.

Or let the flame itself, rushing down, in a growing explosion of wooden fruits, of scales and scabs, drive with its flame whip the mad herd of the living! to your place of asylum, O Sea, and your bronze altars without stairs or banisters! joining with the same lash the Master and the servant, the rich and the destitute, the Prince and all his guests with the daughters of the intendant, and all the fauna too, familiar or sacred, the boar's head and the pelt, horn and hoof, and the wild stallion and the doe with the golden bough . . .

(And let no one think of shouldering the Penates and Lares, nor the blind ancient, founder of the caste. Behind us there is no wife turned to salt, but in front of us excess and lust. And man hunted, from stone to stone, to the last spur of schist and basalt, leans over the ancient sea, and sees, in a flash of slate-colored eternity, the immense convulsive vulva with a thousand streaming crests, like the divine entrails themselves laid bare for one lightning moment.)

*

. . . Towards you the universal Wife in the midst of the congregation of waters, towards you the licentious Wife in the abundance of her springs and the high flood of her maturity, all the earth itself streaming descends the gorges of love: all the ancient land, your answer, infinitely offered—and from so far so lengthily, and from so far, so slowly, modulated—and we ourselves with her, in a great flow of people and a great trampling of the crowd, in our festival dress and our light tissues, like the final recitation after the strophes and the epode, and with this same dance step, O crowd! which towards the strong wide sea, a drunken sea, leads the docile grave land, a drunken land . . .

Affluence, O favor! And the navigator under sail who toils at the entrance of the straits, approaching in turn each of the coasts, sees on the alternate shores men and women of two races, with their spotted animals, like gatherings of hostages at the limits of the earth—or shepherds, with long strides, still walking over slopes, in the fashion of ancient actors waving their staffs.

And over the near-by sea go the great ploughing claws, at the narrowing of the waters. And beyond, opens the foreign Sea, at the exit from the straits, which is no longer a sea of labor, but the major threshold of the greatest Orb and the signal threshold of the greatest Age, where the pilot is discharged—Sea opening of the forbidden world, on the other face of our dreams, ah! like the step beyond the dream, and the very dream none ever dared! . . .

4

—And it is to Her we tell our age of men, and it is to Her our praises go:

". . . She is like the anointing stone out of its coverings; she is of the color of the sword resting on its mound of white silk.

In her lustral purity reign the lines of force of her grace; she takes the reflection of the mobile sky, which is oriented in her image.

She is federal sea and sea of alliance, at the confluence of all seas and of all births.

. . . She is sea of drunken sea and sea of the greatest laughter; and comes to the lips of the most drunken, on her great open books like the stone of temples:

Sea innumerable in her numbers and her multiples of numbers; tireless Sea in her nomes and enumeration of empires!

She grows without figures or numbers and comes to the lips of the most drunken, like that spoken numbering which is mentioned in secret ceremonies.

. . . Magnanimous Sea of divergence, and Sea of the greatest lapse, where empty kingdoms and unsurveyed provinces are idle,

She is the wandering one without return, and sea of blind migration, leading on her great deserted ways and on her seasonal trails, among her great figurations of painted grass,

Leading the crowd of her people and her tributary hordes, towards the distant fusion of a single and same race.

". . . Are you presence for me?"—cry of the most drunken—"or survival of the portent?" . . . It is you, Presence, who dream us.

We summon you: "Be there!" But you made us that other sign which cannot be evaded, and cried to us those things without measure.

And our heart is with you amid the prophetic foam and the distant numbering, and our spirit denies itself access to the place of your mating.

. . . We called you the half-earthly Bride: like woman, periodic, and like glory, seasonal;

But you go on and ignore us, rolling your thickness of idiom over the sadness of our glories and the fame of submerged sites.

Must we cry out? must we pray? . . . On you go, and on, Immense and Vain, and spread yourself, as a peacock, on the threshold of another Immensity . . ."

*

And now we have said who you are, and now we shall be on the watch for you, and shall avail ourselves of your presence in our human affairs:

"Listen, and you will hear us; listen, and you will assist us.

O you who sin infinitely against death and the decline of things,

O you who sing infinitely the arrogance of gates, yourself shouting at other gates,
And you who prowl in the land of the Great like the growling of the soul without a lair,
You, in the depths of the abyss of woe so prompt to reassemble the great irons of love,
You, in the trial of your great masks of joy so prompt to cover yourself with deep ulcerations,
Be with us in weakness and in strength and in the strangeness of living, higher than joy,
Be with us the One of the last evening, who makes us ashamed of our works, and will also release us from our shame,
And be willing, when we are forsaken, under our faltering sails,
To help us again with your great confidence, and with your strength, and with your breath, O natal Sea of the very great Order!
And may increase come to us in our dream at your single name of Sea! . . ."

*

At last we invoke you yourself, outside the strophe of the Poet. May we no longer have, between the crowd and you, the unbearable radiance of language:

". . . Ah! we had words for you and we did not have enough words,
And behold, love makes us one with the very object of these words,
And words for us they are no longer, being no longer signs or adornments,
But the thing itself which they signify and the thing itself they adorned;
Or better, reciting yourself, who are the recital, behold we become you, the recital,
And we are now you, who were to us the Irreconcilable: the very text and its substance and its sea movement,
And the very great robe of poetry with which we clothe ourselves . . ."

In you, who move, we move also, in you, living, we keep silence, and we live you at last, sea of alliance,
O Sea luminous instance and sea very glorious substance, we acclaim you at last in your radiance of sea and in your own essence:
On all bays struck with flashing oars, on all shores whipped by chains of the Barbarian,
Ah! on all roadsteads torn by the noon eagle, and on all harbor courts paved with round stones, which open before you as before the Citadel in arms,
We acclaim you, O Recital!—And the crowd is standing with the Reciter, the Sea at every gate glowing red, and crowned with evening gold.
And here is a great wind descending into the evening to meet the sea evening, and here the crowd marching out of the arena, and all the flying of yellow leaves of the earth,
And the entire City moving towards the sea, with led animals in hand adorned with copper jewelry, performers bearing horns sheathed with gold, and all women stirred to fever, and the star also taking fire from the first city lights in the streets —all things moving towards the sea and the evening of high sea and the smoke of alliance over the waters,
In the divine promiscuity, and the depravation of man among the gods . . .

5

Over the deserted City, above the arena, a leaf floating in the gold of evening, still in quest of a man's brow . . . God the stranger is in the city, and the Poet, coming home alone, with the melancholy Daughters of glory:

". . . Sea of Baal, Sea of Mammon, Sea of every age and every name!

Uterine Sea of our dreams and Sea haunted by the true dream,

Open wound in our side, and ancient chorus at our gate,

O you the offense and you the radiance! all madness and all peace,

And you love and you hate, the Inexorable and the Exorable,

O you who know and do not know, O you who speak and do not speak.

You of all things aware and in all things keeping silence,

And in all things again rising against the poignant taste of tears,

Nurse and mother, not harsh mother, lover and mother to the younger son,

O Consanguineous and very distant one, O you incest and you the ancestry,

And you immense compassion for all things perishable, Sea forever irrepudiable, and Sea at last inseparable! Scourge of honor, monster of love! O plenary Sea conciliated,

Is it you, Nomad, who this evening will pass us over to the banks of the real?"

THE LIFE AND WORKS OF ST.-JOHN PERSE

By ROGER CAILLOIS

Marie-René Alexis Saint-Léger Léger, who was to assume the pen name of St.-John Perse, was born on May 31, 1887, at Guadeloupe in the French West Indies, on a tiny islet off the seaport of Pointe-à-Pitre. His parents were descendants of old French families who had lived in the Antilles for several generations.

His earliest poems were full of images drawn from his childhood and fixed on the page with the fresh, transparent tints, sharp, simple outlines, and sheer enchantment of magic-lantern views. As a child he lived in a princely world, a life at once free and ritualistic in a setting of giant plants and luminous insects, haunted by silhouettes, shades, and phantoms of many races, customs, and beliefs, ending and beginning every day in bright sunshine and the darkness of the palm groves. This was the only world he knew or could conceive of. It must have seemed marvelous and exotic indeed, a dream rather than a reality, outside time and space. At the age of twelve, he left his island for good, taking with him in his young memory the fertile and ineffaceable sediments of arching ferns, canna flowers, bronze-colored natives, and the grace, decorum, serenity, and remoteness of his home.

Perse's entire work stems from this background, and though his early life steadily receded and dwindled, like ripples circling outward till they become imperceptible, his work never ceased to reflect his earliest impressions in their every varying shapes gaining continually in breadth, allusiveness, and gravity.

From 1896 to 1899 he attended school in Pointe-à-Pitre. He studied botany and in the first form he won the natural history prize. At the same time, he learned to ride horseback and was initiated into the joys of sailing: a dual apprenticeship in self-mastery and the mastery of a rebellious force, two disciplines and two pleasures which he has practiced all his life.

It was in 1899 that his family returned to France. He continued his schooling in Pau, at the foot of the Pyrenees. In 1905, at the age of eighteen, as a law student at Bordeaux, he wrote *Images à Crusoé* (*Images of Crusoe,* 1909) and translated Pindar. That same year, visiting the poet Francis Jammes at Orthez, near Pau, he met Paul Claudel, who had just returned from the Far East. In 1906 he did his military service, first at Pau, then at Fort Urdos near the Spanish frontier. Meanwhile, he studied geology and did some mountain climbing. He lost no opportunity to extend and deepen his concrete, detailed, precise knowledge of nature. This became a lifelong passion.

His father died in 1907. He continued his law studies at Bordeaux, made the acquaintance of Jacques Rivière, commenced a correspondence with Claudel, and went botanizing with Francis Jammes in the Pyrenees, where he wrote the first poems of *Eloges* (*Eulogies*). In August, 1909, in the seventh number of the *Nouvelle Revue Française* (*N.R.F.*), edited by Jacques Rivière, *Images of Crusoe* was published; in the same magazine, in April and June of 1910, appeared several poems from *Eulogies*. Thanks to André Gide, these same poems were published in book form in 1911 by the *Nouvelle Revue Française,* not quite anonymously but with blank wrappers, the name Saint-Léger Léger figuring only on the title page.

It was also in 1911, under the influence of Paul Claudel, Arthur Fontaine, and Philippe Berthelot, that Perse decided on a diplomatic career. He traveled in Spain, Great Britain, and Germany where he studied mining, factories, harbor installations, big business, banking, and the trade unions. These travels, made with a view to preparing himself for the foreign service examinations, also brought him into contact with some of the leading writers and personalities in the countries he visited: Eugenio d'Ors and Antonio Gaudi in Spain; Joseph Conrad in England, at whose home in Ashford he met the novelist and naturalist W. H. Hudson; in London, Rabindranath Tagore, whom he urged Gide to translate; at Blankenese, Richard Dehmel, whom he introduced to Paul Claudel. In 1914 he passed the foreign service examinations. Sent to Peking in 1916, he remained there for five years, during which he traveled in Korea, Manchuria, and Outer Mongolia. It was then that he crossed the Gobi Desert and wrote his epic poem *Anabase* (*Anabasis,* 1924).

In 1921, he returned to Europe by a roundabout route. After visiting Japan, Honolulu, Samoa, and the Fiji Islands, he went on a schooner cruise through the South Seas and skirted the Pacific coast of the United States. Back in France, he was sent to the United States as political expert to the Washington Conference (1921–1922) on naval armaments and Far Eastern questions. During an excursion on the Potomac, in the course of a conversation with Aristide Briand, as if to justify his aversion to the printed page by his love of nature, he uttered one of the phrases in which he has best summed up his ambitions and misgivings: "A book is the death of a tree."

In France, the peculiar originality and excellence of his early poems were now recognized by the very small circle of writers alert to the highest literary qualities. In the *Nouvelle Revue Française* of January, 1924, using for the first time the pen name of St.-John Perse, he published most of his *Anabasis,* and in the second issue of *Commerce* (Summer 1924) appeared his *Amitié du Prince* (The Prince's Friendship). That same year these two works were issued in book form; and in 1925, *Eulogies* was republished, this time under the name of St.-John Perse instead of Saint-Léger Léger.

Then, for nearly twenty years, nothing more was heard of him in the literary world, and there began for him a long period of private renown based on less than a hundred pages of text and the esteem of a select few. It was in 1925 that the French Foreign Minister Aristide Briand chose Perse as his *"Directeur du Cabinet"* and involved him closely with the policies he advocated in Europe. Perse considered any literary activity at this time to be incompatible with his new responsibilities. He published nothing more, and even saw to it that none of his published writings were reissued. In 1933, after Briand's death, he was appointed ambassador and secretary-general of the Ministry of Foreign Affairs in Paris, a post he held until the early months of World War II. During these years he lived the life—to use his own words—of a "dual personality."

On June 10, 1940, after being abruptly retired from his position of secretary-general, he was offered the French ambassadorship in Washington. He declined it, however, and boarded a British cargo boat bound for London. So began his long exile from France. After a short stay in England, he crossed the Atlantic and landed in the United States on July 14. Released now from any political responsibilities, he cast off the personality of the diplomat and resumed that of a poet. A private endowment made in his behalf was placed in the keeping of Archibald MacLeish, head of the Library of Congress, and in February, 1941, Perse became literary advisor to the Library, at no cost to the American taxpayer. This also enabled him to serve as an advisor to President Roosevelt for French affairs during the war, a decision prompted by the fact that after the armistice and the advent of Marshal Petain, Perse had been deprived of his nationality and had lost all his possessions in France. It was only after the Liberation that he could regain his full civil rights.

It was during this period that he wrote *Exil* (*Exile*), which was published in March, 1942, in *Poetry* (Chicago), in May in *Les Cahiers du Sud* (Marseille), and in July in *Les Lettres Françaises* (Buenos Aires). At the same time, the poem was issued by *Les Cahiers du Sud,* and *Les Lettres Françaises* in Argentina brought out a large-type quarto edition of it, some copies on fine paper, others on meat-packing paper. In October, 1942, a token edition of fifteen copies was published clandestinely in German-occupied Paris by the *Nouvelle Revue Française.* In Switzerland, the Baconnière Press at Neuchâtel reprinted the poem in its enterprising series of French writings, *Les Cahiers du Rhone.*

Exile was followed in 1943 by *Poème à l'Etrangère* (*Poem to a Foreign Lady*) and *Pluies* (*Rains*) and in 1944, by *Neiges* (*Snows*). These were published together as *Quatre Poemes* by *Les Lettres Françaises* in Buenos Aires in 1944, in a collective edition published for the benefit of French war relief. At the same time, a limited edition of his first volume of prose appeared: the text of a speech in memory of Aristide Briand given at New York University on March 28, 1942.

Meanwhile, the poet was able to give himself up again to his love of sailing and natural history. He traveled widely in the United States, to Maine, Georgia, South Carolina, Texas, Arizona, Key West, and Cape Cod, studying migratory swans, eagle rays, the flora and fauna of the forest lands, deserts, and ocean deeps, attracted by every unusual manifestation of the forces of nature and life. Even when the war ended, he stayed on in the United States, continuing his travels and studies of natural history. In 1945, on a privately owned island off the coast of Maine where he had been spending the summer each year, he wrote *Vents* (*Winds*). This poem was published in Paris in 1946.

The 1950 Summer–Autumn issue of the *Cahiers de la Pléiade* was devoted entirely to *Homage to St.-John Perse,* with numerous contributions signed by some of the greatest names in contemporary literature. This fresh recognition brought an end to the private phase of Alexis Léger. From now on, he enjoyed public recognition as well as honors, distinctions, and awards both national and international. Books were written on his work, and his poems were translated into more and more foreign languages. He had gained unqualified recognition as one of the foremost poets of the century.

In 1957, he finished and published *Amers* (*Seamarks*), a long poem on which he had been working for seven years. Then, after an absence of seventeen years, he returned to France—but without visiting Paris—to take possession of an estate in the peninsula of Giens, which had just been presented to him by a group of American friends and admirers. Henceforth, he spent each summer there and, except for the journeys he undertook (for example to Tierra del Fuego in 1960), he lived for the rest of the year in his Washington home.

In 1958, he married Dorothy Russell. In 1959, he published *Chronique* (*Chronicle*), a backward glance and meditation over his destiny as a man and a poet. In 1960, he was awarded the Nobel Prize for Literature. Since then he has published *Oiseaux* (*Birds*) and *Pour Dante* (*For Dante*).

There is scarcely any precedent or parallel in contemporary French literature for the nature and scope of Perse's achievement. Indeed, there are few writers who so completely baffle the reader by confronting him with such a self-contained world, for nothing in the reader's previous experience of literature can have prepared him for this encounter.

At first, everything seems alien and obscure. Even the vocabulary is disconcerting. Many words in current use, especially abstract nouns and derivatives, have been discarded. On the other hand, the commonest words, those which designate objects of prime necessity or the basic emotions of human life, are favored. To these are added many rare but concrete terms seldom heard in everyday speech; words which widen and enrich the reader's personal experience of life. They bridge the gap between the real world and the dictionary. They are precise terms used by men engaged in delicate operations or meticulous inquiries. For most of us, these objects and actions have no reality: it is the poet's task to point them out and name their names. Sometimes (but not very often), the poet explains and comments on them—as when he uses the unfamiliar word *ber* (the launching cradle in a shipyard) and aptly explains it as being a *berceau de bois* (a wooden cradle). Or again he speaks of *ces petites algues sèches de literie appelées posidonies* (those small dry algae of bedding called posidonias).

Perse's terminology was not collected at random by leafing through an encyclopedia. His range of knowledge is exceptionally wide and varied, and most of his specialized vocabulary comes from fields of activity in which he has thorough, firsthand experience: botany, in particular the special field of tropical flora, and sailing and horsemanship.

This unusual vocabulary, drawn for the most part from experience rather than culture, is accordingly employed with unfailing accuracy at the right time and place. Knowledge here enriches and refines experience.

His private vocabulary, however, is by no means limited to the nomenclature of natural history or to riding or seafaring terms. His West Indian childhood and his diplomatic career have provided him with further verbal resources from which he drew at will the word or image he needed for the impeccable execution of a work in which no inaccuracy could be allowed.

The poems of Perse do more than present an abundance of technical terms. He contrived, especially in his early poems, to multiply the meanings of familiar words by a system of happy alliances and calculated transplants. The commonplace word is suddenly new-minted. Take *écheance,* deriving from *échoir* (to fall): from its usual sense of expiration or falling due, Perse extended it in conjunction with *rives* (banks of a river or lake) to mean limit, declivity, a sudden dip in the ground—a boundary and downgrade. To seduce the brim of a hat (*seduire le bord d'un chapeau*) means to finger it gently, as if to coax and caress it into the desired shape. The meaning is perfectly clear from the etymology of these words, but who would have expected a writer to extract so neatly the original sense of "falling" from *écheance* or "leading aside" from *seduire.*

Moreover, the poet has used the language to describe attitudes, customs, and occupations quite as unusual as the idiom he devised. It is as if he were recording the annals of a civilization so long extinct or so remote that no traveler had yet reached it, no historian yet heard of it. And what he has to tell us about it is only hinted at, never explained. Long, solemn enumerations go to sum up manners which, though puzzling and inexplicable, seem steeped in an immemorial dignity. Again, disembodied voices coming out of nowhere, addressed to unspecified listeners, pour into the void their apparently purposeless panegyrics, linger confidingly over dark secrets or, like a pure expression of soul, utter a succession of rapturous or disconsolate exclamations.

Nothing is more baffling than the subject matter of Perse's bursts of song. One would swear that the things uttered are the freakish creation of a lawless imagination. Such images as a horse's skull dangling from a pole, a ram's hide painted red, a sickly man's carcass burning in the open air, the spice and the green seed swelling in the moonlight of the rainy season, azalea in search of rock salt, or public ceremonies in honor of a pond seem to be nothing but the antics or delusions of a mind at play or unhinged. In reality, it is all quite factual, all taken from different places in the world and marshaled here in a sumptuous collection of wonders. The ethnographer, the archaeologist, the explorer may recognize their own: rites prevailing in some South Sea islands, funeral sacrifices or works of art of the Siberian steppe, the order of precedence as fixed in an Asiatic court by the strictest etiquette. The whole world contributes to this total museum where the rarest, most moving things conceived by man everywhere are laid out in ordered sequences.

Writing to a friend, the poet once confided the small store of memories remaining from the invariably fragmentary collections he had visited, from each of which a single privileged object had stamped its image on his mind: "In London at the British Museum, a crystal head in the pre-Columbian collection, and in the South Kensington Museum a child's toy boat picked up by Lord Brassey in the middle of the Indian Ocean; at the Kremlin in Moscow, a woman's bracelet with the pastern of a stuffed horse, under the rough trappings of a nomad conqueror; in the Armeria of Madrid, a child's armor; in Warsaw, a princely letter on beaten gold leaf; in the Vatican, a similar letter on goat's hide; in Bremen, a historical collection of unreal pictures for cigar-box lids . . ."

The poetry of St.-John Perse is made up of such treasures as these. Into it goes nothing but what has already demanded much artistry and a high cost in the way of patience, courage, and pains. It is the poet himself who enters "the Lighthouse Station where fables and lanterns lie about"; it is he who lights up the "beautiful troughs of lapis where the brittle princess carved in bone and pricked with gold comes down the course of the centuries under her head of sisal-hemp hair."

But he does not visit only the repositories of masterpieces and curios. His rounds have taken him over the whole world in search of booty. And what he could not see he has read about, drawing upon mankind's vast accumulation of written records to complete what his wanderings have taught him and to add the experience of others to his own. He has cultivated some of the less prestigious sciences to which little attention is paid: those whose business it is to work out the lineage of illustrious families, to classify coins and medals, to draw up sea charts, to determine each year the calendar date of the movable feasts. The numismatist, the philologist, and the historian of religions have each given him some of the terms of their art, some of the fruits of their diligence. From the newspapers he has culled rare items. His references to "the man who saved from the advancing armies a very rare hybrid of the Himalayan briar rose" or "those large iron coins unearthed by a thunderbolt" seem to come straight from the news-in-brief column: items of no consequence, but fairylike in their oddity, each a fluke, a whim of nature, a lucky gamble or intrepid act on the part of an unknown individual who at once relapses into obscurity. Thus it happened during his childhood in the West Indies that a boat was swept up in a cyclone and deposited in the middle of his native island; there, soon overrun by the tropical vegetation, it was transformed into a great basket of flowers.

Perse gathers into his poems, as into an ideal gallery, a rich harvest of deliberate or fortuitous deeds that came from the thinking mind or the blind play of chance: the brilliant achievements brought off by the ingenuity of man; the fleeting emotions of the human heart, elusive but thrillingly keen and felt but once; the vicissitudes of great kingdoms and the nobility of their military, civil, and religious institutions. But this is only the quintessential substance of a poetry that celebrates other miracles. All at once, against this grandiose background, there are flashes of terse confessions of happiness or sadness, of longed-for glory or rankling bitterness. Recurring insistently, they infuse each piece with its hidden meaning. In this fabulous miscellany, drawn from every age and latitude, Perse records the manifold stirrings of human emotion, lifting them from a vulgar and unstable world, remounted and bejeweled, aglow with the simplicity and power of things that do not pass away.

Immemorial customs, actions, and emotions are conjured up; every detail has the stamp of an unobtrusive scholarship. Every statement of fact is backed by the authority of some standard work of reference. Every particular is adduced for judgment as exactly the thing it is: truth as truth, fable as fable, imagery as imagery.

Perse never explains, rather, he evokes and praises. This is why his poetry is not didactic, but allusive; and the sciences to which he is devoted are not causal, but concrete and classifying. They set the whole animal and vegetable kingdom in graded and bracketed tables, ramified according to successive kinds and specific differences. This microscopic view of the world keeps him continuously informed about the quality and singularity of things and beings.

His attitude toward society is exactly the same. He is a man of pacts and clauses, rules of procedure and schedules. He puts his trust in administrative provisions, the precautions of jurisprudence, the conventions of diplomacy.

St.-John Perse is one of the few poets who have sided with civilization against the disorder of nature. Probably no other poet has carried it to such lengths and abided by it with such tenacity and consistency. He tolerates nothing but what has been given its due place and rank.

The grand design of species, genera, and varieties has served to classify the wild profusion of nature. An elaborate system of obligations and prerogatives, franchises and restrictions, rights and immunities, laws, liturgies, and statutes likewise introduces some degree of order into the endless maze of human affairs. Here and there, momentarily, rites and ceremonies check the universal riot. In the midst of the struggle and tumult they contrive a place apart for the delight of the poet and any who care to share it—a haven of serenity, a demonstration of grandeur.

Roger Caillois, director of literary services for UNESCO, is a journalist who has won the French Legion of Honor's prize for peace.

Translated by James Emmons.

THE 1960 PRIZE

By KJELL STRÖMBERG

IN THE AUTUMN of 1959 there was a lively debate in the French press on the subject of the Nobel Prize, in which François Mauriac, who had received the prize in 1952, took part. With his customary forthrightness, Mauriac launched into some tart criticism of the general principles which, in his view, had guided the Swedish Academicians in particular in their choice of French Prizewinners, arguing that a French author not very easily accessible and having little or no impact upon the public, could not be among the Prizewinners. ("How happy I would be to feel myself mistaken!")

In point of fact, Mauriac was mistaken, and the proof of this was not long in coming to light. Precisely one year later, on October 26, 1960, the Swedish Academy decided to award the Nobel Prize for Literature to St.-John Perse, otherwise Marie-René Alexis Saint-Léger Léger, whose "lofty flight and imaginative richness convey a visionary reflection of the present time."

Possibly François Mauriac made use of his double right—both as an Academician and a Nobel Prizewinner himself—in order to propose his favored candidate for the high award, but surely one of the first to suggest the candidacy of Perse was his English translator, T. S. Eliot, who won the Prize in 1948. Perse's nomination for the Prize was also supported by the American Academy of Arts and Letters of New York. Certainly behind these proposals—the first one was in 1955—was a very persuasive inspirer, the then newly elected Secretary-General of the United Nations, the Swedish Academician Dag Hammarskjöld, a personal friend and fervent admirer of St.-John Perse, whose works he subsequently translated into Swedish.

It was Dag Hammarskjöld, a distinguished man of letters as well as a diplomat, who drew up the report on Perse in 1955 for the use of his colleagues of the Swedish Academy. This report is a model of lucid analysis and concise explanation of this difficult poet. While indicating his affinities with a surrealism free from arbitrary pedantry, Hammarskjöld was careful to link the "discontinuous poetry" of Perse with the classic French tradition, as this tradition had been transformed by Baudelaire, Rimbaud, Mallarmé, and others, bringing Perse closer to Claudel. But while Claudel was (as the report stated) a "believer," Perse is a "mystic."

In the literary circles of Stockholm, Perse was not unknown. In 1939, Arthur Lundkvist, who had introduced so many foreign poets to Sweden and was himself a much admired avant-garde poet, had published a first translation of *Anabasis,* with the help of Eliot's version. A second translation, perhaps more faithful to the original, was done fifteen years later by Erik Lindegren, later a member of the Academy, and was set to music in the form of an oratorio for a full orchestra by Karl-Birger Blomdahl, the young leader of the "atonal" school.

Thus prepared, Swedish criticism hailed the Academy's choice with almost unanimous acclamation, though there was some surprise at the boldness of the choice. In France, François Mauriac was the first to render public tribute to the friend of his youth, of whom he avowed himself one of the oldest admirers. In the Parisian press, attention centered upon the brilliant career of Perse the diplomat as much as upon that of Perse the poet. Upon the relation between diplomacy and literature thus brought into focus, Dag Hammarskjöld, in an interview given to *Le Figaro Litteraire,* made a statement of principle which was all the more significant in that Perse had been awarded the Prize almost immediately after two other diplomat-poets: Ivo Andrić and Giorgos Seferis. Hammarskjöld said:

> Between diplomacy and literature there is a sort of rapport which might appear to be mysterious, or at least odd, but which is not without a rational basis. The diplomat, like the poet, works with words, uses them as he would a key—though not necessarily a passkey! We have the case of Alexis-Léger Léger, but we have also the cases of Claudel, of Giraudoux. It is not just a coincidence. Let us not forget either the sort of world in which we live today. The problem of translation, of transposing, of expressing things in different languages is one which is with us always. Translation, transposition—this is a part, a permanent part, of our daily lives. I have often discussed this question with my friend Léger. It fascinated him, as it does myself.

In answer to questions by the France-Presse agency Saint-John Perse made a statement in his turn apropos his award of the Nobel Prize:

> I am not a literary person by career, for I do not wish to be a slave of my profession. But I am very happy that for the fourth time for several years the Nobel Prize has been awarded to a poet. This, moreover, accords perfectly with the feelings which animated the founder of the Prize. Was he not desirous above all to insure that a certain idealism should be safe-guarded? By crowning a poetical work I think one means to help to revive a humanism which is seriously threatened by the progress of modern technology and constitutes a real danger to the functioning of the mind.

It was not Dag Hammarskjöld, however, delayed in New York by the affairs of the Congo, who greeted his friend St.-John Perse on the occasion of the award, as had been hoped, but Anders Österling, permanent secretary of the Swedish Academy. After comparing him with Hölderlin, that "miracle-maker with words," Österling recognized in Perse a continuation "in his own manner of the great tradition of French poetic art," borrowing his metaphors from "all disciplines, all epochs, all mythologies, all climates, so that the cycle of his poems recalls to mind one of those great seashells from which a cosmic music seems to flow."

There was a little moment of surprise at the award ceremony when Perse, the former diplomat, very dignified, very erect, impeccably dressed but wearing no decorations, walked down the few steps of the floral-decked platform to receive his Prize from the hands of King Gustav Adolph VI. It was well known that Perse was a Grand Officer of the Legion of Honor and the holder of an impressive collection of foreign stars and crosses. He wore none of these, as he was later to explain, because all these distinctions had been conferred on him as the diplomat and not as the poet.

Translated by F. Gay.

Luigi Pirandello

1934

"For his bold and ingenious revival of dramatic and scenic art"

Illustrated by UMBERTO ROMANO

PRESENTATION ADDRESS

By PER HALLSTRÖM

PERMANENT SECRETARY
OF THE SWEDISH ACADEMY

THE WORK OF Luigi Pirandello is extensive. As an author of novellas he certainly is without equal in output, even in the primary country of this literary genre. Boccaccio's *Decameron* contains one hundred novellas; Pirandello's *Novelle per un anno* (1922–1937) has one for each day of the year. They offer much variation in subject matter as well as in character: descriptions of life either purely realistic or philosophically profound or paradoxical, as often marked by humor as by satire. There are also creations of a jaunty poetic imagination in which the demands of reality give way to an ideal and creative truth.

The common feature of all these novellas is the effortless improvisation that gives them spontaneity, *élan,* and life. But since the limited scope of the novella demands a particularly strict composition, we also find the result of improvisation. In his hurried treatment of the subject Pirandello may soon lose control, without any concern for the overall impression. Although his novellas reveal much originality, they are hardly representative of the accomplished master; this is readily apparent when one notes the many motifs which were later employed in his dramatic work.

Nor do his novels mark the zenith of his literary achievement. Although his early novels were imbued with the same ideas with which he made his profoundly original contribution to the modern theater, he reserved the definitive shaping of these ideas for the theater.

In the short survey that is possible here, we can mention only one of these novels in which a distinctive feature of his concept of our times, his disgust and fear of materialism which mechanizes life, appears most strongly. The novel is *Si gira* (*Shoot!,* 1916) titled after a technical term of the cinema, "Shoot one." The expression warns the actors when the shooting of a scene begins. The narrator is the one who "shoots," that is, the cameraman of a large film company. He finds a special meaning in his work. For him, life with all its good and evil is reduced to the material of images mechanically produced for a thoughtless pastime; it has no other purpose. The photographic apparatus becomes a demon which swallows everything and unrolls it on the film reel, thus giving it an outward appearance of reality, an appearance which is, in essence, spiritual death and emptiness. Our modern existence revolves and runs with the same lifeless speed, completely mechanized as if it were destroyed and annihilated. The author's attitude is expressed with extreme intensity. The mere plot is devastating enough.

That is the background of Pirandello's dramas, limited as they most often are to purely psychological problems. The bitterness of our present era must have had much influence on the play's pessimistic philosophy even if this philosophy is based on the author's nature.

Maschere Nude (1918–1921), the title he gave to his collection of plays, is difficult to translate because of its complexity. Literally this expression means "naked masks," but "masks" usually indicates a bare surface. In this case, however, the word is applied to the disguise which hides one from others and from one's self and which signifies to Pirandello the form of the self—a surface with an unfathomable being behind it. "Veiled" masks, analyzed and dissolved with penetrating clarity: this is the portrayal of human beings in his dramas—men are unmasked. That is the meaning of the phrase.

The most remarkable feature of Pirandello's art is his almost magical power to turn psychological analysis into good theater. Usually the theater requires human stereotypes; here the spirit is like a shadow, obscurity behind obscurity, and one cannot decide what is more or less central inside. Finally one racks his brains, for there is no center. Everything is relative, nothing can be grasped completely, and yet the plays can sometimes seize, captivate, and charm even the great international public. This result is wholly paradoxical. As the author himself explained, it depends on the fact that his works "arise out of images taken from life which have passed through a filter of ideas and which hold me completely captive." It is the image which is fundamental, not, as many have believed, the abstract idea disguised afterwards by an image.

It has been said that Pirandello has but a "single" idea, the illusory nature of the personality, of the "I." The charge is easy to prove. The author is indeed obsessed with that idea. However, even if the idea is expanded to include the relativity of everything man believes he sees and understands, this charge is unfair.

Pirandello's dramatic art did not at first break with general literary tendencies. He treated social and ethical problems, the conflict between parenthood and the social structure with its inflexible notions of honor and decency, and the difficulties that human goodness finds in protecting itself against the same adversaries. All this was presented in morally as well as logically complicated situations and ended either in victory or defeat. These problems had their natural counterpart in the analysis of the "I" of the characters who were as relative as the idea against which they were fighting.

In several of his plays it is the idea others have of a personality and the effect they experience from it which becomes the principal subject. Others know us only as we know them, imperfectly; and yet we make definitive judgments. It is under the atmospheric pressure of these judgments that the consciousness of one's self can be changed. In *Tutto per bene* (*All for the Best,* 1920) this psychological process is carried to its conclusion. In *Vestire gli ignudi* (*To Clothe the Naked,* 1923) the motif is turned upside down and assumes a moving tragic character. A lost life, an "I," no longer finding anything in itself, desires death but, turning entirely to the outside, has a last pathetic wish to have a proper shroud in the beautifying idea which others have of its former being. In this gripping play even lying appears by its anguish as a kind of innocence.

But the author does not stop here; several of his plays deal with the lie in the world of relativity and examine with a penetrating logic how more or less criminal this lie is. In *La vita che ti diedi* (*The Life I Gave You,* 1924) the right to unreality receives beautiful and great expression. A woman, having lost her only son, no longer has anything which holds her to life; yet the very violence of the blow reawakens in her a strength which dispels death, as light dispels darkness. All has become shadows;

she feels that not only herself but all existence is "such stuff as dreams are made of." In her heart she guards both the memory and the dream, and now they are able to surpass all other things. The son to whom she gave life, who always filled her soul, fills it still. There no void is possible; the son cannot be removed. He remains in her presence, a form she cannot grasp; she feels him there as much as she is able to feel anything. Thus the relativity of truth has taken the shape of a simple and sublime mystery.

The same relativity appears as an enigma in *Così è (se vi pare)* (*Right You Are* [*If You Think You Are*], 1918). The play is called a parable, which means that its singular story makes no pretensions to reality. It is a bold and ingenious fabrication which imparts wisdom. The circumstances of a family, recently settled in a provincial city, become intolerable to the other inhabitants of the town. Of the three members of the family, the husband, the wife, and the mother-in-law, either the husband or the mother-in-law, each otherwise reasonable, must be viewed as seized with absurd ideas about the identity of the wife. The last speaker always has the final say on the issue, but a comparison of the conflicting statements leaves it in doubt. The questionings and the confrontation of the two characters are described with great dramatic art and with a knowledge of the most subtle maladies of the soul. The wife should be able to resolve the puzzle, but when she appears she is veiled like the goddess of knowledge and speaks mysteriously; to each of the interested parties she represents what she must be in order for that person to preserve his image of her. In reality she is the symbol of the truth which no one can grasp in its entirety.

The play is also a brilliant satire on man's curiosity and false wisdom; in it Pirandello presents a catalogue of types and reveals a penetrating self-conceit, either partially or completely ridiculous, in those attempting to discover truth. The whole remains a masterpiece in its own right.

The central problem in the author's dramatic work, however, is the analysis of the "I"—its dissolution in contrary elements, the negation of its unity as illusory, and the symbolical description of the *Maschere nude*. Thanks to the inexhaustible productivity of his mind, Pirandello attacks the problem from different sides, some of which have already been mentioned.

By sounding the depths of madness, he makes important discoveries.

In the tragedy of *Enrico IV* (*Henry IV,* 1922), for example, the strongest impression comes from the struggle of the personality for its identity in the eternally flowing torrent of time. In *Il giuoco delle parti* (*The Rules of the Game,* 1919) Pirandello creates a drama of pure abstractions: he uses the artificial notions of duty to which members of society can be subjected by the force of tradition with resolute logic for an action completely contrary to expectation. As if by a stroke of a magic wand, the game of abstractions fills the scene with an extremely captivating life.

Sei personaggi in cerca d'autore (*Six Characters in Search of an Author,* 1921) is a game similar to that described earlier and at the same time its very opposite; it is both profoundly serious and full of ideas. Here unrestrained creative imagination rather than abstraction dominates. It is the true drama of poetic creation; it is also the settling of accounts between the theater and truth, between appearance and reality. Moreover, it is the half-despairing message of art to the soul of a ravaged age, of fragmentary scenes both fulminating and explosive. This flood of violent feeling and superior intellectuality, rich in poetry, is truly the inspiration of genius. The worldwide success of the play, which proves that it has to some extent been understood, is as extraordinary as the piece itself. There is neither the necessity nor the time to recall its magically startling details.

The skeptical psychology on which Pirandello has based his remarkable production is purely negative. If it were adopted by the general public with the same naiveté with which new and bold ideas are generally received, it would indeed entail more than one risk. But there is no danger that this will happen. It applies itself to purely intellectual realms and the general public scarcely follows it there. If by chance someone might be persuaded that his "I" is a fiction, he would soon be convinced that in practice this "I" does possess a certain degree of reality. Just as it is impossible to prove the freedom of the will, which is however constantly proved by experience, so the "I" manifestly finds means to make itself remembered. These means are gross or subtle. The most subtle of them perhaps consists in the faculty of thought itself; among others, the thought which wants to annihilate the "I."

But the analytical work of this great writer retains its value, especially if compared to several other things to which we have been treated in our time. Psychological analysis has given us complexes, which have spread immense pleasure and joy. They have even been worshiped as fetishes by apparently pious minds. Barbarous fetishes! To a person with some visual imagination, they resemble seaweed entangled in the water. Small fish often hover before this seaweed meditating until, their heads clear at last, they sink into it and disappear. Pirandello's skepticism protects us from such adventures; furthermore, he can help us. He warns us not to touch the delicate tissue of the human soul in a coarsely dogmatic and blind manner.

As a moralist, Pirandello is neither paradoxical nor destructive. Good remains good, and evil, evil. A nobly old-fashioned humanity dominates his ideas about the world of men. His bitter pessimism has not stifled his idealism; his penetrating analytical reason has not cut the roots of life. Happiness does not occupy a large place in the world of his imagination, but what gives dignity to life still finds enough air to breathe in it.

Dear Dr. Pirandello—Mine was the difficult task of presenting a concise synopsis of your profound literary work. Although such a brief sketch is hardly adequate, I have carried out my charge with pleasure.

May I now ask you to receive from His Majesty the Nobel Prize for Literature, of which the Swedish Academy has deemed you worthy.

ACCEPTANCE SPEECH

By LUIGI PIRANDELLO

I TAKE DEEP SATISFACTION in expressing my respectful gratitude to Your Majesties for having graciously honored this banquet with your presence. May I be permitted to add the expression of my deep gratitude for the kind welcome I have been given as well as for this evening's reception, which is a worthy epilogue to the solemn gathering earlier today at which I had the incomparable honor of receiving the Nobel Prize for Literature for 1934 from the august hands of His Majesty the King.

I also wish to express my profound respect and sincere gratitude to the eminent Royal Swedish Academy for its distinguished judgment, which crowns my long literary career.

For the success of my literary endeavors, I had to go to the school of life. That school, although useless to certain brilliant minds, is the only thing that will help a mind of my kind: attentive, concentrated, patient, truly childlike at first, a docile pupil, if not of teachers, at least of life, a pupil who would never abandon his complete faith and confidence in the things he learned. This faith resides in the simplicity of my basic nature. I felt the need to believe in the appearance of life without the slightest reserve or doubt.

The constant attention and deep sincerity with which I learned and pondered this lesson revealed humility, a love and respect for life that were indispensable for the assimilation of bitter disillusions, painful experiences, frightful wounds, and all the mistakes of innocence that give depth and value to our experiences. This education of the mind, accomplished at great cost, allowed me to grow and, at the same time, to remain myself.

As my true talents developed, they left me completely incapable of life, as becomes a true artist, capable only of thoughts and feelings; of thoughts because I felt, and of feelings because I thought. In fact, under the illusion of creating myself, I created only what I felt and was able to believe.

I feel immense gratitude, joy, and pride at the thought that this creation has been considered worthy of the distinguished award you have bestowed on me.

I would gladly believe that this Prize was given not so much to the virtuosity of a writer, which is always negligible, but to the human sincerity of my work.

THE EMPEROR

(HENRY IV)

By LUIGI PIRANDELLO

English version by Eric Bentley

CHARACTERS

FIRST VALET
SECOND VALET
HARALD (*whose real name is Franco*)
LANDOLF (*whose real name is Lolo*)
ORDULF (*whose real name is Momo*)
BERTOLD (*whose real name is Fino*)
(Harald, Landolf, Ordulf, Bertold: *supposed Privy Councillors*)
GIOVANNI, *the butler*
MARQUIS CARLO DI NOLLI
BARON TITO BELCREDI
DR. DIONISIO GENONI, *a psychiatrist*
COUNTESS MATILDA SPINA, *the Baron's mistress*
FRIDA, *her daughter, engaged to the Marquis*
"HENRY THE FOURTH, EMPEROR OF GERMANY" (*the Marquis' uncle*)

The scene is laid in a solitary villa in the Umbrian countryside.

The time is "the present"—the play was first performed in 1922.

THE EMPEROR

ACT I

A hall in the villa got up in every way to pass for the throne room of the German Emperor Henry the Fourth in his imperial residence at Goslar, Hanover. But in the middle of the ancient furnishings two large modern oil paintings—life-size portraits—stand out from the back wall. They are supported, not far above the ground, on a sort of pedestal or ledge of carved wood which runs the whole length of the wall. (It is broad and protrudes so you can sit on it as on a long bench.) Between the two portraits is the throne itself—the imperial chair and its low baldachin—which is, as it were, inserted in the pedestal dividing it into two parts. The two portraits represent a lady and a gentleman, both young, rigged up in carnival costumes, one as the Emperor Henry the Fourth and the other as Countess Matilda of Tuscany. Doors to left and right.

Two valets, in eleventh-century costume, are lying on the ledge. Suddenly they jump down, in surprise, apparently, running to place themselves, stiff as statues, at the foot of the throne, one on each side, with their halberds. Soon afterward, by the second door on the right, HARALD, LANDOLF, ORDULF, *and* BERTOLD *come in. These young men are paid by the Marquis Carlo Di Nolli to pretend to be privy councillors—regal vassals, belonging to the lower aristocracy, at the court of the Emperor. They are therefore dressed as German knights of the eleventh century. The last of them,* BERTOLD *(his real name is Fino), is doing the job for the first time. His three companions are amusing themselves telling him everything. The whole scene should be played with extreme vivacity.*

LANDOLF (*to* BERTOLD, *as if following up an explanation*). And this is the throne room!

HARALD. At Goslar!

ORDULF. Or, if you'd prefer that, in his castle in the Harz Mountains!

HARALD. Or at Worms.

LANDOLF. It jumps around a bit. According to the scene we're acting out. Now here, now there——

ORDULF. Now in Saxony——

HARALD. Now in Lombardy——

LANDOLF. Now on the Rhine.

FIRST VALET (*holding his position, hardly moving his lips*). Sss, Sss!

HARALD (*hearing and turning*). What's the matter?

FIRST VALET (*still like a statue, in an undertone*). Well, is he coming or isn't he? (*The allusion is to the Emperor.*)

ORDULF. He isn't. He's sleeping. Take it easy.

SECOND VALET (*dropping the pose as his partner does so, taking a long breath, and going to lie down again on the ledge*). Well, for Christ's sake, why didn't you say so before?

BERTOLD (*who has been observing everything in mixed amazement and perplexity, walking around the room and looking at it, then looking at his clothes and his companions' clothes*). But look . . . this room . . . these clothes. . . . *What* Henry the Fourth? . . . I don't quite get it—is it Henry the Fourth of France or Henry the Fourth of England?

(*At this demand,* LANDOLF, HARALD, *and* ORDULF *burst into loud laughter.*)

LANDOLF (*laughing all the time and pointing at* BERTOLD *as if inviting the others—who also go on laughing—to continue making fun of him*). Is it Henry the Fourth of France?

ORDULF. Or Henry the Fourth of England?

HARALD. Why, my dear child, it's Henry the Fourth of *Germany!*

ORDULF. The great and tragic emperor——

LANDOLF. —who repented and knelt in the snow before the Pope at Canossa! And day by day in this room we keep the war going—the terrible war between Church and State——

ORDULF. —between Pope and emperor!

BERTOLD (*covering his head with his hands to protect himself against this avalanche of information*). I see, I see! I just didn't get it. Clothes like this. A room like this. I was right: these are *not* sixteenth-century clothes!

HARALD. Sixteenth century, indeed!

ORDULF. We're between the year 1000 and the year 1100.

LANDOLF. Count it up yourself: if we're in the snow at Canossa on January 25, 1077 . . .

BERTOLD (*more distressed than ever*). My God, this is a disaster!

ORDULF. It certainly is, if you thought it was the *French* court.

BERTOLD. The *English* court, I studied up on *English* history, I was reading Shakespeare and everything . . .

LANDOLF. My dear man, *where* were you educated? Still, you're only a couple of centuries out.

BERTOLD (*getting angry*). But why in God's name couldn't they have told me it was Henry the Fourth of Germany! I had two weeks to study the thing up—I can't tell you the number of books I've had my nose in!

HARALD. Look, dear boy. Didn't you know that poor Tony was called Adalbert, Bishop of Bremen, in this house?

BERTOLD. Adalbert, Bishop of . . . ? How'd I know that?

LANDOLF. Well, you see how it was: when Tony died, the Marquis . . .

BERTOLD. Ah, so it *was* the Marquis. Then why on earth didn't he tell me that . . . ?

HARALD. Maybe he thought you knew, dear boy.

LANDOLF. He wasn't going to take anyone else on. There were three of us left, and he thought we'd be enough. But then *he* took to shouting, "Adalbert driven out, Adalbert driven out!" Poor Tony, you see, it didn't seem to *him* Tony had died, it seemed to *him* the bishops of Mainz and Cologne had driven Adalbert out!

BERTOLD (*taking his head in his two hands and keeping it there*). But I never heard a word of all this!

ORDULF. So here you are, my dear fellow.

HARALD. And the trouble is that we don't know who *you* are either, dear boy!

BERTOLD. Even you don't know? You don't know what part I'm to play?

ORDULF. Well, um—Bertold.

BERTOLD. Bertold? Who's he? *Why* Bertold?

LANDOLF. "They've driven Adalbert away from me? Then I want Bertold, I want Bertold!"—He took to shouting *that.*

HARALD. The three of us just stared at each other. Who the devil could this Bertold be?

ORDULF. So here you are, my dear fellow—Bertold.

LANDOLF. And what a wonderful job you'll make of it.

BERTOLD (*rebelling and starting to go*). Oh, no! Not for me, thank you! I'm going, I'm going.

HARALD (*while he and* ORDULF *hold him back, amid laughter*). Calm down, dear boy, calm down!

ORDULF. You won't be the Bertold of the story.

LANDOLF. Comfort yourself with the thought that even we don't really know who we are. He's Harald, he's Ordulf, I'm Landolf. . . . That's what we're *called,* and by now we've got used to it, but who *are* we? Names. Names of the period. And that's what you'll be—a name—of the period: Bertold. Only one of us, the late lamented Tony, ever had a good part, a part out of the story—the Bishop of Bremen. He looked like a real bishop, he was marvelous, poor Tony!

HARALD. God, how the dear boy would study: read, read, read!

LANDOLF. And he gave orders. Even to his Majesty. Oh, yes, he knew how to put himself over. Guided him. Was a tutor. An adviser, in effect. *We're* privy councillors, for that matter. But with us it's just for appearances: because the history books say the Emperor was hated by the *higher* aristocracy for surrounding himself at court with young men of the *lower* aristocracy.

ORDULF. That's us, my dear fellow.

LANDOLF. It really is a shame, because, well, with these clothes we could make a sensational appearance on the stage. In a costume play. They go over big these days. The Life and Loves of Henry the Fourth—what a story! Material not for one but for half a dozen tragedies! And now look at us! Just look at the four of us—and those two unfortunates standing by the throne like stuck pigs. (*He points at the two valets.*)—No one—no one puts us on stage, no one gives us scenes to act. We've got the—what do you call it?—we've got the *form*—but we don't have the *content!* We're worse off than the Emperor's real privy councillors because, well, it's true no one had given *them* a part to play either, but they didn't know they *had* to play one, they played it because they played it, it wasn't a part, it was their life, see what I mean? They acted in their own interests, they fought their rivals, they sold investitures, and so forth, while we . . . here are we in this beautiful court, dressed up as you see, and for what? To do what? To do nothing. . . . Six puppets hanging on the green room wall.

HARALD. No, no, dear boy, pardon me, but our replies do have to be in character.

LANDOLF. Yes, as far as that goes—

BERTOLD. And you said we do nothing! How'm I going to reply in character? I've got myself all prepared for Henry of England, and now someone calling himself Henry of Germany comes . . . comes butting in!

(LANDOLF, ORDOLF, HARALD *start laughing again.*)

HARALD. You'd better attend to it, dear boy—

ORDULF. —and we'll help you, my dear fellow—

HARALD. —we've lots of books in there, my dear man—but first we'll just run through the main points—

ORDULF. —so you'll have a general idea—

HARALD. Look at this! (*Turns him around and shows him the Countess Matilda's portrait on the back wall.*) Who's that, for example?

BERTOLD (*looking*). That? Well, in the first place, if you don't mind my saying so, it's out of place. Two modern paintings in the midst of all this medieval stuff?

HARALD. You're right, dear boy. And as a matter of fact they weren't there originally. Behind the pictures there are two niches—for two statues they were going to put in—in the style of the period. The niches stayed empty—then they were covered by these two canvases——

LANDOLF (*interrupting and continuing*). —which would certainly be out of place—if they really were paintings!

BERTOLD. They're not paintings? What are they, then?

LANDOLF. If you go and touch them, yes, they're paintings. But for *him* (*He points mysteriously out right, alluding to the* EMPEROR.)—since he does *not* touch them . . .

BERTOLD. He doesn't? What are they, then—for him?

LANDOLF. Well, this is just my interpretation, don't forget. All the same, I think it's pretty good. They're—images. Images—like, um, like images in a mirror, you see? That one there is him (*pointing*), the living image of him, him in this throne room—which is also—as it should be—in the style of the period. What are you so amazed about, may I ask? If we place you in front of a mirror, won't you see *your* living image? Won't you see the "you" of today in the trappings of yesteryear? Well, then, it's as if we had two mirrors here—two living images—in the midst of a world which . . . well, you'll see for yourself, now you live with us, you'll see how this world, too, every part of it, will come to life.

BERTOLD. Now, really, I didn't come here to go mad!

HARALD. Go mad, dear boy? Ts, ts. You're going to have fun!

BERTOLD (*to* LANDOLF). You certainly have quite a line in philosophy!

LANDOLF. My dear man, you can't go behind the scenes of history—eight hundred years of it—and not bring back a bit of experience!

HARALD. Let's be going, dear boy. We'll fix you up in no time—

LANDOLF. We'll fasten the wires on and have you in full working order: the perfect marionette!

ORDULF. Let's go. (*Takes him by the arm, to lead him off.*)

BERTOLD (*stopping and looking toward the other portrait*). Just a minute. You haven't told me who *she* is. The Emperor's wife?

HARALD. No, dear boy. The Emperor's wife is called Bertha of Susa.

ORDULF. The Emperor can't stand her. He wants to be young like us. He's planning to get rid of her.

LANDOLF. That's his fiercest enemy: Countess Matilda. Of Tuscany.

BERTOLD. Wait. Wasn't it her castle the Pope was staying in . . .

LANDOLF. At Canossa.

ORDULF. Precisely.

HARALD. Now *do* let's get going!

(*They are all moving over toward the door on the right by which they had entered when the old butler* GIOVANNI, *in modern cutaway, comes in at the left.*)

GIOVANNI (*in a great hurry, and worked up*). Sss, sss! Franco! Lolo!

HARALD (*stopping and turning*). Hey! What do *you* want?

BERTOLD (*amazed to see him come into the throne room in his modern coat.*) What's this? *He* comes in *here?*

LANDOLF. A visitor from the twentieth century! Away!

(*He and his two comrades make a joke of running over to threaten him and drive him out.*)

ORDULF. The Pope's ambassador—away with him!

HARALD. Away with the rogue!

GIOVANNI (*defending himself, annoyed*). Oh, come on, stop this!

ORDULF. No, you're not allowed in here!

HARALD. Get away, old man!

LANDOLF (*to* BERTOLD). It's witchcraft! He's a demon conjured up by the Great Magician of Rome! Out with your sword! (*And he reaches for his own.*)

GIOVANNI (*shouting*). Stop this, I say! This is no time for fooling; the Marquis is here, and there's company with him. . . .

LANDOLF (*rubbing his hands*). Oh, wonderful! Ladies?

ORDULF (*doing the same*). Old? Young?

GIOVANNI. Two gentlemen.

HARALD. But the ladies; who are they, dear boy?

GIOVANNI. Countess Matilda and her daughter.

LANDOLF (*amazed*). What? (*Pause.*) What's that?

ORDULF (*also amazed*). The Countess, you say?

GIOVANNI. Yes, yes, the Countess!

HARALD. And the two men, dear boy?

GIOVANNI. I don't know.

HARALD (*to* BERTOLD). Landolf told you we have form without content in here, but keep your eyes open, dear boy.

ORDULF. The Pope has sent a whole *bevy* of ambassadors! We'll have fun all right.

GIOVANNI. Will you let me speak?

HARALD. Speak! (*Pause.*) Speak, dear boy!

GIOVANNI. Well, one of the two men seems to be a doctor.

LANDOLF. Oh, sure, we're used to *them.*

HARALD. Many thanks, Bertold, you bring us luck!

LANDOLF. You'll see how we'll manage *him.*

BERTOLD. I'm walking into a fine old mess, I can see that.

GIOVANNI. Now, listen. They'll be coming into this room.

LANDOLF (*in amazement and consternation*). What? Is that true? Even she? The Countess will come in here?

HAROLD. This is content—with a vengeance, dear boy.

LANDOLF. This'll be a real tragedy!

BERTOLD (*his curiosity aroused*). But why? What are you talking about?

ORDULF (*pointing to the portrait*). The Countess is the woman in the portrait.

LANDOLF. Her daughter is engaged to the Marquis.

HARALD. But what have they come for? That's the question.

ORDULF. If *he* sees her, there'll be fireworks.

LANDOLF. Maybe he won't recognize her anymore.

GIOVANNI. If he wakes up, you'll just have to keep him in there.

ORDULF. Are you joking? How'd we do that?

HARALD. You know what he's like, dear boy!

GIOVANNI. Good heavens, use force if need be! Those are the Marquis's orders. Now get going! Get going!

HARALD. Yes, we'd better go; he may be awake already.

ORDULF. Let's go.

LANDOLF (*leaving with the others, to* GIOVANNI). You must explain it all later!

GIOVANNI (*shouting after them*). Lock the door on that side and hide the key! This other door, too. (*He points to the other door at right.*)

(LANDOLF, HARALD, *and* ORDULF *leave by the second door on the right.*)

GIOVANNI (*to the* TWO VALETS). You must go, too; go on, that way! (*He points to the first door on the right.*) Lock the door and take the key out of the lock!

(*The* TWO VALETS *leave by the first door on the right.* GIOVANNI *goes to the door on the left and opens it for the* MARQUIS CARLO DI NOLLI.)

MARQUIS. You have given the orders properly, Giovanni.

GIOVANNI. Yes, Marquis. Certainly, Marquis.

(THE MARQUIS *goes out again for a moment to bring the others in. First comes* BARON TITO BELCREDI *and* DR. DIONISIO GENONI, *then* COUNTESS MATILDA SPINA *and her daughter* FRIDA. GIOVANNI *bows and goes out. The* COUNTESS *is about forty-five, still beautiful and shapely, though she too patently repairs the inevitable ravages of time with a violent if expert makeup which gives her the haughty head of a Valkyrie. This makeup stands out in high and painful relief from her mouth, which is very lovely and very sad. Many years a widow, she now has* BARON TITO BELCREDI *for friend. Neither she nor other people have ever taken him seriously, or so it appears. What the* BARON *really means to her, he alone fully knows. He can therefore laugh if she needs to pretend she doesn't know, can laugh at the laughter of other people, caused, as it is, by the Countess's jests at his expense. Slim; prematurely gray, a little younger than she, he has a curious, bird-shaped head. He would be very vivacious if his agility—which makes him a formidable swordsman and is in itself live enough—were not actually encased in a sleepy, Arab laziness that comes out in his strange voice, which is rather nasal and drawling.* FRIDA, *the* COUNTESS'*s daughter, is nineteen years old. Having grown sad in the shade to which her imperious and showy mother relegates her, living in this shade she is also offended by the easy gossip which the mother provokes to the detriment of them both equally. And yet, as luck will have it, she is already engaged—to the* MARQUIS CARLO DI NOLLI, *a stiff young man, very indulgent toward others, yet rigid and shut up in the small space of what he thinks he can be, of what he thinks he is worth, in the world, though at bottom even he doesn't know what this worth is. At any rate his consternation is great at the many responsibilities which he believes weigh him down. Yes, the others can talk, the others can have their fun, lucky they. He cannot. Not that he wouldn't like it. Just that he cannot. He is dressed in the deepest mourning for the death of his mother.* DR. DIONISIO GENONI *has a fine, satyr's face, insolent and rubicund, with protruding eyes, a short, pointed beard that shines like silver. He has refined manners and is almost bald. They enter in a state of consternation, almost afraid, looking with curiosity about the room—all except the* MARQUIS. *And at first they speak in low voices.*)

BARON. Splendid, it's very splendid!

DOCTOR. Most interesting, how one can see the madness in the room itself, in inanimate objects, it really *is* splendid, quite splendid!

COUNTESS (*who has been looking around the room for her portrait, finding it, and moving toward it*). Ah, so here it is! (*Looking at it from a certain distance while different feelings arise within her.*) Yes, ye-es . . . why, look . . . heavens . . . (*She calls her daughter.*) Frida, Frida. . . . Look. . . .

FRIDA. Ah! Your portrait?

COUNTESS. No, just look, it's not me at all, it's you!

MARQUIS. It's true, isn't it? I told you so.

COUNTESS. I'd never have believed it—to this extent. (*She shakes with a sudden tremor along the spine.*) Heavens, what a strange sensation! (*Then, looking at her daughter.*) What's the matter, Frida? (*Slipping an arm about her waist, she pulls her close.*) Come here, don't you see yourself in me—in that picture?

FRIDA (*with a gasp*). But it's me, why . . .

COUNTESS. Wouldn't you think so? You couldn't miss it, could you? (*Turning to the* BARON.) You look, Tito, and *you* tell me!

BARON (*not looking*). I say it's not you. I know without looking.

COUNTESS. How stupid, he thinks he's paying me a compliment. (*Turning to the* DOCTOR.) You tell me, Doctor!

DOCTOR (*starts to come over*).

BARON (*with his back turned, pretending to speak to him secretly*). Sss! No, Doctor! For heaven's sake, have nothing to do with it!

DOCTOR (*bewildered, smiling*). But why not, why not?

COUNTESS. Pay no attention to him, just come. He's insufferable.

FRIDA. Don't you know he's a professional fool?

BARON (*to the* DOCTOR, *seeing him go*). Watch your feet, watch your feet, Doctor, your feet!

DOCTOR (*as above*). What's wrong with my feet?

BARON. You've got hobnailed boots on!

DOCTOR. What?

BARON. And you're walking toward four little feet of delicate Venetian glass.

DOCTOR (*laughing out loud*). What nonsense! There's nothing staggering, it seems to me, in the fact that a daughter resembles her mother . . .

BARON. Crash! Now it's over.

COUNTESS (*exaggeratedly angered, coming toward the* BARON). What do you mean: Crash! What is it? What has he been saying?

DOCTOR (*sincerely*). Don't you think I'm right?

BARON (*answering the* COUNTESS). He said there's nothing staggering in it. While *you* are extremely staggered. Why?—if it's all so natural?

COUNTESS (*still more angered*). You fool! It's *because* it's so natural. Because it's *not* my daughter. (*Pointing to the canvas.*) That is *my* portrait. To find my daughter in it instead of myself is a staggering experience. Believe me, I was quite sincerely staggered, I can't let you say I wasn't!

(*After this violent outburst there is a moment of embarrassed silence.*)

FRIDA (*quite annoyed*). Always the same story: arguments about absolutely nothing.

BARON (*also quiet, almost with his tail between his legs, apologetically*). I wasn't saying anything of the sort. (*To* FRIDA.) I simply noticed that, from the outset, *you* weren't . . . staggered like your mother. If *you're* staggered, it's merely because the portrait resembles you so strongly.

COUNTESS. Obviously! Because there's no way for her to see herself in *me*—as I was at her age. Whereas I, the girl in the portrait, can perfectly well see myself in her—as she is now.

DOCTOR. True. A portrait stays just as it is. Fixed! It can't move away from the moment when it was made, a distant moment now, and, for the young lady, a moment without memories. Whereas for her mother it brings back many things: movements, gestures, looks, smiles, things that aren't *in* the portrait at all . . .

COUNTESS. Exactly.

DOCTOR (*continuing, turning to her*). For you, naturally, the same things are to be found in your daughter, too.

COUNTESS. It's so seldom I give way to my feelings, and when I do, *he* has to come and spoil it for me! Just for the pleasure of hurting me!

DOCTOR (*impressed with his own perspicacity, starts up again in a professional tone, turning to the* BARON). Resemblance, my dear Baron, oftentimes has its roots in intangibles. On these lines, it seems eminently explicable that . . .

BARON (*to interrupt the lecture*). Someone might find a resemblance between you and me, my dear professor.

MARQUIS. Drop it now, drop it, I beg you. (*He points to the doors on the right, indicating that someone is there who might hear.*) We've been sidetracked too much already, coming . . .

FRIDA. Of course! With him here . . . (*Indicating the* BARON.)

COUNTESS (*promptly*). That's why I so much wished he wouldn't come.

BARON. Now you've had a lot of fun at my expense. Don't be ungrateful!

MARQUIS. Tito, please, that's quite enough. The doctor is with us, and we're here for a very serious purpose. You know how much it means to me.

DOCTOR. Precisely. Now let's see if we can't begin by getting certain points quite clear. This portrait of yours, Countess, may I ask how it comes to be here? Was it a gift from you? Did you make him a present of it—I mean in the days—before . . .

COUNTESS. Oh, no. How could I have given him presents in those days? I was just a girl—like Frida now—and not engaged at that. No, no, I let him have it three or four years after the accident. I let him have it because his (*indicating the* MARQUIS) mother urged me to.

DOCTOR. His (*with a gesture toward the doors on the right, the reference being to* EMPEROR HENRY) sister, that is to say?

MARQUIS. Yes, Doctor: my mother was his sister. She died a month ago. It's for her sake we've come here—the payment of a debt to her, you might say. In the normal course of events, she (*indicating* FRIDA) and I would be traveling . . .

DOCTOR. On business of quite another sort, hm?

MARQUIS. Please! My mother died in the firm conviction that her beloved brother's recovery was imminent.

DOCTOR. You couldn't tell me, perhaps, from what evidence she reached this conclusion?

MARQUIS. I believe it was from certain strange things he said to her not long before she died.

DOCTOR. Strange things? Aha! It would be terribly useful to me to know what those things were, by Jove!

MARQUIS. I don't know myself. I only know Mother came home after that last visit extremely upset. It seems he'd shown her a most unusual tenderness, as if he foresaw the coming end. On her deathbed she made me promise never to neglect him, to make sure that people see him, visit him . . .

DOCTOR. I see. Very good. Now, to begin with . . . Oftentimes the most trivial causes lead . . . well, take this portrait . . .

COUNTESS. Heavens, Doctor, how can you attach such overwhelming importance to the portrait? It happened to make a big impression on me for a moment just because I hadn't seen it in so long.

DOCTOR. Just a minute, please, just . . .

BARON. But it's so. It must have been there fifteen years . . .

COUNTESS. More! More than eighteen by now!

DOCTOR. I beg your pardons, but you don't yet know what questions I'm going to ask. I set great store—very great store—by those two portraits. I fancy they were painted before the famous—and most unfortunate—cavalcade, isn't that so?

COUNTESS. Why, of course.

DOCTOR. So it was when he was . . . normal . . . quite . . . sane . . . that's what I'm really getting at.—Was it he who suggested having it painted—to you?

COUNTESS. No, no, Doctor. Lots of us were having them done. I mean, of those who took part in the cavalcade. They were something to remember it by.

BARON. I had one of me done!

COUNTESS. We hardly waited for the costumes to be ready!

BARON. Because, you see, it was proposed to collect them all in the drawing room of the villa that the cavalcade came from. As a memorial. A whole gallery of pictures. But afterward each of us wanted to keep his own picture for himself.

COUNTESS. As for mine, as I told you, I let *him* have it—and without very much regret—because his mother . . . (*Indicating the* MARQUIS *again.*)

DOCTOR. You don't know if he actually asked for it?

COUNTESS. No, I don't. Perhaps he did. Or perhaps it was his sister—as a loving gesture . . .

DOCTOR. Just one other point: the cavalcade—was it his idea?

BARON (*promptly*). Oh, no! It was mine!

DOCTOR. Now, please . . .

BARON. The idea was mine, I tell you! After all, there's nothing to boast of in *that*—seeing how it all turned out! It was . . . oh, I remember it well: one evening, early in November, at the club, I was leafing through an illustrated magazine, a German one—just looking at the pictures, you understand, I don't know German—and there was a picture of the German Emperor in . . . what was the university town he'd been a student in?

DOCTOR. Bonn, Bonn.

BARON. Possibly, Bonn. He was on horseback and dressed in one of the strange traditional costumes of the oldest student fraternities. He was followed by a cortege of other students of noble birth, also on horseback and in costume. Well, the idea came to me from that picture. I should have told you some of us at the club had been thinking of possible masquerades for the next carnival. I proposed this . . . historical cavalcade. Historical, in a manner of speaking. It was really a Tower of Babel: each of us was to choose a character, from this century or that, king or emperor or prince, with his lady beside him, queen or empress. All were to be on horseback. With the horses harnessed and dressed up—in the style of the period of course. Well, my proposal was accepted.

DOCTOR. So *he* chose the character of Henry the Fourth?

COUNTESS. Because—thinking of my own name—and, well, not taking the whole thing any too seriously—I said I'd like to be Countess Matilda of Tuscany.

DOCTOR. I don't . . . I don't see the connection . . .

COUNTESS. I didn't understand it myself in the beginning—I just heard him saying, "Then I'll be at your feet at Canossa—like Henry the Fourth." Oh, yes, I knew about Canossa, but to tell the truth I didn't remember much of the story, and it made quite an impression on me when I studied it. I found I was a loyal and zealous friend of the Pope in the fierce struggle he was waging against the German Empire. I now understood why *he* wanted to be next to me in the cavalcade—as the Emperor.

DOCTOR. Ah! You mean because . . .

COUNTESS. . . . because I'd chosen to present his implacable enemy.

DOCTOR. Ah! Because——

BARON. Because he was courting her all the time! So she (*indicating the* COUNTESS) naturally . . .

COUNTESS (*stung, fierily*). Yes, naturally! I *was* natural in those days . . .

BARON (*pointing to her*). You see: she couldn't abide him!

COUNTESS. That's not true! I didn't even dislike him. Just the opposite! But with me, if a man wants to be taken seriously——

BARON (*finishing her sentence*). —he gives the clearest proof of his stupidity!

COUNTESS. Don't judge others by yourself, Baron B. *He* wasn't stupid.

BARON. But then *I* never asked you to take me seriously.

COUNTESS. Don't I know it! But with him it was no joke. (*Changing her tone and turning to the* DOCTOR.) My dear Doctor: a woman has a sad life, a silly life. And some time or other it's her lot to see a man's eyes fixed upon her, steady and intense and full of—shall we say?—the promise of enduring sentiment! (*She bursts into a harsh laugh.*) What could be funnier? If only men could see their looks of enduring sentiment!—I've always laughed at them. More at *that* time than any other.—And let me tell you something: I can still laugh at them, after more than twenty years.—When I laughed like that at *him,* it was partly from fear, though. Perhaps one could have believed a promise in *those* eyes. It would've been dangerous, that's all.

DOCTOR (*with lively interest and concentration*). Aha! I'd be interested to know about *that.*—Why dangerous?

COUNTESS (*with levity*). Because he wasn't like the others. And because I too am . . . I can't deny it . . . I'm a little

. . . more than a little, to tell the truth, more than a little (*She searches for a modest word.*) intolerant, that's the word. I don't like stuffiness, I don't like people who take life hard.—Anyway, I was too young at that time, you understand? And I was a woman: I couldn't help champing at the bit.—It would have needed *courage,* and I didn't have any.—So *I* laughed at him, too. With remorse. With real self-hatred eventually—my laughter mingled with the laughter of fools, and I knew it. With the laughter of all the fools who made fun of him.

BARON. More or less as they do of me.

COUNTESS. My dear, you make people laugh at your . . . your perpetual affectation of self-abasement—they laughed at him for the opposite reason: it makes a difference, hm?—And, with you, people laugh right in your face!

BARON. Better than behind my back, *I* say.

DOCTOR (*coughing nervously*). Ahem, yes, um . . . he was already rather . . . strange . . . exalted, as it were—if I've been following you properly?

BARON. Yes. But after a very curious fashion, Doctor.

DOCTOR. Namely?

BARON. Well, I'd say . . . he was damned cold-blooded about it—

COUNTESS. Cold-blooded? What nonsense! This is how it was, Doctor. He was a little strange, it's true, that was because there was so much life in him. It made him eccentric.

BARON. I don't say this . . . exaltation was just an act. Not at all. He was often genuinely exalted. But I could swear, Doctor: he was looking at himself, looking at his own exaltation. And I believe the same is true of every move he made, however spontaneous: he *saw* it. I'll say more: I'm certain it was this that made him suffer. At times he had the funniest fits of rage against himself.

COUNTESS. That is true.

BARON (*to the* COUNTESS). And why? (*To the* DOCTOR.) As I see it, the lucidity that came from acting all the time . . . being another man . . . shattered, yes, shattered at a single blow the ties that bound him to his own feelings. And these feelings seemed—well, not exactly a pretense, no, they were sincere—but he felt he must give them an intellectual status, an intellectual form of expression—to make up for his lack of warmth and spontaneity—so he improvised, exaggerated, let himself go, that's about it, to deafen his own ears, to keep his eyes from seeing himself. He seemed fickle, silly, and sometimes . . . yes, ridiculous, let's face it.

DOCTOR. Was he . . . unsociable?

BARON. Not in the least. He was a regular fellow. He was famous for his *tableaux vivants,* he was always getting up dances, benefit performances, all just for fun, of course. He was an awfully good actor, believe me.

MARQUIS. And he's become a superb and terrifying one—by going mad.

BARON. Even before that. I still remember how—when the accident happened—and he fell from his horse, you know—

DOCTOR. He hit the back of his head, didn't he?

COUNTESS. Oh, what a horror! He was next to me. I saw him between the horse's hooves. The horse reared up——

BARON. At first we'd no idea any great harm was done. There was a stop—a bit of a scrimmage in the cavalcade—people wanted to know what had happened. . . . But he'd been picked up and carried into the villa.

COUNTESS. There was *nothing,* you understand: not a sign of a wound, not one drop of blood.

BARON. We all believed he'd merely fainted——

COUNTESS. —so, about two hours later, when——

BARON (*nervously*). —that's right, he reappeared in the hall of the villa—this is, what I was going to say——

COUNTESS. His face at this moment! I saw the whole thing in a flash.

BARON. No, no, *that's* not true, nobody had the least idea——

COUNTESS. You didn't—you were all behaving like madmen!

BARON. Everyone was performing his own part! As a joke! Oh, it was a real Tower of Babel——

COUNTESS. You can imagine our horror, can't you, Doctor, when we realized *he* was playing his part—in earnest?

DOCTOR. Oh, so he too . . .

BARON. Exactly. He entered. Came into the midst of us. We assumed he'd recovered and that he was just acting—like the rest of us . . . only better—he was a fine actor, as I told you—in short, we assumed he was joking.

COUNTESS. Some of the others started fooling with him, jostling, fighting . . . and at a certain point he was hit . . .

BARON. At that instant . . .—he was armed—he drew his imperial sword and bore down on a couple of us. What a moment! Scared the pants off us.

COUNTESS. I shall never forget the scene: all those masked faces, distorted, panic-stricken, turned toward that terrible mask, which was now no mask at all, but the very face of lunacy!

BARON. The Emperor! It was Henry the Fourth himself in a moment of fury!

COUNTESS. His obsession with the masquerade was taking effect, Doctor. He'd been obsessed with it for over a month. And everything he did was an obsession of this sort.

BARON. The things he studied for the purpose! Down to the smallest details . . . minutiae . . .

DOCTOR. Yes, I see. What with the fall, and the blow on the head that caused the damage to his brain, the momentary obsession was perpetuated. Became a fixation, as we say. One can go raving mad, one can become simpleminded . . .

BARON (*to* FRIDA *and the* MARQUIS). You see the tricks life plays, my dears? (*To the* MARQUIS). You weren't more than four or five. (*To* FRIDA.) It seems to your mother that you've taken her place in the portrait though at the time she hadn't even dreamed of bringing into the world. I have gray hair now. And as for him—(*He clicks finger and thumb.*)—he was hit in the neck—and he's never moved since. He is the Emperor—Henry the Fourth!

DOCTOR (*who has been lost in thought, now takes his hands from before his face as if to focus everyone's attention upon himself, and starts to give his scientific explanation*). Well, ladies and gentlemen, it all comes down to this . . .

(*But all of a sudden the first door on the right—the one nearest the footlights—opens, and* BERTOLD *emerges, his face very excited.*)

BERTOLD (*rushing in like a man at the end of his tether*). Excuse me, everybody . . .

(*But he stops directly when he sees the confusion that his entry has created.*)

FRIDA (*with a cry of horror, drawing back.*) My God, it's he!

COUNTESS (*stepping back, upset, with an arm raised so as not to see him*). It's he. He?

MARQUIS (*promptly*). No, no, no! Don't be excited!

DOCTOR (*astonished*). Then who is it?

BARON. A fugitive from the masquerade!

MARQUIS. He's one of the four young fellows we keep here to . . . um, back him up in his lunacy.

BERTOLD. I beg your pardon, Marquis . . .

MARQUIS. So you should! I'd given orders for the doors to be locked! No one was to come in!

BERTOLD. Yes, I know, Marquis. But I

can't bear it! I've come to beg off! I want to quit!

MARQUIS. Ah! So you're the one who was to start work this morning?

BERTOLD. Yes, Marquis. But I can"t bear it, I tell you—

COUNTESS (*to the* MARQUIS *in lively consternation*). Then he *isn't* calm—you said he was!

BERTOLD (*promptly*). That's not it, madam, it isn't him! It's my three comrades. You say they "back him up," Marquis. Back him up! They don't back him up—because it's them that's mad! I come here for the first time, and instead of helping me, Marquis . . .

(LANDOLF *and* HARALD *come to the same door on the right, in haste, anxiously, but stopping at the door.*)

LANDOLF. May we come in?

HARALD. May we, dear Marquis?

MARQUIS. Come in then! But what on earth is the matter? What are you all up to?

FRIDA. O God, I'm going, I'm scared out of my wits! (*She starts to go toward the door on the left.*)

MARQUIS (*who at once holds her back*). No, no, Frida!

LANDOLF. Marquis, this dumbbell . . . (*Indicating* BERTOLD.)

BERTOLD (*protesting*). No: thanks very much, my friends! I'm not staying!

LANDOLF. What do you mean, you're not staying?

HARALD. He's ruined *everything,* Marquis, running in here like this! Ts, ts, ts!

LANDOLF. He's driven him absolutely crazy. We can't keep him in there any longer. He's given orders for this fellow's arrest. Wants to pass judgment on him. From the throne. What's to be done?

MARQUIS. Lock the door of course! Go and lock that door!

(LANDOLF *starts to do so.*)

HARALD. But Ordulf won't be able to hold him all by himself!

LANDOLF (*stopping*). Marquis, if we could just announce your visit: it would be a distraction for him. Have you gentlemen thought what you'll wear in his presence . . .

MARQUIS. Oh. yes, we've thought the whole thing out. (*To the* DOCTOR.) Doctor, if you think we can make the call at once. . . .

FRIDA. I won't, I won't, Carlo! I'm leaving. You come with me, Mamma, please!

DOCTOR. Tell me, Marquis . . . he won't be armed, will he?

MARQUIS. Armed? Of course not, Doctor. (*To* FRIDA.) Forgive me, Frida, but these fears of yours are really childish. You wanted to come . . .

FRIDA. I didn't! I didn't at all: it was Mother!

COUNTESS (*firmly*). Well, I'm ready! So what are we to do?

BARON. Is all this dressing up really necessary?

LANDOLF. Oh, yes, Baron, it's essential! Unhappily, he just sees *us* . . . (*He shows his costume.*) He *mustn't* see you gentlemen in modern dress!

HARALD. He'd think it was some devilish travesty, dear Baron!

MARQUIS. Just as these men seem a travesty to you, to him *we*—in our modern clothes—would seem a travesty.

LANDOLF. And maybe it wouldn't much matter, Marquis, only he'd think it was the work of his mortal enemy!

BARON. The Pope?

LANDOLF. Right. He says he's a pagan.

BARON. The Pope a pagan? Not bad!

LANDOLF. A pagan who conjures up the dead! He accuses him of all the black arts. Lives in constant fear of him.

DOCTOR. Ha! Persecution mania!

HARALD. Oh, he'd be furious, dear sir—

MARQUIS (*to the* BARON). But you don't have to be there, if I may say so.

We'll leave that way. It's enough if the doctor sees him.

DOCTOR. You mean . . . just me?

MARQUIS. They'll be present. (*Indicating the three young men.*)

DOCTOR. It's not that . . . I mean, if the Countess . . .

COUNTESS. That's right: *I* want to be there! I want to see him!

FRIDA. But why, Mother? Come with us, do!

COUNTESS (*imperiously*). Leave me alone, I came for this! (*To* LANDOLF.) I shall be his mother-in-law, Adelaide.

LANDOLF. Marvelous. Yes. Adelaide, the Empress Bertha's mother. Marvelous! Your ladyship need only put on a cloak —to hide these clothes. And the ducal crown on your head, of course. (*To* HARALD.) Go on, Harald, go on!

HARALD. Just a moment, dear boy, what about this gentleman? (*indicating the* DOCTOR.)

DOCTOR. Oh, yes . . . they told me the Bishop, I believe . . . the Bishop of Cluny.

HARALD. You mean the Abbot, dear sir? That'll be simply divine: the Abbot of Cluny!

LANDOLF. He's been here so often before . . .

DOCTOR (*astonished*). He's been here before?

LANDOLF. Don't be afraid, sir. I only mean it's an easy disguise and . . .

HARALD. And it's been used *often,* dear sir.

DOCTOR. But . . . but . . .

LANDOLF. No, no, he won't remember. It's the clothes he looks at—not the man inside them.

COUNTESS. That'll be just as well. For me, too.

MARQUIS. You and I'll be going, Frida. You come with us, Tito.

BARON. What? Oh. No, no, if she stays, um, (*indicating the Countess*) I'll stay, of course.

COUNTESS. I don't need you in the least, my dear Baron.

BARON. I didn't say you needed me! But you're not the only one who wants to see *him.* Surely I can stay if I want?

LANDOLF (*helping out*). Yes, um, maybe it's better if there are three!

HARALD. Then the gentleman will surely——

BARON. Yes, I'll need a disguise. Make it an easy one.

LANDOLF (*to* HARALD). I have it! *He* can be from Cluny, too.

BARON. From Cluny; how do you mean?

LANDOLF. The cassock of a monk from Cluny Abbey. He can be in attendance on the Abbot. (*Still to* HARALD.) Now, go, go! (*To* BERTOLD.) You go too, and keep out of sight all day today! (*But as soon as he sees him going.*) Wait! Bring the clothes he gives you! (*To* HARALD.) And you go and announce the arrival of his mother-in-law and the Abbot of Cluny.

HARALD. It shall be done, dear boy.

(HARALD *shepherds* BERTOLD *out by the first door on the right.*)

MARQUIS. Now we can go, Frida.

(*With* FRIDA *he leaves by the door on the left.*)

DOCTOR (*to* LANDOLF). I take it he should think rather well of me—when I'm the Abbot of Cluny?

LANDOLF. Quite right, you can count on it, sir. The Abbot has always been received with great respect. So have you: *you* needn't worry either, my lady. He hasn't forgotten it was due to the intercession of the two of you that he was admitted to the castle at Canossa and brought before the Pope, who hadn't *wanted* to receive him at all. Kept him waiting in the snow for two days—he almost froze.

BARON. What about me, may I ask?

LANDOLF. You, sir? Oh, yes. You should, um—stand deferentially apart.

COUNTESS (*irritated, very nervous*). Oh, why didn't you leave?

BARON (*quietly, but nettled*). You're certainly very worked up over . . .

COUNTESS (*with pride*). I am as I am! Leave me in peace!

(BERTOLD *returns with the clothes.*)

LANDOLF (*seeing him enter*). Oh, good, here are the clothes! —This cloak for the Countess.

COUNTESS. Wait, I must take my hat off.

(*She does so and gives it to* BERTOLD.)

LANDOLF. Put it over there, Bertold. (*Then to the* COUNTESS, *preparing to place the ducal crown on her head.*) May I, Countess?

COUNTESS. But, heavens, isn't there a mirror here?

LANDOLF. There are mirrors in there. (*He points through the left entrance.*) If your ladyship would prefer to put it on yourself?

COUNTESS. Oh, yes, it'll be much better, give it to me, it won't take a minute.

(*She takes the hat back and goes out with* BERTOLD, *who is carrying the crown and the cloak. In the meantime the* DOCTOR *and the* BARON *put on the monks' cassocks as best they can.*)

BARON. Well, I must say, I never expected to be a Benedictine monk! Think what a heap of money this madness is costing!

DOCTOR (*defensively*). Oh, well, my dear Baron, lots of other kinds of madness cost . . .

BARON. Surely, if you have a fortune to put into them!

LANDOLF. Yes, indeed. In there we have an entire wardrobe of costumes of the period. Tailored to perfection after ancient models. It's my special job—I commission theatrical costumers, experts. It costs plenty.

(*The* COUNTESS *reenters, wearing cloak and crown.*)

BARON (*immediately, in admiration*). Ah, magnificent, truly royal!

COUNTESS (*seeing the* BARON *and bursting out laughing*). Good God, no! Take it off! You're impossible! You look like an ostrich in monk's feathers!

BARON. Well, look at the doctor for that matter!

DOCTOR. Don't be hard on *me,* Countess.

COUNTESS. Oh, you'll do, *you're* all right. (*To the* BARON.) But you're ludicrous!

DOCTOR (*to* LANDOLF). You have many receptions here then?

LANDOLF. It depends. Many times he gives orders for such and such a person to be presented to him. Then we have to hunt up someone who'll serve the purpose. Women, too . . .

COUNTESS (*touché but trying to hide the fact*). Ah! Women, too?

LANDOLF. At one time there were rather a lot of women.

BARON (*laughing*). Wonderful! In costume? (*Indicating the* COUNTESS.) Like that?

LANDOLF. Well, you know: any women who'd . . .

BARON. Who'd serve the purpose? I see! (*With innuendo, to the* COUNTESS.) Take care, it may get dangerous for you!

(*The second door on the right opens and* HARALD *appears. First he gives a furtive sign to stop all conversation in the room. Then he announces, solemnly*)

HARALD. His Majesty the Emperor!

(*First, the* TWO VALETS *enter, taking up their positions at the foot of the throne. Then, between* ORDULF *and* HARALD, *who hold themselves back a little, deferentially,* EMPEROR HENRY *enters. He is nearly fifty, very pale, and already gray at the back of his head—while on the temples and forehead he seems blond because of very obvious, almost childish hair dye. High on each cheek, in the midst of that tragic pallor, is a patch of red, doll makeup, this too very obvious. Over his regal habit he wears a penitent's sack, as at Canossa. His eyes are characterized by a horrifying, convulsive fixity. At the same time he expresses the attitude of a penitent who wishes to be all humility and repentance. One feels that the humility is as ostentatious as the humiliation is deserved.* ORDULF *carries the imperial crown in both hands,* HARALD *the scepter and eagle and the globe and cross.*)

HENRY (*bowing first to the* COUNTESS, *then to the* DOCTOR). My Lady . . . My Lord Abbot . . .

(*He then looks at the* BARON, *starts to bow to him, too, but turns to* LANDOLF, *who has gone over to his side, and asks, suspiciously, and in an undertone,*)

Is it Peter Damiani?

LANDOLF. No, your Majesty, it's a monk of Cluny: he came with the Abbot.

HENRY (*turns to scrutinize the* BARON *with increasing suspicion and, noting that the latter, hesitant and embarrassed, turns to the* COUNTESS *and the* DOCTOR *as if to take counsel from their eyes, draws himself up very straight and shouts*). It is the Pope's henchman Father Damiani—It's no use, Father, looking at her like that! (*Suddenly turning to the* COUNTESS *as if to ward off a danger.*) I swear, my lady, I swear to you, my mind is changed toward your daughter, though I confess that I'd have divorced her if he (*indicates the* BARON) hadn't come to stop me. Oh, yes: there were people prepared to favor such a divorce. The Bishop of Mainz would have arranged it in return for one hundred and twenty farms. (*Steals a look, rather perplexed, at* LANDOLF *and then suddenly says:*) But at this time I should say nothing against the bishops. (*Humble now, he is in front of the* BARON). I'm grateful to you, believe me, Peter Damiani, I'm glad you stopped me!—My whole life is made up of humiliations! My mother, Adalbert, Tribur, and now Goslar with my young men of the lower aristocracy! (*Of a sudden he changes his tone and speaks like someone who, in a clever parenthesis, runs through a part he is rehearsing.*) But it doesn't matter! Clarity in one's ideas, insight, firmness in behavior, and patience in adversity! (*Then he turns to them all and with contrite gravity says,*) I know how to correct my errors, and I abase myself even before you, Peter Damiani! (*Bows low to him, and then stays with his back bent, as if under the impulsion of an oblique suspicion. It is new, but it makes him add, almost in spite of himself, in a threatening tone,*) Except that it was you who started the obscene rumor about my mother Agnes and Henry, Bishop of Augsburg!

BARON (*since Henry stays bent over, with one finger pointed threateningly at him, places his hands on his breast and then speaks in denial*). No . . . no, it was not . . .

HENRY (*straightening up*). You say it wasn't? Sheer infamy! (*Glares at him and then says,*) I wouldn't have thought you could! (*Approaches the* DOCTOR *and pulls at his sleeve a little, winking with some cunning.*) It's them! It always is, isn't it, my Lord Abbot?

HARALD (*quietly, whispering, as if prompting the* DOCTOR). That's it: the rapacious bishops!

DOCTOR (*turned toward* HARALD, *trying to stick to his "part"*). Oh, them . . . of course, them!

HENRY. They were insatiable! When I was a little child, my Lord Abbot—even an emperor has a childhood—he doesn't know he's an emperor in fact—he's just a kid at play, letting time go by . . . I was six years old and they snatched me from my mother and made use of me against her without my knowing, against her and against the dynasty itself, profaning, robbing, marauding, one greedier than the other—Anno greedier than Stefan, Stefan greedier than Anno!

LANDOLF (*in a persuasive undertone, to get his attention*). Your Majesty . . .

HENRY (*turning of a sudden*). You're right! At this time I shouldn't speak ill of the bishops.—But this infamous slander against my mother, my Lord Abbot, goes beyond the bounds! (*Melting, as he looks at the* COUNTESS.) And I may not even weep for her, my Lady.—I turn to you, you are a mother, you must feel it here. (*Indicates the pit of his stomach.*) She came from her convent to seek me out a month ago now. They had told me she was dead. (*Sustained pause, dense with emotion. Then with a most mournful smile,*) I cannot mourn her because if you are here and I am dressed like this (*shows his sackcloth*) it means I am twenty-six years old.

HARALD (*almost in an undertone, sweetly, to comfort him*). It means she is still alive, your Majesty.

ORDULF (*in the same manner*). And still in her convent.

HENRY (*turns to look at them*). True. So I can postpone my grief to another occasion. (*Almost coquettishly he shows the* COUNTESS *the dye on his hair.*) Look, I'm still blond . . . (*Then quietly, confidentially,*) for you!—*I* wouldn't need it, but externals do help. Milestones of time, aren't they, my Lord Abbot? (*He returns to the* COUNTESS *and, observing her hair*) Ah, but I see that . . . you too, my Lady . . . (*He winks, makes an expressive sign with one hand as if to say her hair is false—but without a hint of scorn, rather with mischievous admiration.*) Heaven keep me from amazement or disgust!—O vanity of human wishes: we try to ignore the obscure and fatal power that sets limits to our will! What *I* say is, if one is born and died—did you wish to be born, Lord Abbot, did you will your own birth? I didn't—and between birth and death, both of them independent of our will, so many things happen that we all wish wouldn't happen. Willy-nilly, we resign ourselves to them.

DOCTOR (*just to say something while he scrutinizes* HENRY). It's true, alas!

HENRY. But when we're not resigned, we always start wishing and willing! A woman wishes to be a man, an old man wishes to be young. . . . None of us is lying, there's no conscious deception in it, it's simply this: in entire good faith we are fixed in some fine conception of ourselves, as in a shell or a suit of armor. However, my lord, while you keep this firm grip on yourself, holding onto your holy cassock with both hands, something is slipping away from you unnoticed, slithering down your sleeves, gliding off like a serpent. That something is LIFE, my lord. And when you see your life suddenly taking shape, coagulating outside you in this way, you are surprised. You despise yourself, you're furious with yourself. And the remorse, the remorse! How many times I've seen my own remorse—with a face that was my own and yet so horrible I couldn't behold it! (*He returns to the* COUNTESS.) Has this never happened to you, Countess? You can recall being always the same, can you? But, once upon a time, I tell you . . . how can it be? How *could* you do such a thing? (*He looks her so sharply in the eyes, she nearly faints.*) Such a thing as . . . precisely . . . we understand each other. But don't worry, I won't breathe a word to anyone! And you, Peter Damiani, how could you be a friend to *that* man . . .

LANDOLF (*as above*). Your Majesty . . .

HENRY (*at once*). No, no, I won't name him, I know it would be too annoying for you. (*Turning on the* BARON, *as if by stealth.*) What an opinion, what an opinion you had of him, eh?—All the same, every one of us clings to his idea of himself—like a man who dyes his hair when he grows old. What if the color of the dye in my hair cannot, for you, be that of my real hair? You, Lady, certainly don't dye your hair to deceive others or even yourself. You only deceive—and ever so little at that—your own image in the glass. I do it as a joke. You do it in earnest. But, however much in earnest, you too are in disguise, Lady, and I don't mean the venerable crown that rings your forehead and which I bow before, I don't mean your ducal mantle, I mean you wish to fix a memory in your mind, artificially, the memory of your blond hair as it was when, one day, it pleased you—or of your dark hair if you were dark—the fading image of your youth. With you it's different, isn't it, Peter Damiani? You're not interested in *fixing* your memories, are you? For you, to remember what you have been, what you have done, is but to recognize the realities of the past which have lived on inside you, isn't that so? Like a dream. Like a dream! *My* memories are like that too, inexplicable to me as I think them over. . . . Oh, well, don't be amazed, Peter Damiani: it'll be the same tomorrow with your life of today! (*Suddenly getting into a rage and seizing his sackcloth.*) This sackcloth here! (*With almost fierce joy he begins to take it off while* HARALD *and* ORDULF *at once run up in horror to stop him.*) Oh, God! (*Drawing back and taking off the sackcloth he shouts to them.*) Tomorrow, at Brixen, twenty-seven German and Lombard bishops will sign with me the deposition of the Pope!

ORDULF (*with the other two, imploring him to be silent*). Your Majesty! In God's name!

HARALD (*motioning to him to put the sackcloth on again*). Take care, your Majesty!

LANDOLF. The Abbot is here with the Countess Matilda to intercede in your favor! (*Furtively makes urgent signs to the* DOCTOR *to say something at once.*)

DOCTOR (*worried*). Um, yes, of course . . . we came to intercede . . . sire . . .

HENRY (*repenting at once, almost terrified, lets the three of them put the sackcloth back on for him. He pulls it down over him with convulsive hands*). Pardon! That's it: pardon, pardon, my Lord Abbot, pardon, Lady! . . . I swear to you, I feel the weight of the anathema, I do!

(*He bends down with his head in his hands as if expecting something to fall and crush him. He stays like this a moment. Then, in a changed voice but in an unchanged position, he says softly and confidentially to* LANDOLF, HARALD, *and* ORDULF,)

I don't know why, but somehow I *can't* be humble before that man! (*Indicating the* BARON *quasi-secretly.*)

LANDOLF (*in an undertone*). But, your Majesty, why do you persist in believing it's Peter Damiani? It isn't at all!

HENRY (*looking at them askance, fearfully*). It isn't Peter Damiani?

HARALD. No, no, it's just a poor monk, your Majesty!

HENRY (*mournfully, with plaintive exasperation*). Perhaps you, Lady, can understand me better than the others because you are a woman. This is a solemn and decisive moment. I could, look you, accept the aid of the Lombard bishops, capture the Pope, run to Rome, and set up a pope of my own choosing!—But I do not give way to the temptation, and believe me, I'm right. I know the drift of the times. I know the majesty of a man who *can* be what he should be, a pope!—Would you be inclined to laugh at me in my present situation? You're stupid if you do. You don't understand the political shrewdness which enjoins this penitential habit upon me. I tell you that, tomorrow, the roles could be reversed. And then what would you do? Would you laugh to see a pope in captive's clothes?—No.—Yet the two cases are the same. Today I wear the mask of a penitent, tomorrow he wears the mask of a prisoner. Woe betide the man who knows not how to wear his mask, whether of pope or emperor!—Perhaps his Holiness is, at present, a little too cruel, that's true. Think, Lady, how Bertha—your daughter and my wife—toward whom, I repeat, my heart is changed (*He turns suddenly on the* BARON *and shouts in his face as if the latter had said him nay.*) changed, CHANGED—because of the affection, the devotion she was able to show me in that terrible moment!

(*He stops, convulsed by his angry outburst, and makes an effort to hold himself in, a groan of exasperation in his throat; then, with sweet and mournful humility, he turns again to the* COUNTESS.)

She has come with me, Lady. She is below, in the courtyard. She insisted on following me as a beggar. And she is frozen, frozen from two nights in the open, in the snow. You are her mother. May the bowels of your compassion be moved: with his aid (*indicating the* DOCTOR) beg the Pope's pardon! Induce him to receive us!

COUNTESS (*trembling, a thin thread of voice*). Yes, sire, at once, yes . . .

DOCTOR. Yes, sire, we'll do it!

HENRY. And one more thing, one more! (*He summons them round about him and speaks quietly, as if telling a great secret.*) You see me? I am a penitent, and I swear I'll remain one till the Pope receives me. But it's not enough that he receive me. (*Pause. He starts again.*) You know how he can do anything, literally anything, even to calling up the dead? Now, my Lord Abbot, now, my Lady: my real punishment is (*pointing to himself*)—*here*—or (*pointing to the picture of himself*) if you like, *there*—for it consists in the fact that I cannot cut myself loose from that piece of magic! When the excommunication is revoked, I want you two to make another request of him who can do everything, namely, that he cut me loose from that picture and let me live! Let me live my poor life, the life I've been excluded from, let me have it intact, entire! One cannot go on being twenty-six forever, Lady! I ask this favor for your daughter, too. So that, well disposed as I am toward her, and so deeply affected by her compassion, I may love her as she deserves. That's all. Just that. I am in your hands. (*He bows.*) My Lady! My Lord Abbot!

(*Still bowing, he starts to withdraw by the door through which he entered. The* BARON, *who had come forward a little to hear the proceedings, now turns to go back again to his place.* HENRY *assumes he wishes to steal the imperial crown which is on the throne. Amid general concern and astonishment,* HENRY *runs over, takes it, hides it under his sackcloth, then, with a cunning smile on his lips and in his eyes, he starts bowing again and disappears. The* COUNTESS *is so deeply disturbed she falls into a chair with a crash, almost fainting.*)

ACT II

Scene I

Another room in the villa. Antique and austere furniture. On the right, about eighteen inches from the floor, is a raised platform very like a church choir, with a ring of wooden pilasters around it, the ring being broken at the front and sides by two steps. On the platform are a table and six stools of the period, one at the head and two on each side. The main door is at the rear. On the left there are two windows looking out on the garden. On the right there is another door.

It is later in the afternoon of the same day. The COUNTESS, *the* DOCTOR, *and the* BARON *are on stage. They are conversing, but the* COUNTESS *stands gloomily on one side, clearly very irritated by what the other two are saying, though she can't help listening because in her present disturbed state everything interests her in spite of herself—so that she can't concentrate on perfecting the plan which hovers before her mind's eye and beckons and is stronger than she is. The words which she hears the others speak attract her attention because she instinctively feels something like a need to be held fast in the present.*

BARON. Well, my dear Doctor, you *may* be right, but that's my impression.

DOCTOR. I won't gainsay you but I rather think it's only . . . well, yes, an impression.

BARON. But he said it in so many words, my dear Doctor! (*Turning to the* COUNTESS.) Didn't he, Countess?

COUNTESS (*interrupted in her thoughts, turning*). Said what? Oh, yes . . . But not for the reason you think.

DOCTOR. He was referring to the clothes we'd put on. (*To the* COUNTESS.) Your cloak, our Benedictine cassocks. The whole thing is childish!

COUNTESS (*in a little burst, indignant, again turning*). Childish? Doctor, what are you saying?

DOCTOR. On the one hand, it's childish —let me speak, Countess, I beg—and on the other hand, it's much more complicated than you could possibly imagine.

COUNTESS. Not at all. To me, it's crystal-clear.

DOCTOR (*with the expert's pitying smile for the nonexpert*). All the same! One must take account of that special psychology of madmen according to which, you see, one can be sure that the madman sees, sees right through the disguise we confront him with, sees through it and at the same time accepts it, believes in it, like a child, to whom it is both reality and a game. That's why I said it's all childish. But then it's highly complicated, too—in this respect: that he is, he must be, perfectly aware of being—an image. To himself, I mean. In his own eyes. He is an image. The image in the picture. (*He points out left where the picture is.*)

BARON. He said that!

DOCTOR. Precisely.—Now: to this image, other images have just presented themselves. Ours. The images we created in those clothes. Don't imagine he isn't clever and clear-sighted in his lunacy! On the contrary, he was at once aware of the difference between his sort of image and ours. He knew there was in ours an element of deliberate fiction. So he was suspicious. All madmen are fortified by constant, vigilant suspicion. Not that he could see any further than that. He couldn't see compassion in the way we adapted our game to his. His own game seemed the more tragic to us the more he tried to reveal that it was only a game. Coming before us with paint on his cheeks and temples! To tell us he'd done it on purpose, as a joke! That's how suspicious he is! And how defiant!

COUNTESS (*again breaking out*). No, Doctor, that's not it, that's not it at all!

DOCTOR. What do you mean, that's not it?

COUNTESS (*positively trembling*). I am quite sure he recognized me.

DOCTOR. Out of the question, out of the question!

BARON (*at the same time as the* DOCTOR). Nonsense, nonsense!

COUNTESS (*even more positively, almost convulsed*). He recognized me, I tell you. When he came over to talk to me at close quarters, he looked me in the eyes, deep in the eyes, and recognized me!

BARON. But if he talked of your daughter . . .

COUNTESS. He didn't!—It was me, he was speaking of me!

BARON. Perhaps so, when he said . . .

COUNTESS (*at once, without restraint*). About my dyed hair? But didn't you notice how he right away added: "or the memory of your dark hair if you were dark"?—He remembered perfectly well that in those days I *was* dark.

BARON. Nonsense, nonsense!

COUNTESS (*taking no notice of him, turning to the* DOCTOR). My hair is dark really, Doctor, like my daughter's. *That* is why he started talking of her!

BARON. But he doesn't even know your daughter; he's never seen her!

COUNTESS. Exactly! You understand nothing. By my daughter, he meant me. Me—as I was "in those days"!

BARON. Great heavens, this is catching!

COUNTESS (*quietly, with contempt*). What's catching? You fool!

BARON. Tell me, were you ever his wife? In his lunacy your daughter is his wife, Bertha of Susa.

COUNTESS. That's precisely it! Not being dark anymore—as he remembers me—but like this, blond, I was introduced to him as his wife's mother.—For him my daughter doesn't exist—he never saw her—you said so yourself. So how can he know if she's blond or dark?

BARON. Oh, he just happened to say dark, sort of in general, for heaven's sake. Like anyone who wants to tie down a memory of youth with the color of a girl's hair—blond, brunette, what have you. As ever, you go off into foolish fantasies.—Doctor, you say *I* oughtn't to have come here, but what about *her?*

COUNTESS (*is defeated for a moment by the* BARON*'s argument. She has been lost in thought but now she takes hold of herself, the more excited because she is unsure of herself*). No . . . no, he was speaking of me . . . He talked *to* me, *with* me, *of* me . . .

BARON. Not so bad! He never left *me* for a moment, I couldn't *breathe,* and you say he was talking with you the whole time? Maybe you think he was alluding to you when he spoke with "Peter Damiani?"

COUNTESS (*defiantly, almost breaking the bounds of decorum*). Who knows?—Can you explain to me why, from the very first moment, he felt an aversion to you, to you in particular?

(*The answer must be almost explicitly expressed in the tone of the query. It is: "Because he understood that you are my lover." The* BARON *gets the point. Discomfited, he stands there emptily smiling.*)

DOCTOR. May I say the reason could also be that only two persons' arrival had been announced: the Emperor's mother-in-law, Adelaide and the Abbot of Cluny. When he discovered a third person who hadn't been announced, suspicion at once . . .

BARON. Of course: suspicion at once made him see in me an enemy, Peter Damiani.—But if *she's* got it into her head that he recognized her . . .

COUNTESS. There's not the least doubt of it!—His eyes told me, Doctor. There's a way of looking at someone that leaves no doubt whatsoever, *you* know that. Perhaps it was only for an instant, but what more do you want?

DOCTOR. It's entirely possible he could have a lucid interval . . .

COUNTESS. It's possible—you admit it! But that's not all. His talk seemed to me full, brim-full, of regret for my youth and his, regret for the horrible thing that happened to him, the thing that has held him here in a mask he can't cut from his face. But he'd like to, Doctor. Oh, how he longs to cut loose!

BARON. Yes: and why? He wants to start loving your daughter. Or even you. Softened, as you think, by the pity you feel for him.

COUNTESS. Which is great, don't make light of it.

BARON. I won't, my dear Countess. I'm sure a faith healer would consider the miracle more than likely.

DOCTOR. May *I* speak? I don't perform miracles. I am not a faith healer. I am a doctor. I've been listening to everything that's been said, and I must repeat what I've told you already. Every elaborate or, as we say, systemized form of lunacy is characterized by what we call analogical elasticity. In him this elasticity is no longer . . . well, um, elastic. It has worked loose, it's limp. In short, the various elements of his lunacy aren't holding together. Years ago he superimposed a second personality upon himself, but now it's proving next to impossible for him to maintain his equilibrium within it—because (and this is very reassuring) of the attacks this second personality is being subjected to. Sudden recollections are wrenching him free from what has been his state of mind hitherto, a state of mind we call incipient apathy—no, that's not right either, it's really a morbid wallowing in reflective melancholy, accompanied by, yes, considerable cerebral activity. Very reassuring, I say. And now, if by the trick—I should say, the shock treatment—we've planned . . .

COUNTESS (*turning toward the window, in the tone of a querulous invalid*). How is it the car hasn't come back yet? In three and a half hours . . .

DOCTOR (*stunned*). What do you say?

COUNTESS. The car, Doctor. It's more than three and a half hours now!

DOCTOR (*taking out his watch and looking at it*). Yes, more than four, for that matter!

COUNTESS. They could have been here half an hour ago at least, that chauffeur . . .

BARON. Perhaps he couldn't find the dress.

COUNTESS. But I told him exactly where it was. (*She is very impatient.*) And where's Frida?

BARON (*leaning out of the window a little*). Maybe she's in the garden with Carlo.

DOCTOR. He'll talk the fear out of her!

BARON. It isn't fear, Doctor, don't you believe it: It's just that she's annoyed.

COUNTESS. Do me the favor of not asking her to do this! I know how she is!

DOCTOR. Let's wait. Patiently. Anyhow, it'll only take a moment, and it has to be in the evening.—If, as I was saying, our shock treatment shakes him up till, at a single blow, he breaks the threads that still bind this fiction of his together, threads that are slack enough as it is, if, I say, we give him back what he himself demands—"One cannot go on being twenty-six forever," he said—namely, liberation from this punishment, which even he regards as a punishment, in short, if we can help him regain, all at once, his sense of time, his sense of duration——

BARON (*stepping in*). He will be cured! (*Then underlining his words with irony.*) We shall have cut him loose from his delusion!

DOCTOR. We can hope he'll start going again—like a clock stopped at a certain hour. Here we stand, so to speak, watch in hand, waiting for that watch to start up. A shake, like this! And now let's hope it'll begin to tell the time again, it's been stopped quite long enough.

(*At this point the* MARQUIS *enters by the main door.*)

COUNTESS. Carlo . . . where's Frida? Isn't she here?

MARQUIS. Yes, Countess. She'll be in at any moment.

DOCTOR. The car got back?

MARQUIS. Yes, Doctor.

COUNTESS. He found the dress, that chauffeur?

MARQUIS. Yes, yes, he found it.

DOCTOR. Well, that's a relief!

COUNTESS (*shuddering*). Then where is it? Where is it?

MARQUIS (*shrugging his shoulders and smiling sadly with the air of one who lends himself unwillingly to a jest that is out of place*). You'll see soon enough, Countess. (*Indicating the direction of the main entrance.*) Watch . . .

(BERTOLD *presents himself at the threshold solemnly announcing,*)

BERTOLD. Her Ladyship the Countess Matilda—of Canossa!

(*Magnificent and very lovely,* FRIDA *at once enters. She is dressed in her mother's old dress, that is, as the Countess Matilda of Tuscany, and appears a living version of the dead image we have seen in the throne-room portrait.*)

FRIDA (*as she passes the bowing figure of* BERTOLD, *says to him with contemptuous gravity*). Of Tuscany, Matilda of Tuscany, please! Canossa is just a castle of mine!

BARON (*admiring her*). Ah! Well! She looks like someone I know!

COUNTESS. Like me!—God in heaven, do you see?—Stop, Frida!—Do you see? It's my picture come to life!

DOCTOR. Yes, yes . . . to a T, to a T! The portrait!

BARON. No question of that, the portrait! Just look at her: what a girl!

FRIDA. Now don't make me laugh or I'll burst. Heavens, what a wasp waist you had, Mamma! I could hardly squeeze myself into it.

COUNTESS (*convulsed, helping to fix the dress*). Wait . . . keep still . . . Now these pleats . . . Does it really feel so tight?

FRIDA. Stifling! For heaven's sake, let's be quick . . .

DOCTOR. Oh, but we must wait till evening . . .

FRIDA. No, no, I can't! I can't hold out that long!

COUNTESS. But why on earth did you put it on so early?

FRIDA. When I saw it . . . the temptation . . . was irresistible . . .

COUNTESS. At least you could have taken me with you. Or had someone help you. . . . It's all crumpled—oh, dear! . . .

FRIDA. I know, Mamma, but they're such old creases . . . it'd be hard to get them out.

DOCTOR. It doesn't matter, Countess. The illusion is perfect. (*Then, approaching and asking her to stand in front of her daughter, though without concealing her.*) Pardon me. We place them . . . thus . . . at a certain distance . . . will you stand a little further forward? . . .

BARON. And in this way we learn to appreciate the passage of time!

COUNTESS (*turning slightly to him*). Twenty years after: isn't it a catastrophe?

BARON. You exaggerate, my dear Countess.

DOCTOR (*highly embarrassed, trying to put matters to rights*). No, no! I meant . . . I mean, the dress . . . I wanted to see . . .

BARON (*laughing*). For the dress, Doctor, it's *more* than twenty years: it's eight hundred. An abyss. You want to make him jump across? You'll hit him that hard? From here (*pointing to* FRIDA) to here (*pointing to her mother*). You'll need a basket to pick up the pieces. My friends, just think for a moment: joking aside, for us it's a matter of twenty years, two dresses, and a disguise. But, for him, if, as you say, Doctor, time is fixed, if he's really living back there with her (*indicating* FRIDA) eight hundred years earlier, I tell you the jump will simply make him dizzy, make his head reel. He'll fall in our midst like a . . . (*The*

DOCTOR *shakes a finger in dissent.*) You deny it?

DOCTOR. Yes. Life, my dear Baron, renews itself. *Our* life—here—will at once be real—even to him. It will take hold of him and, at a blow, strip him of his illusion and reveal your eight hundred years as a bare twenty. It will be like certain practical jokes—the leap into space, for example, as the Freemasons do it: you think you're making a tremendous jump, then you find you've taken a single step down.

BARON. Now we're onto something. Doctor: look at Frida and her mother. We say youth goes on ahead. We imagine youth to be in front. But it isn't true, is it, Doctor? We oldsters are ahead, we are in front, we are rightly called "advanced in years," for—time is something we have a lot more *of.*

DOCTOR. Except that the past is all the time receding from us.

BARON. No, no, the point is this. They (*indicating* FRIDA *and the* MARQUIS), have still to do what we have already done, they have still to grow old, they have still to do more or less the same foolish things . . . The idea that you start out in life ahead of those who've already started—this is the great illusion, the great untruth! You are no sooner born than you start dying. He who started first is therefore furthest along of all, *he* is ahead, *he* is in front. The youngest of men is our common father Adam. Behold the Countess Matilda of Tuscany: (*Shows* FRIDA) She is eight hundred years younger than any of us! (*He makes a low bow before her.*)

MARQUIS. Please, Tito, this is no laughing matter.

BARON. Oh, if you think I'm joking . . .

MARQUIS. Certainly I do, for heaven's sake . . . ever since you arrived . . .

BARON. What? I've even dressed up as a Benedictine . . .

MARQUIS. Why, yes, for a *serious* purpose . . .

BARON. That's what I'm saying . . . if it's been serious for the others . . . Frida, now, for example . . . (*Then, turning to the* DOCTOR.) Doctor, I swear I still don't understand what you wish to do.

DOCTOR (*annoyed*). Give me a chance! —Naturally, with the Countess in the wrong costume——

BARON. You mean, she too must . . .

DOCTOR. Surely; she must wear a dress exactly like that one. (*Indicating* FRIDA'S.) The young lady enters, he see Matilda of Tuscany, then the Countess enters, and——

BARON. There'll be two Matildas of Tuscany!

DOCTOR. Two Matildas of Tuscany. Precisely. Such is our shock treatment. After that, the watch starts going again.

FRIDA (*calling him to one side*). Doctor, one moment, please!

DOCTOR. Here I am.

(*He goes over to* FRIDA *and the* MARQUIS *and is explaining things to them during the following dialogue.*)

BARON (*quietly, to the* COUNTESS). Good heavens, then . . .

COUNTESS (*turning on him with a firm expression*). Then what?

BARON. Are you really interested? You'll lend yourself to . . . this sort of thing?

COUNTESS. I owe it to *him!*

BARON. What you're doing is an insult to me, my dear.

COUNTESS. Who's thinking of *you?*

MARQUIS (*coming forward*). That's it, yes, that's what we'll do . . . (*Turning toward* BERTOLD.) You! Go and call one of the other three, will you?

BERTOLD. Yes, sir. (*He leaves by the main door.*)

COUNTESS. But first we must pretend to take our leave!

MARQUIS. Exactly. I'm sending for a

valet to prepare the leave-taking. (*To the* BARON.) *You* needn't bother, of course, you can just stay here.

BARON (*nodding ironically*). Of course, *I* needn't bother!

MARQUIS. So as not to arouse his suspicions again, you understand?

BARON. I'm a negligible quantity. Of course.

DOCTOR. His certainty that we've gone away must be absolute. Absolute.

(LANDOLF, *followed by* BERTOLD, *enters by the door on the right.*)

LANDOLF. May we come in, Marquis?

MARQUIS. Yes, come in. Now . . . you're Lolo, are you?

LANDOLF. Lolo or Landolf, as you please, Marquis.

MARQUIS. Good. Now look. The Doctor and the Countess are about to take their leave . . .

LANDOLF. Very good. All we need say is that the Pope has agreed to receive him as a result of their entreaties. He's in his apartment, groaning at the thought of what he's been saying. He's penitent, but quite sure the Pope won't oblige him. Will you come in to him? . . . You must be good enough to put those clothes on again . . .

DOCTOR. Yes, let's be going.

LANDOLF. One moment, Doctor. May I make another suggestion? You should say that Countess Matilda of Tuscany implored the Pope to receive him.

COUNTESS. So he did recognize me!

LANDOLF. No! I beg your pardon, Countess. It's because he so fears Matilda—fears her dislike. The Pope was staying in her castle. It's strange—in the version of the story I know—though doubtless you all know the truth of the matter better than I do—there's nothing about Henry being secretly in love with Matilda, is there?

COUNTESS (*at once*). Nothing at all! Quite the reverse!

LANDOLF. That's what I thought. But *he* says he loved her—he's always saying so . . .—And now he fears that her indignation on this score will hurt him with the Pope.

BARON. We must make him understand she no longer dislikes him.

LANDOLF. That's it! Precisely!

COUNTESS (*to* LANDOLF). Yes, yes, quite! (*Then, to the* BARON.) Because, in case you didn't know, it was to the prayers of Matilda and the Abbot of Cluny that the Pope yielded. And let me tell you this, my dear Baron: at that time—the time of the cavalcade, I mean—I was going to exploit this fact—I was going to show him my heart was no longer so unfriendly to him as he imagined.

BARON. Well, isn't that marvelous, Countess? You're just following history . . .

LANDOLF. Yes. So my lady could easily spare herself the trouble of wearing two disguises and present herself from the start, with the Abbot here (*indicating the* DOCTOR) in the costume of Matilda of Tuscany.

DOCTOR (*at once, with force*). No! No! For heaven's sake, not that! That would spoil everything! His impression of the confrontation must be instantaneous. A sudden blow. No, Countess, let's be going: you will again appear as his mother-in-law, Adelaide. And we'll take our leave. The essential thing is that he know we've gone. Come on now, don't let's waste any more time, there's still plenty to be done.

(*Exeunt the* DOCTOR, *the* COUNTESS, *and* LANDOLF *by the door on the right.*)

FRIDA. I'm beginning to be terribly afraid, Carlo—

MARQUIS. All over again?

FRIDA. Wouldn't it have been better if I'd seen him before? . . .

MARQUIS. Believe me, Frida, there's nothing to it! All you've got to do is stand there.

FRIDA. But isn't he raving?

MARQUIS. No, no, he's quite calm.

BARON (*with an ironic affectation of sentimentality*). He's melancholy, poor chap. Haven't you heard he loves you?

FRIDA. Thank you, but that's *why* I'm afraid.

BARON. He won't want to hurt you!

MARQUIS. And it'll only be a matter of a moment anyway . . .

FRIDA. Yes. But to be in the dark! With him!

MARQUIS. For one moment. And I'll be at your side. And the others will be in ambush at the door, ready to run to your assistance. As soon as he sees your mother, understand? As soon as he sees your mother your part is finished . . .

BARON. I'm afraid what we're doing is like digging a hole in water.

MARQUIS. Oh, don't start *that* again, Tito! I think the doctor's remedy will work perfectly!

FRIDA. So do I! I can feel it in me already . . . I'm trembling all over!

BARON. That's all very well, my friends, but madmen—little, alas, as they know it—are blessed with a certain characteristic which we're forgetting——

MARQUIS (*interrupting, annoyed*). What characteristic is that?

BARON (*forcibly*). They do not reason things out!

MARQUIS. What's reasoning got to do with it, for heaven's sake?

BARON. Why, what else is he supposed to do but reason out the situation we're confronting him with—seeing her (*indicating* FRIDA), and her mother at the same time? That's how we planned it, hm?

MARQUIS. Not in the least, it's not a matter of reasoning at all. We're confronting him with . . . "a double image of his own fiction." That's what the doctor said.

BARON (*suddenly taking off*). I've never understood why they graduate in medicine.

MARQUIS (*stunned*). Who?

BARON. The psychiatrists.

MARQUIS. Heavens above, what should they graduate in?

FRIDA. They're psychiatrists, aren't they?

BARON. They're psychiatrists, my dear: an exact legal definition! And all they do is talk. The best talker, the best psychiatrist. "Analogical elasticity," "the sense of time, of duration!" They tell you right off the bat they can't work miracles—when a miracle is precisely what we need. Of course, the more they say they're not faith healers, the more people believe they're serious—and don't they know it! They don't work miracles—but they always land on their feet—not bad, huh?

BERTOLD (*who has been spying at the door on the right, looking through the keyhole*). Here they are! They're coming!

MARQUIS. They are?

BERTOLD. I think he wants to show them out . . . Yes, yes, here he is!

MARQUIS. Let's get out then, get out at once! (*Turning to* BERTOLD *before leaving.*) You stay here!

BERTOLD. I'm to stay?

(*Without answering him, the* MARQUIS, FRIDA, *and the* BARON *make their escape by the main door, leaving* BERTOLD *lost and irresolute. The door on the right opens.* LANDOLF *enters first and at once bows. Then the* COUNTESS *enters with cloak and ducal crown as in Act One, the* DOCTOR *in the cassock of the Abbot of Cluny.* EMPEROR HENRY, *in regal robes, is between them. Behind,* ORDULF *and* HARALD.)

HENRY (*continuing what we suppose him to have been saying in the throne room*). Now I ask you, how could I possibly be clever, as you now describe me, if I'm also considered obstinate . . .

DOCTOR. Obstinate, sire? Nothing of the sort . . .

HENRY (*smiling, pleased*). For you, I'm really clever?

DOCTOR. Neither obstinate nor clever, sire, no . . .

HENRY (*stops and exclaims in the tone of someone who wishes, benevolently yet ironically, to observe that matters can't rest here*). My Lord Abbot, if obstinacy is not a vice that consorts with cleverness, I did hope that in denying it to me you might have conceded me a little cleverness instead. I assure you I could use some! But if you insist on keeping it all for yourself . . .

DOCTOR. I? You think me clever, sire?

HENRY. Oh, no, my Lord, what are you saying? You don't seem very clever to me! (*Cutting this short, so he can turn to the* COUNTESS.) With your permission—a word in confidence with our Empress' lady mother. Here on the threshold. (*He draws her a little on one side and with a great air of secrecy anxiously asks her,*) Your daughter is very dear to you, is she?

COUNTESS (*lost*). Why, of course . . .

HENRY. Would you like me to make amends for the grave wrong I have done her—by offering all my love, all my devotion? Of course you mustn't believe what my enemies say about my debauches.

COUNTESS. I don't believe it, no, I never have . . .

HENRY. So you *would* like it?

COUNTESS (*lost again*). Like—what?

HENRY. You *would* like me to love your daughter again? (*He looks at her and at once adds in a mysterious tone of mingled admonition and pain,*) Don't be friendly to Matilda of Tuscany, please don't!

COUNTESS. But I tell you again she has begged the Pope, she has pleaded with him, as much as we have . . .

HENRY (*at once, quiet, trembling*). Don't say that, don't say that, in heaven's name, don't you see how it affects me?

COUNTESS (*looks at him, then very quietly indeed as if in confidence*). You love her still?

HENRY (*dismayed*). Still? You say *still?* How do you know? No one knows, no one *must* know!!

COUNTESS. But wouldn't *she* know? She who has been on her knees for you?

HENRY (*looks at her for a moment, then says*). Do you love your daughter? (*A short pause. Turns to the* DOCTOR, *laughingly.*) Ah, my Lord, it was only afterwards I realized my wife existed, and that was rather late in the day. . . . Even now, well, I suppose I have a wife, yes, I certainly have a wife, but I assure you I hardly ever give her a thought. It may be a sin, but I don't feel her, I don't feel her in my heart. It's an extraordinary thing but her own mother doesn't feel her in her heart either. She doesn't mean very much to you, does she, Lady, confess! (*Turning to the* DOCTOR, *in exasperation.*) She talks to me of another woman, *the* other woman. (*Getting more and more excited.*) She *insists* on talking of her, she insists, I can't understand it!

LANDOLF (*humbly*). Perhaps, Majesty, you have formed an unfavorable opinion of Matilda of Tuscany and my Lady would like to remove it? (*Upset at having allowed himself this remark, he at once adds,*) I mean of course at this particular time . . .

HENRY. *You* maintain that she's my friend?

LANDOLF. At this time, yes, your Majesty!

COUNTESS. Yes, of course, that's the reason . . .

HENRY. I see. So you don't believe I love her. I see, I see. No one ever did believe it, no one ever dreamed of it, so much the better, let's change the subject.

(*He breaks off, turning to the* DOCTOR, *his face and mind completely different.*) My Lord Abbot, have you noticed? The Pope will revoke the excommunication on certain conditions. Have you noticed that these conditions have nothing, nothing to do with the original reason he had for excommunicating me? Go tell Pope Gregory I'll settle accounts with him at Brixen! And you, Lady, should you chance to meet your daughter—let's say down in the courtyard of your friend's castle—your friend Matilda of Tuscany —well, what shall I say? Have her come up. And we'll see if I don't succeed in keeping her at my side: wife and empress. Many women, before now, have come here telling me, assuring me, they were she—the wife I knew I had . . . and, well, sometimes I actually tried—there's nothing shameful in that, is there?—with one's wife—But every one of them, when she tried to say she was Bertha, that she came from Susa, I don't know why, burst out laughing! (*As if in confidence.*) We were in bed, understand? I didn't have these clothes on. For that matter, well, she had no clothes on either . . . heavens, it's natural, isn't it? For a man and a woman? At those moments we don't think who we are, do we? Our clothes, on the hook, are—phantoms! (*Changing his tone again, to the* DOCTOR, *in confidence.*) In general, my Lord, I think phantoms are nothing but slight disorders of the spirit, images we don't succeed in holding within the bounds of sleep. They come out even in the daytime when we're awake and frighten us. I'm always so afraid when I see them before me at night. A confused mob of images, alighting from their horses, laughing! Sometimes I'm afraid of my own blood: it pulses in my arteries like the dull sound of footsteps in distant rooms in the silence of the night! But enough! I have kept you far too long on your feet. Your humble servant, Lady. Your servant, my Lord.

(*He has accompanied them to the threshold of the main door. He takes his leave of them and they bow. Exeunt* MATILDA *and the* DOCTOR. *He shuts the door and at once turns. Another change of expression.*)

The clowns, the clowns, the clowns! Like a color organ: touch it and, look! White, pink, yellow, green. . . . And the other fellow, Peter Damiani, ha-ha! He's hit, a bull's-eye. He's scared even to appear before me now!

(*He says this with gay, bursting frenzy, pacing and looking first in this direction, then in that, till of a sudden he sees* BERTOLD, *more than astounded and terror-struck by the sudden change. He stops in front of him and points him out to his three comrades, who also are lost in astonishment.*)

Just look at this idiot here! He stands gaping at me with his mouth open! (*Shaking him by the shoulders.*) Don't you understand? Don't you see how I dress them up, how I fool them, how I like to have them parade before me like terrified clowns! What is there to be terrified by? The fact that I tear off the comic mask and reveal all their trappings as mere disguises? As if it were not I who had forced them to wear the mask in the first place—because it pleased me to play the madman!

LANDOLF, HARALD, ORDULF (*their heads swimming, flabbergasted, looking from one to the other*). What? What do you say? Then . . . ?

HENRY (*when they speak, turning at once, and shouting imperiously*). Enough, then, let's have done with it! The whole thing annoys me! (*Then at once, as if on second thought, he isn't satisfied, he can't believe it.*) God, the effrontery of the woman, coming here, to me, now, her gigolo on her tail . . . Pretending they were doing me a favor, coming out of pity, to keep me within bounds—as if I weren't beyond everything already, beyond this world, beyond life, beyond time! The other fellow, their Peter Damiani, wouldn't have permitted such presumption, but *they* would. They would: every day, every minute, they claim that other people are what they would have them be. That isn't presumption, is it? Oh, dear no! It's their way of thinking, their way of seeing, of feeling, every man has his own! You have yours, haven't you? By all means. But what can yours be? That of a flock of sheep: miserable, frail, uncertain . . . They profit by this, they make you swallow their way, so you'll see and feel what they see and feel, or at least so they can kid themselves you will. For what, after all, do they manage to impose on you? Words! Words which each of you understands and repeats in his own fashion. That's the way so-called public opinion is formed! Woe betide the man who, one fine day, finds himself labeled with one of the words that people have been repeating. The word Madman for instance. Or the word—what's another example?—the word Idiot. Tell me something: if someone went around persuading people you are as *he* sees you—went around fixing his own judgment of you in the minds of others—could you stand idly by? "Madman, madman!"—I'm not saying right now that I do it as a joke. Earlier, before I hurt my head falling from a horse . . . (*He stops short, noting their agitation, more than ever upset and astounded.*) You're looking each other over? (*With bitter mimicry he mocks their astonishment.*) Ha? Huh? What's the revelation? Am I or am I not?—I'll tell you: I am! I am mad! (*Becoming terrible.*) And so, by God, down on your knees, down on your knees before me! (*One by one he forces them to kneel.*) I order you all to kneel before me! That's it! Now touch the floor three times with your foreheads! Down! That's how everyone should be before madmen! (*At the sight of the four kneeling men, he feels his fierce gaiety evaporate at once. He is indignant now.*) Off your knees, you cattle, get up!—You obeyed me when you might have put a strait-jacket on me?—Is a word heavy enough to crush a man with? It's a mere nothing, it's . . . like a fly!—Yet words are heavy enough to crush us all. Oh, the weight of the dead!—Here am I. Can you seriously believe Henry the Fourth is still alive? And yet: I speak and give orders to you, the living! I want you that way!—Do you think this a jest, too—the way the dead continue to take part in life? *Here,* yes, it is a jest. But go outside. Into the living world. Day is dawning. Time lies before you. Break of day. The day that lies before us, you say, will be of our own making. Hm? Of your own making? What about tradition then? Time-honored customs? Come on: speak for yourselves. You will not utter a word that has not been uttered thousands of times before. You think you are living? You are remasticating the life of the dead! (*He is now right in front of* BERTOLD, *who by this time is completely stupefied.*) You don't get it, do you, my boy?—What's your name?

BERTOLD. Me? . . . er . . . Bertold.

HENRY. Bertold? You fool! Between the two of us, what's your name?

BERTOLD. My . . . um . . . real name . . . is Fino . . .

(*No sooner have the other three started to give signs to* BERTOLD, *advising and chiding him, than* HENRY *at once turns to silence them.*)

HENRY. Fino?

BERTOLD. Fino Pagliuca, yes sir.

HENRY (*turning again to the others*). I've heard the names you use among yourselves so many times. (*To* LANDOLF.) You are called Lolo?

LANDOLF. Yes, sir. (*Then, with a burst of joy.*) Heavens! . . . So you . . . ?

HENRY (*at once, very abrupt*). So what?

LANDOLF (*straightaway growing pale*). Nothing . . . I mean . . .

HENRY. So I'm not mad anymore? No. You see me, don't you?—It's all a joke on those who believe it. (*To* HARALD.) I know your name's Franco . . . (*To* ORDULF.) And yours—one second now—

ORDULF. Momo.

HENRY. Momo, that's it! A nice state of affairs, hm?

LANDOLF (*still hesitant*). Then . . . then . . . heavens.

HENRY (*not changing*). What? No: not in the least! Let's all have a big, long, lovely laugh about it . . . (*And he bursts out laughing.*)

LANDOLF, HARALD, ORDULF (*looking each other over, uncertain, lost between joy and pain*). He's cured? It's true? What?

HENRY. Sh, sh! (*To* BERTOLD.) You don't laugh? Are you still offended? I wasn't addressing you in particular, you know.—*Everybody* finds it convenient, understand? everybody finds it convenient to believe certain people mad—as an excuse for keeping them locked up. You know why? Because they can't bear to hear what they say. What do I say of these people who've just left? That one is a harlot, another a lecher, another an impostor . . . "It's not true! No one can believe it!"—All the same, they listen to me. Terrified. *Why* do they listen—if what I say is untrue? One simply cannot believe the words of madmen. And yet they listen! Their eyes goggling with terror. Why? You tell me, you tell me why. I am calm, look!

BERTOLD. Well, because . . . maybe they think . . .

HENRY. No, my dear fellow, no! Look at me, look me right in the eyes . . . I don't say it's true, don't worry! Nothing is true! But just look me in the eyes!

BERTOLD. Very well, how's that?

HENRY. There: you see, you see! You, too! You have terror in your eyes!—Because you think I'm mad.—That's the proof!

(*He laughs.*)

LANDOLF (*representing all four, plucking up courage, exasperated*). What's the proof?

HENRY. The distress you're all in because again you think I'm mad!—And, by God, you know it! You believed me: up to now you believed I was mad. Didn't you? (*Looking at them for a moment, he sees the alarm they are in.*) You see this distress? You feel how it can turn into terror? Terror at something that takes the ground from under your feet, that deprives you of the air you breathe? You *do* see it, you *must* feel it! For what does it mean to find yourself face to face with a mad man, eh? It means being face to face with one who takes what you have painstakingly constructed within yourself, takes it and shakes it, shakes it down to the very foundations! Your logic—the logic of all these constructions of yours—totters!—Well? Who is it that constructs without logic? The madman! Blessed are the mad—they construct without logic. Or with a logic of their own that floats on air like a feather. They chop and change. Like this today, but tomorrow who knows?—You stick to your guns, they take to their heels. Choppers and changers!—You say: this cannot be! For them, anything can be.—You say it's not true, because—because what?—because it doesn't seem true to (*indicating three of them in turn*) you, you, you, or to a hundred thousand others! Then, my dear friends, we'd have to see what seems true to a hundred thousand others, a hundred thousand who're *not* considered mad. We'd have to see what account *they* can give us of the things they agree on—the fruits of their logic. But this I know: when I was a child, the moon in the pond was . . . true . . . to me. Lots of things were true. People told me about them; I believed; and I was happy. Hold fast to whatever you think true today! Hold fast to whatever you think true tomorrow—even if it's the opposite of what you thought true yesterday! Or woe betide you! Woe betide you if, like me, you are swallowed up by a thought—a thought that will *really* drive you mad. You are with no other human being, you're at their side, you look into their eyes—how well I remember doing it, that day—and . . . you might as well be a beggar before some door you must never pass through! Open it if you wish: the man who enters is not you, will never be you, will never carry your world within him, the world you see, the world you touch. You don't know the man. He is another person like *any* other person who, from his own impenetrable world, sees you, touches you . . .

(*A long, sustained pause. The shadows in the room begin to thicken, increasing that sense of distress and deepest consternation which fills the four masqueraders, increasing also the distance between them and the great masquerader, who is lost in the contemplation of a terrible misery which is not his alone but everyone's. Then he pulls himself together, and, not feeling their presence around him, starts to look for them, and says,*)

It's been getting dark in here.

ORDULF (*at once, coming forward*). Shall I go and get the lamp?

HENRY (*with irony*). The lamp, yes. . . . Do you think I don't know that as soon as I turn my back and go off to bed, oil lamp in hand, you switch the electric light on! Both here and in the throne room!—I pretend not to see it . . .

ORDULF. Ah! Then you want me to . . .

HENRY. No! It would only blind me.—I want my lamp.

ORDULF. Very well, it'll be here at the door, ready. (*He goes to the center door, opens it, goes out, and returns at once with an ancient oil lamp, the kind you hold by a ring on top.*)

HENRY (*taking the lamp and pointing to the table on the platform*). There, a little light. Sit there, around the table, all of you. No, not like that! In special attitudes, handsome attitudes! (*To* HARALD.) You, like this. (*Putting him in position. Then to* BERTOLD, *putting him in position, too.*) You, like this. That's right. I'll sit here. (*Turning his head toward one of the windows.*) One should be able to say: "O Moon, shed your light on us! Give us one little ray, a pretty one!" The moon is so good for us, so good! For my part I feel the need of the moon. I often spend my time gazing at her from my window. To look at her, who would think she knows eight hundred years have passed and that this man seated at the window moon-gazing cannot really be the Emperor Henry the Fourth? But look, look at the scene: what a picture! a nocturne! "The Emperor Henry with his trusty councillors." Don't you relish that?

LANDOLF (*quietly to* HARALD *so as not to break the spell*). You see now? To think that it wasn't true . . .

HENRY. True? What?

LANDOLF (*wavering, as if to apologize*). Nothing . . . I mean . . . (*pointing to* BERTOLD) he's only just started work here—and I was telling him only this morning what a pity it was . . . with us dressed up like this . . .

and with all the other fine clothes in the wardrobe . . . and a room like that one . . . (*Pointing to the throne room.*)

HENRY. Well? What's a pity?

LANDOLF. That . . . that we never knew . . .

HENRY. That it was all just playacting, a comedy, a jest?

LANDOLF. Because we thought . . .

HARALD (*coming to his assistance*). It was all done in earnest, dear sir!

HENRY. And wasn't it? Don't you really think it was?

LANDOLF. Well, sir, if you say . . .

HENRY. I say you are fools. Call it a deception, if you wish. The point is you should have been smart enough to accept this deception—for your own sakes. Not just as a play to enact before me or those who came to visit me from time to time. For your own sakes, for your natural selves, day in, day out, before nobody. (*Taking* BERTOLD *by the arms.*) For your own sake, my boy, so you can eat, sleep, within a . . . a piece of fiction that's your own—so you can scratch your back when it itches! (*Turning again to all four.*) Feeling alive, really alive in the eleventh century, here, at the court of your Emperor, Henry the Fourth! And, from this vantage point, the vantage point of an age long past, sepulchral, yet colorful, to think that nine centuries down the road of time, down, down, the men of the twentieth century live in the utmost confusion. Their life is all strain, all anxiety to know what will happen to them. To see to what issue the crises will come that keep them in such anguish and turmoil. Whereas—you are history already! With me! What has happened to me may be sad, the situations I've found myself in may have been horrendous, oh, yes, there were bitter struggles, painful vicissitudes . . . BUT they are history! They have stopped changing! They cannot change anymore! You understand? Fixed forever! You can take your ease and marvel at every effect as it follows from every cause in perfect obedience, with perfect logic, at the unfolding of every event—precise and coherent in every particular! The pleasure of history, in fact, the pleasure of history! And how great that is!

LANDOLF. Wonderful!

HENRY. Wonderful! But over with. Now that you know, I can't go through with it. (*He takes the lamp in order to go to bed.*) Nor can you, for that matter. If you've never understood the real reason. It gives me nausea to think of! (*Almost to himself, with violent, contained rage.*) By God, I'll make her sorry she came! In a mask of a mother-in-law, pah! With him as Father Abbot!—And they bring me a doctor with them—to study me! Who knows if they don't even hope to cure me? . . . Clowns!—How nice it would be to smack one of them in the face, at least one—*that* one!—A famous swordsman, is he? He'll run me through, will he? We'll see about that. (*He hears a knocking at the center door.*) Who is it?

GIOVANNI'S *voice. Deo Gratias!*

HARALD (*delighted at the thought that here's a trick one could still play*). It's Giovanni the butler. He comes here every evening. As a monk!

ORDULF (*rubbing his hands, lending himself to the jest*). Yes, let him do his act as usual, sir, let him do his act!

HENRY (*at once severe*). You fools! Play a prank on a poor old man who's doing this for love of me? Why?

LANDOLF (*to* ORDULF *and* HARALD, *whispering*). It must be as if it were true, don't you see?

HENRY. Oh, very good—*as if it were true*. Only in that way does the truth cease to be a jest. (*He goes and opens the door and lets* GIOVANNI *in. The latter is dressed as a humble friar with a roll of parchment under his arm.*) Come in, Father, come in! (*Then, taking on a tone of tragic gravity and deep resentment.*)

All the documents of my life, of my reign, that were favorable to me have been destroyed, deliberately destroyed, by my enemies. All that has escaped destruction is this one—my life, as written by a humble monk who is devoted to me. And you would laugh at him? (*With love in his eyes, he turns again to* GIOVANNI *and invites him to sit at the table.*) Be seated, Father, sit there. With this lamp beside you. (*He places at his side the lamp he is still carrying.*) Now write, write!

GIOVANNI (*unrolls the parchment and prepares to write from dictation*). Ready, your Majesty!

(*The lights fade, but go up almost at once on.*)

Scene II

(HENRY *is just finishing the dictation.*)

HENRY. ". . . the proclamation of peace issued at Mainz was of benefit to the poor and good while it did harm to the bad and powerful. It brought prosperity to the former, hunger and poverty to the latter." (*Henry's voice is tired. He notices that* GIOVANNI *and the four young men are drowsy. Quietly:*) Enough! (*As he rises, the five others are suddenly alert and on their feet.*) No, No! Just stay where you are, I can manage! Good night! (*They continue to watch him as he leaves the room.*)

(*At this point the revolving stage starts to rumble. The throne room set is being brought on.* HENRY *is on the turntable walking in the direction opposite to its movement and at the same speed; hence, in relation to the audience, he is stationary. The rumbling stops; we are in the throne room.**

In the dark, the back wall is hardly visible. The canvases have been removed from the portraits. Within the frames which are now in the two empty niches, in exact imitation of the two portraits, are FRIDA, *dressed as Matilda of Tuscany* [*i.e. as we saw her in Scene I*] *and the* Marquis *dressed as Henry the Fourth.*)

FRIDA (*as soon as she sees* HENRY *has just passed the throne, whispering from her niche like someone who feels she's about to faint with fright*). Henry! . . .

HENRY (*stopping at the sound, as if by some treachery he has suddenly received a knife in his back. In his alarm he turns his face toward the back wall and instinctively starts to raise his arms as if in self-defense*). Who's calling me?

(*It is not a question. It is an exclamation which slipped out in a tremor of terror and which asks no answer from the darkness and terrible silence in the room, a darkness and silence which have for him been suddenly filled with the suspicion that he is mad in earnest.*)

FRIDA (*at this act of terror is the more alarmed at what she is to do. She repeats a little more loudly*). Henry! . . .

(*But although she wishes to stick to the part they have assigned her, she stretches her head out a little from the one niche toward the other.*)

HENRY (*gives a mad yell, lets the lamp fall in order to shield his head with his hands, and starts to flee.*)

FRIDA (*jumping from the niche onto the ledge and shouting as if she'd gone mad*). Henry . . . Henry . . . I'm afraid . . . I'm afraid! . . .

(*The* MARQUIS *jumps onto the ledge and then to the floor, running over to* FRIDA, *who continues to shout convulsively, on the point of fainting. Meanwhile the others rush in from the door on the left: the* DOCTOR, *the* COUNTESS *who is also dressed as Matilda of Tuscany, the* BARON, LANDOLF, HARALD, ORDULF, BERTOLD, GIOVANNI. *One of them suddenly*

* These directions are an interpolation by the translator, designed to eliminate the need for a second intermission. In the original, what follows is called Act III.—E. B.

turns on the light: a strange light emanating from small bulbs hidden in the ceiling and arranged in such a fashion that only the upper part of the stage is brightly lit. Without paying attention to HENRY, *who, after the moment of terror is past [though it continues to vibrate through his whole body], just stays looking on, astonished at the unexpected inrush of people, they anxiously run to support and comfort* FRIDA, *who still trembles and groans and rages in her fiancé's arms. General confusion of voices.*)

MARQUIS. No, no, Frida . . . *I* am here . . . I am with you!

DOCTOR (*coming up with the others*). That will do! Nothing more is needed . . .

COUNTESS. He's cured, Frida, look! He's cured, do you see?

MARQUIS (*astonished*). Cured?

BARON. The whole thing was a joke, don't worry!

FRIDA (*unchanged*). I'm afraid, I'm afraid.

COUNTESS. Afraid of what? Look at him! It wasn't true, it isn't true!

MARQUIS (*unchanged*). It isn't true? What are you saying? He's cured?

DOCTOR. It seems so, Marquis. As for myself . . .

BARON. Yes, yes, *they* told us . . .

COUNTESS. He's been cured for some time. He told those four attendants about it.

MARQUIS (*now more indignant than astonished*). What? Up to a short time ago . . .

BARON. My dear Marquis, he put on an act so he could have a good laugh behind your back, behind the backs of all of us who—in good faith——

MARQUIS. Is it possible? He even deceived his own sister on her deathbed?

HENRY (*who has stayed apart, peering now at one, now at another, as he feels their accusations and their ridicule; for all now believe it has been a cruel jest on his part, and that it is at last unveiled. His flashing eyes have shown that he is pondering a revenge, though up to now his scorn, in tumult within him, has prevented him seeing precisely what it will be. Wounded, he bursts forth at this point with one clear idea: to accept as true the fiction which they have insidiously worked out. He shouts to his nephew*). Go on talking, go on!

MARQUIS (*stopped by this shout, stunned*). What, go on?

HENRY. Your sister isn't the only one who's dead.

MARQUIS (*unchanged*). *My* sister? I'm talking of yours. To the very end you forced her to come here as your mother Agnes!

HENRY (*again having regard to the* MARQUIS'*s present disguise*). And she wasn't your mother?

MARQUIS. *My* mother, *my* mother, exactly.

HENRY. To the old man, old and far away, that I am, your mother is dead. But you're newly come down out of that niche! How should *you* know that I've not mourned her in secret—mourned her year in, year out—even in these clothes?

COUNTESS (*in consternation, looking at the others*). What's he saying?

DOCTOR (*very disturbed, observing him*). Quiet, for heaven's sake, quiet!

HENRY. What am I saying? I'm asking everyone if Agnes wasn't the Emperor's mother! (*He turns to* FRIDA *as if she were really Matilda of Tuscany.*) It seems to me, my Lady, you should know!

FRIDA (*still scared, holding on to the* MARQUIS). I? Oh, no, no!

DOCTOR. Here's the lunacy back again . . . Be careful, everyone!

BARON (*scornfully*). Lunacy? That's not lunacy, Doctor, it's the same old play acting!

HENRY (*at once*). I? You have emptied those two niches, and it's *he* that stands here as the Emperor!

BARON. Oh, let's have done with this perpetual jesting!

HENRY. Who says it's jesting?

DOCTOR (*to the* BARON, *loudly*). Don't excite him, Baron, for the love of God!

BARON (*taking no notice of him, more loudly*). *They* said so! (*Pointing at the four young men.*) *They* said so!

HENRY (*turns to look at them*). You said that? You said it was all a jest?

LANDOLF (*timidly, embarrassed*). No . . . what we said was, you were cured.

BARON. Very well, let's have done! (*To the* COUNTESS.) His appearance—(*pointing to the* MARQUIS) and for that matter yours, Countess—is coming to seem insufferably childish, don't you see that?

COUNTESS. You be quiet! Who cares about clothes if he's really cured?

HENRY. Cured? Yes, I'm cured! (*To the* BARON.) Oh, but not to make an end of things all at once as you think! (*Attacking him.*) Do you know that for twenty years no one has ever dared to appear before me here like you and this gentleman? (*Indicating the* DOCTOR.)

BARON. Of course I know. Only this morning, after all, I myself came in dressed.

HENRY. Dressed as a monk, yes . . .

BARON. And you took me for Peter Damiani. And I didn't even laugh, thinking of course . . .

HENRY. That I was mad. It makes you laugh to see her like that—now I'm cured? And yet you might have realized that in my eyes, her present appearance . . . (*He interrupts himself with a burst of scorn and an:* Ach! *He turns at once to the* DOCTOR.) You are a doctor?

DOCTOR. Yes, I . . .

HENRY. And you dressed *her* as Matilda of Tuscany, too? (*Indicating the* COUNTESS.) Don't you know, Doctor, that in that moment you risked driving my poor brain back into the night? By heaven, to make the portraits speak, to make them jump, living, from their frames . . . (*He contemplates* FRIDA *and the* MARQUIS, *then he looks at the* COUNTESS, *finally he looks at his own costume.*) Oh, quite a coincidence: two couples. Not bad, Doctor, not bad—for a madman . . . (*With a gesture in the direction of the* BARON.) He thinks it's a carnival out of season, does he? (*Turns to look at him.*) Then away with my masquerade costume, I'm coming with you, why not?

BARON. Why not indeed?

HENRY. Where shall we go? To the club? White tie and tails? Or home with the Countess—a happy threesome?

BARON. Wherever you like, my dear fellow. I can quite see you wouldn't want to stay here—perpetuating, by yourself, what was after all only the unhappy joke of a carnival day! It's incredible, it's incredible to me that you've been able to do it—even before today—once the effects of the accident were over.

HENRY. Surely, but it was like this, don't you see? After I fell from the horse and was hit on the head, I was *really* mad for quite a time . . .

DOCTOR. Aha! A long time?

HENRY (*very quickly to the* DOCTOR). Yes, Doctor, a long time: about twelve years. (*Then, at once, turning to the* BARON.) Can you imagine how it was, my dear fellow, to see nothing of what happened after that carnival day, what happened for you and not for me—how things changed, how friends betrayed me? Can you imagine having your place taken by others? Maybe . . . let's say . . . in the heart of the woman you loved? Not knowing who had died, who had disappeared! It wasn't such a . . . jest to me as you think!

BARON. Pardon me, but that's not what I meant, I meant afterwards!

HENRY. Did you? Afterwards? Well, one day . . . (*He stops and turns to the* DOCTOR.) A fascinating case, Doctor, study me, study me carefully! (*He shakes from head to foot while speaking.*) One day, all by itself, heaven knows how, the trouble here (*he touches his forehead*) shall we say? stopped. Little by little I opened my eyes again. At first I didn't know if it was sleep or wake. Why yes, I was awake. I touched one thing, then another, I could see clearly again . . . (*He breaks off and makes a gesture toward the* BARON.) I agree with him! away with these clothes, they're a mask, an incubus! Let's open the windows, let in the breath of life! Come on, let's run out of doors! (*Putting the brakes on.*) But where? To do what? To have everyone secretly pointing at me and whispering "Emperor Henry!" when I'm no longer like this but out there in the streets with my friends and arm in arm with you?

BARON. Not at all! What are you talking about? What makes you think that?

COUNTESS. Who could conceive of such a thing? An accident is an accident.

HENRY. They all said I was mad—even before—all of them! (*To the* BARON.) And you know it! No one was more furious than you if anybody defended me!

BARON. Oh, come, that was only a joke!

HENRY. Look at this hair. (*Shows the hair on his neck.*)

BARON. I have gray hair, too.

HENRY. There's a difference: mine went gray here! While I was Emperor! Understand? I never noticed it. I noticed it all at once—one day as I opened my eyes—I was terror-struck! For I realized that my hair wasn't the only thing that was gray, I must be gray all through, decayed, finished! Hungry as a wolf I would arrive at the banquet after it had been cleared away!

BARON. That's all very well, my dear man, but you couldn't expect other people . . .

HENRY (*at once*). —to wait till I was cured. I know. (*Pause.*) Not even those who came up behind and pricked my horse, harnessed and dressed up as he was, with their spurs . . .

MARQUIS. (*disturbed*). What? What was that?

HENRY. Pricked my horse, with their spurs! To make him rear up! Treachery, don't you see? So I'd fall!

COUNTESS (*at once, with horror*). It's the first I've heard of that!

HENRY. That must have been a joke, too!

COUNTESS. But who was it? Who was behind us?

HENRY. No matter who. All of them! All who went on with the banquet, all who would now leave the scraps, Countess—the scraps of their piddling pity! Whatever leavings of remorse have stuck to their filthy plates they'll give to me! No thanks! (*Turning to the* DOCTOR *on a sudden impulse.*) So you see, Doctor: isn't this case absolutely new in the annals of madness? I preferred to stay mad. Everything had been prepared for this new kind of pleasure: to *live* my madness, to live it with the clearest consciousness of it, and so avenge myself on the brutality of a stone which had struck me on the head: to take solitude—*this* solitude—squalid and empty as it seemed when my eyes reopened—to take solitude and straightway clothe it in all the colors and splendors of that distant carnival day when you—(*he points* FRIDA *out to the* COUNTESS) ah! there you are, Countess! —when you had your day of triumph: to oblige all those who came to see me, to live out, by God, that famous masquerade of long ago which—for you but not for me—was the jest of a single day! To make it last forever—not a jest, no, a reality, the reality of a true madness! So here we were with our masks on—here was the throne room—here were my four privy councillors—traitors, of course! (*He suddenly turns in their direction.*) I'd like to know what you hoped to gain by letting out the fact that I was cured! —Once I'm cured, I don't need *you* anymore, you're fired!—To confide in anyone, now *that,* that is really the act of a madman!—But now it's my turn, and I accuse you! (*He turns to the others.*) Do you know, they thought they and I could play the joke on you now, take *you* in! (*He bursts out laughing. The others manage to laugh, embarrassed, except the* COUNTESS.)

BARON (*to the* MARQUIS). Just think . . . not bad, hm? . . .

MARQUIS (*to the four young men*). You?

HENRY. We must forgive them. For me, these clothes (*indicating his own costume*) are a caricature, a voluntary and overt caricature, of that other masquerade, the one that's going on all the time. You take part in it whether you know it or not. If without knowing it you wear the mask of what you think you are, you are still a puppet in this masquerade, though an *in*voluntary one. That's why we must forgive these four young men if they don't yet see these clothes of theirs as in character. (*Again he turns to the* BARON.) You know this? One soon gets used to it. And one walks around like this—(*He does so.*) a tragic character—there's nothing to it—in a room like this!—Look, Doctor. I remember a priest—an Irish priest undoubtedly —good-looking, too—and one November day he was sleeping in the sun in a public park. He'd laid his arm along the back of the seat for support. He was basking in the delight of a golden warmth which to him must have seemed almost like summer. One can be sure that at that moment he didn't know he was a priest anymore, he didn't know where he was. He was dreaming, who knows of what?—A small boy passed. He was carrying a flower he'd plucked, with a long stalk. In passing, he tickled the priest, right here in the neck.—I saw laughter in the priest's eyes as they opened. His whole mouth laughed with the happy laughter of his dream. He'd let himself go, he had escaped. But I must tell you, he soon put himself together again, he soon belonged to his priest's cassock again. He grew rigid. And back into his eyes came the same seriousness that you have seen in mine—for Irish priests defend the seriousness of their Catholic faith with the same zeal I felt for the sacred rights of hereditary monarchy.—I am cured, gentlemen, for I *know* I'm playing the madman, I do it quite calmly.—Woe betide you if you live your madness unquietly, without knowing it, without seeing it!

BARON. So the obvious conclusion is—that *we* are the madmen!

HENRY (*with a little outburst that he manages to check*). If you were not mad—you and she—would you have come?

BARON. Actually, I came here believing the madman to be you.

HENRY (*loudly of a sudden, indicating the* COUNTESS). And she?

BARON. She? I don't know. I see that she seems bewitched by what you have to say, fascinated by this conscious madness of yours! (*He turns to her.*) Dressed as you are, I'm sure you could stay here and live it out, Countess . . .

COUNTESS. You are impertinent!

HENRY (*at once, placating her*). Don't mind him, don't mind him. He's determined to provoke me—though that was just what the doctor told him not to do. (*Turning to the* BARON.) Do you think I'll trouble myself any more about what happened between me and you—about the part you played in my misfortune with her—(*Indicates the* COUNTESS, *then turns to her, indicating the* BARON.) the part he is now playing in *your* life?—My life is like this! Yours is not!—The life you have grown old in—I have not lived at all! (*To the* COUNTESS.) Is that what you wanted to say, to prove, to me? You were even prepared to take the doctor's advice and dress like that? Well done, Doctor, I say again. Two pictures: "Before and After: what we were then, and what we are today!"—But I'm not mad in your way, Doctor. I well know he (*indicating the* MARQUIS) can't be me because *I* am Henry the Fourth. I've been Henry the Fourth for twenty years, understand? Fixed in this eternity of masquerade! (*Indicating the* COUNTESS.) She has lived them, she has enjoyed them, the twenty years, and she's become—a woman I can't recognize. For I know her thus—(*indicating* FRIDA *and going over to her*) in my eyes, this is she, forever . . . You seem like a child that I can frighten as I will. (*To* FRIDA.) You've been badly frightened, haven't you, my child, by the joke they persuaded you to play? They didn't understand that, to me, it could hardly be the joke they intended, it could only be this terrible prodigy: a dream come alive—in you! More alive than ever! For there (*pointing to the niche*) you were an image. They have made you a living creature. You are mine, mine, mine! And by right!

(*He takes her in his arms, laughing like a madman while the others are scared out of their wits and shout. But, when they try to tear* FRIDA *from his arms, he becomes terrible and shouts to his four young men.*)
Hold them back, hold them back, I order you to hold them back!

(*Stunned, yet fascinated, the four young men automatically set about holding back the* MARQUIS, *the* DOCTOR, *and the* BARON.)

BARON (*liberates himself at once and rushes toward* HENRY). Leave her alone! You are *not* mad!

HENRY (*drawing the sword, swift as lightning, from the side of* LANDOLF, *who is next to him*). Not mad? We'll see about that! (*And he wounds him in the belly.*)

(*A general yell of horror. The* MARQUIS *and* BERTOLD *run to support the* BARON.)

MARQUIS. He's wounded you?

BERTOLD. He's wounded him! He's wounded him!

DOCTOR. I told you so!

FRIDA. God, God!

MARQUIS. Frida, come here!

COUNTESS. He's mad, he's mad!

MARQUIS. Hold him!

BARON (*while they carry him out by the door on the left, fiercely protesting*). No! He's not mad! He's not mad! He's not mad!

(*They are shouting as they leave by the door on the left. And they keep on shouting until, amid the general din, is heard a more piercing shout from the* COUNTESS. *Then silence.*)

HENRY (*is left on stage with* LANDOLF, HARALD, *and* ORDULF. *His eyes are starting from his head. He is thunderstruck at the life of the fiction he himself created. In a single moment it has driven him to crime.* This time . . . we've no choice. (*Calls them around him as if to defend himself.*) We're here . . . forever!

SIX CHARACTERS IN SEARCH OF AN AUTHOR

By LUIGI PIRANDELLO

English version by Eric Bentley

CHARACTERS OF THE PLAY-IN-THE-MAKING

The Father
The Mother
The Son, aged 22
The Stepdaughter, 18
The Boy, 14
The Little Girl, 4
(these two last do not speak)
Then, called into being: Madam Pace

ACTORS IN THE COMPANY

The Director (Direttore-Capocomico)
Leading Lady
Leading Man
Second Actress
Ingenue
Juvenile Lead
Other actors and actresses
Stage Manager
Prompter
Property Man
Technician
Director's Secretary
Stage Door Man
Stage Crew

Daytime. On the stage of a playhouse.

Author's Note

The play has neither acts nor scenes. The performance should be interrupted twice: first—without any lowering of the curtain —when the Director and the chief among the Characters retire to put the scenario together and the Actors leave the stage; second when the Technician lets the curtain down by mistake.

Translator's Note

The theater envisaged is of the type most usual where and when the play was written—Italy, 1921. Attempts to substitute a non-Italian type of theater of a later date break down because unless very drastic changes are made in the script, you are still left with items that don't properly fit. You cannot, for example, pretend this is an Off Broadway theater in 1970 if you then proceed to call a character "Second Actress"—Actor's Equity Association hasn't a single member who would accept the title. With such things in mind, the translator decided simply to translate. And so the reader has the job of imagining a theater he is probably not familiar with—a theater in which, for example, there is a prompter in a prompter's box, center stage.

The second most important personage in the play is called, in the original, Direttore-Capocomico. A Direttore is a managing director or manager. Capocomico one would first be inclined to translate as Actor Manager, and the Actor Managers of the Victorian age did direct the plays. The only trouble here is that Pirandello's Capocomico obviously does not act. He is a Director-Manager, and I think there is, in American English, no alternative to calling him the Director, even though the present-day Italian word for that is Regista. It is a matter of the evolution of this particular profession. The Direttore-Capocomico is an intermediate figure between the old Actor Managers and the new Directors. Pirandello gets to the latter in a later play, *Tonight We Improvise*.

One note on the stage directions. In this play, there are few personal names, so that characters are generally referred to as just *him* or *her*. This forces the author to insert very many parentheses on the pattern of "Pointing to the Father." When possible, the translator has taken the liberty of shortening these to just (to stick to the example) "the Father" in parentheses.

The Italian text followed is that of the *Maschere Nude* as reprinted by Mondadori in 1948. This represents Pirandello's final revision of the play. The translation published in America by the E. P. Dutton Company was based on an earlier Italian text, namely, on the first edition of 1921. The three substantial passages in the first edition which Pirandello cut from his later revisions are included here in footnotes, so that, for the first time, the American reader gets a chance to see what Pirandello's changes amounted to. (No detailed study of *all* the changes has as yet been made, it would seem. The present translator is aware of three different stages of revision: the final version, the second edition [1923], and the first edition [1921].) A British and very free rendering of the final text, by Frederick May, has been published by Heinemann's in London, and there are free adaptations based on the final text by Denis Johnston and Paul Avila Mayer, respectively. The Dutton text, by Edward Storer, is literal but often erroneous. There is an accurate, and therefore helpful, translation of the first edition into French by Benjamin Crémieux.

SIX CHARACTERS IN SEARCH OF AN AUTHOR

When the audience arrives in the theater, the curtain is raised; and the stage, as normally in the daytime, is without wings or scenery and almost completely dark and empty. From the beginning we are to receive the impression of an unrehearsed performance.

Two stairways, left and right respectively, connect the stage with the auditorium.

On stage the dome of the prompter's box has been placed on one side of the box itself. On the other side, at the front of the stage, a small table and an armchair with its back to the audience, for the DIRETTORE-CAPOCOMICO (DIRECTOR).

Two other small tables of different sizes with several chairs around them have also been placed at the front of the stage, ready at need for the rehearsal. Other chairs here and there, left and right, for the actors, and at the back, a piano, on one side and almost hidden.

As soon as the houselights dim, the TECHNICIAN *is seen entering at the door on stage. He is wearing a blue shirt, and a tool bag hangs from his belt. From a corner at the back he takes several stage-braces, then arranges them on the floor downstage, and kneels down to hammer some nails in. At the sound of the hammering, the* STAGE MANAGER *comes running from the door that leads to the dressing rooms.*

STAGE MANAGER. Oh! What are you doing?

TECHNICIAN. What am I doing? Hammering.

STAGE MANAGER. At this hour? (*He looks at the clock*) It's ten-thirty already. The Director will be here any moment. For the rehearsal.

TECHNICIAN. *I* gotta have time to work, too, see.

STAGE MANAGER. You will have. But not now.

TECHNICIAN. When?

STAGE MANAGER. Not during rehearsal hours. Now move along, take all this stuff away, and let me set the stage for the second act of, um, *The Game of Role Playing.*

(*Muttering, grumbling, the* TECHNICIAN *picks up the stage-braces and goes away. Meanwhile, from the door on stage, the* ACTORS OF THE COMPANY *start coming in, both men and women, one at a time at first, then in twos, at random, nine or ten of them, the number one would expect as the cast in rehearsals of Pirandello's play, "The Game of Role Playing"*, which is the order of the day. They enter, greet the* STAGE MANAGER *and each other, all saying good-morning to all. Several go to their dressing rooms. Others, among them the* PROMPTER, *who has a copy of the script rolled up under his arm, stay on stage, waiting for the* DIRECTOR *to begin the rehearsal. Meanwhile, either seated in conversational groups, or standing, they exchange a few words among themselves. One lights a cigarette, one complains about the part he has been assigned, one reads aloud to his companions items of news from a*

* *Il giuoco delle parti,* published in English as *The Rules of the Game.*

theater journal. It would be well if both the Actresses and the Actors wore rather gay and brightly colored clothes and if this first improvised scene [scena a soggetto] combined vivacity with naturalness. At a certain point, one of the actors can sit down at the piano and strike up a dance tune. The younger actors and actresses start dancing.)

STAGE MANAGER (*Clapping his hands to call them to order*). All right, that's enough of that. The Director's here.

(*The noise and the dancing stop at once. The Actors turn and look towards the auditorium from the door of which the* DIRECTOR *is now seen coming. A bowler hat on his head, a walking stick under his arm, and a big cigar in his mouth, he walks down the aisle and, greeted by the Actors, goes on stage by one of the two stairways. The* SECRETARY *hands him his mail: several newspapers and a script in a wrapper.*)

DIRECTOR. Letters?

SECRETARY. None. That's all the mail there is.

DIRECTOR (*Handing him the script*). Take this to my room. (*Then, looking around and addressing himself to the* STAGE MANAGER) We can't see each other in here. Want to give us a little light?

STAGE MANAGER. Okay.

(*He goes to give the order, and shortly afterwards, the whole left side of the stage where the Actors are is lit by a vivid white light. Meanwhile, the* PROMPTER *has taken up his position in his box. He uses a small lamp and has the script open in front of him.*)

DIRECTOR (*Clapping his hands*). Very well, let's start. (*To the* STAGE MANAGER) Someone missing?

STAGE MANAGER. The Leading Lady.

DIRECTOR. As usual! (*He looks at the clock*) We're ten minutes late already. Fine her for that, would you, please? Then she'll learn to be on time.

(*He has not completed his rebuke when the voice of the* LEADING LADY *is heard from the back of the auditorium.*)

LEADING LADY. No, no, for Heaven's sake! I'm here! I'm here! (*She is dressed all in white with a big, impudent hat on her head and a cute little dog in her arms. She runs down the aisle and climbs one of the sets of stairs in great haste.*)

DIRECTOR. You've sworn an oath always to keep people waiting.

LEADING LADY. You must excuse me. Just couldn't find a taxi. But you haven't even begun, I see. And I'm not on right away. (*Then, calling the* STAGE MANAGER *by name, and handing the little dog over to him*) Would you please shut him in my dressing room?

DIRECTOR (*Grumbling*). And the little dog to boot! As if there weren't enough dogs around here. (*He claps his hands again and turns to the* PROMPTER.) Now then, the second act of *The Game of Role Playing*. (*As he sits down in his armchair*) Quiet, gentlemen. Who's on stage?

(*The Actresses and Actors clear the front of the stage and go and sit on one side, except for the three who will start the rehearsal and the* LEADING LADY *who, disregarding the* DIRECTOR*'s request, sits herself down at one of the two small tables.*)

DIRECTOR (*To the* LEADING LADY). You're in this scene, are you?

LEADING LADY. Me? No, no.

DIRECTOR (*Irritated*). Then how about getting up, for Heaven's sake?

(*The* LEADING LADY *rises and goes and sits beside the other Actors who have already gone to one side.*)

DIRECTOR (*To the* PROMPTER). Start, start.

PROMPTER (*Reading from the script*). "In the house of Leone Gala. A strange room, combined study and dining room."

DIRECTOR (*Turning to the* STAGE MANAGER). We'll use the red room.

STAGE MANAGER (*Making a note on a piece of paper*). Red room. Very good.

PROMPTER (*Continuing to read from the script*). "The table is set and the desk has books and papers on it. Shelves with books on them, and cupboards with lavish tableware. Door in the rear through which one goes to Leone's bedroom. Side door on the left through which one goes to the kitchen. The main entrance is on the right."

DIRECTOR (*Rising and pointing*). All right, now listen carefully. That's the main door. This is the way to the kitchen. (*Addressing himself to the Actor playing the part of Socrates*) You will come on and go out on this side. (*To the* STAGE MANAGER) The compass at the back. And curtains. (*He sits down again.*)

STAGE MANAGER (*Making a note*). Very good.

PROMPTER (*Reading as before*). "Scene One. Leone Gala, Guido Venanzi, Filippo called Socrates." (*To the* DIRECTOR) Am I supposed to read the stage directions, too?

DIRECTOR. Yes, yes, yes! I've told you that a hundred times!

PROMPTER (*Reading as before*). "At the rise of the curtain, Leone Gala, wearing a chef's hat and apron, is intent on beating an egg in a saucepan with a wooden spoon. Filippo, also dressed as a cook, is beating another egg. Guido Venanzi, seated, is listening."

LEADING ACTOR (*To the* DIRECTOR). Excuse me but do I really have to wear a chef's hat?

DIRECTOR (*Annoyed by this observation*). I should say so! It's in the script. (*And he points at it.*)

LEADING ACTOR. But it's ridiculous, if I may say so.

DIRECTOR (*Leaping to his feet, furious*). "Ridiculous, ridiculous!" What do you want me to do? We never get a good play from France any more, so we're reduced to producing plays by Pirandello, a fine man and all that, but neither the actors, the critics, nor the audience are ever happy with his plays, and if you ask me, he does it all on purpose.

(*The Actors laugh. And now he rises and coming over to the* LEADING ACTOR *shouts:*) A cook's hat, yes, my dear man! And you beat eggs. And you think you have nothing more on your hands than the beating of eggs? Guess again. You symbolize the shell of those eggs. (*The Actors resume their laughing, and start making ironical comments among themselves.*) Silence! And pay attention while I explain. (*Again addressing himself to the* LEADING ACTOR) Yes, the shell: that is to say, the empty *form* of reason without the *content* of instinct, which is blind. You are reason, and your wife is instinct in the game of role playing. You play the part assigned you, and you're your own puppet—of your own free will. Understand?

LEADING ACTOR (*Extending his arms, palms upwards*). Me? No.

DIRECTOR (*Returning to his place*). Nor do I. Let's go on. Wait and see what I do with the ending. (*In a confidential tone*) I suggest you face three-quarters front. Otherwise, what with the abstruseness of the dialogue, and an audience that can't hear you, goodbye play! (*Again clapping*) Now, again, order! Let's go.

PROMPTER. Excuse me, sir, may I put the top back on the prompter's box? There's rather a draft.

DIRECTOR. Yes, yes, do that.

(*The* STAGE DOOR MAN *has entered the auditorium in the meanwhile, his braided cap on his head. Proceeding down the aisle, he goes up on stage to announce to the* DIRECTOR *the arrival of the Six Characters, who have also entered the auditorium, and have started following him at a certain distance, a little lost and perplexed, looking around them.*

Whoever is going to try and translate this play into scenic terms must take all possible measures not *to let these Six Characters get confused with the Actors of the Company. Placing both groups correctly, in accordance with the stage directions, once the Six are on stage, will certainly help, as will lighting the two groups in contrasting colors. But the most suitable and effective means to be suggested here is the use of special masks for the Characters: masks specially made of material which doesn't go limp when sweaty and yet masks which are not too heavy for the Actors wearing them, cut out and worked over so they leave eyes, nostrils, and mouth free. This will also bring out the inner significance of the play. The Characters in fact should not be presented as ghosts but as created realities, unchanging constructs of the imagination, and therefore more solidly real than the Actors with their fluid naturalness. The masks will help to give the impression of figures constructed by art, each one unchangeably fixed in the expression of its own fundamental sentiment, thus:*

remorse *in the case of the* FATHER; revenge *in the case of the* STEPDAUGHTER; disdain *in the case of the* SON; grief *in the case of the* MOTHER, *who should have wax tears fixed in the rings under her eyes and on her cheeks, as with the sculpted and painted images of the* mater dolorosa *in church. Their clothes should be of special material and design, without extravagance, with rigid, full folds like a statue, in short not suggesting a material you might buy at any store in town, cut out and tailored at any dressmaker's.*

The FATHER *is a man of about 50, hair thin at the temples, but not bald, thick moustache coiled round a still youthful mouth that is often open in an uncertain, pointless smile. Pale, most notably on his broad forehead: blue eyes, oval, very clear and piercing; dark jacket and light trousers: at times gentle and smooth, at times he has hard, harsh outbursts.*

The MOTHER *seems scared and crushed by an intolerable weight of shame and self-abasement. Wearing a thick black crepe widow's veil, she is modestly dressed in black, and when she lifts the veil, the face does not show signs of suffering, and yet seems made of wax. Her eyes are always on the ground.*

The STEPDAUGHTER, *18, is impudent, almost insolent. Very beautiful, and also in mourning, but mourning of a showy elegance. She shows contempt for the timid, afflicted, almost humiliated manner of her little brother, rather a mess of a* BOY, *14, also dressed in black, but a lively tenderness for her little sister, a* LITTLE GIRL *of around 4, dressed in white with black silk sash round her waist.*

The SON, *22, tall, almost rigid with contained disdain for the* FATHER *and supercilious indifference towards the* MOTHER, *wears a mauve topcoat and a long green scarf wound round his neck.*)

STAGE DOOR MAN (*Beret in hand*). Excuse me, your honor.

DIRECTOR (*Rudely jumping on him*). What is it now?

STAGE DOOR MAN (*Timidly*). There are some people here asking for you.

(*The* DIRECTOR *and the Actors turn in astonishment to look down into the auditorium.*)

DIRECTOR (*Furious again*). But I'm rehearsing here! And you know perfectly well no one can come in during rehearsal! (*Turning again toward the house*) Who are these people? What do they want?

THE FATHER (*Stepping forward, followed by the others, to one of the two little stairways to the stage*). We're here in search of an author.

DIRECTOR (*Half angry, half astounded*). An author? What author?

FATHER. Any author, sir.

DIRECTOR. There's no author here at all. It's not a new play we're rehearsing.

STEPDAUGHTER (*Very vivaciously as she rushes up the stairs*). Then so much the better, sir! *We* can be your new play!

ONE OF THE ACTORS (*Among the racy comments and laughs of the others*). Did you hear that?

FATHER (*Following the* STEPDAUGHTER *onstage*). Certainly, but if the author's not here . . . (*to the* DIRECTOR) Unless *you'd* like to be the author?

(*The* MOTHER, *holding the* LITTLE GIRL *by the hand, and the* BOY *climb the first steps of the stairway and remain there waiting. The* SON *stays morosely below.*)

DIRECTOR. Is this your idea of a joke?

FATHER. Heavens, no! Oh, sir, on the contrary: we bring you a painful drama.

STEPDAUGHTER. We can make your fortune for you.

DIRECTOR. Do me a favor, and leave. We have no time to waste on madmen.

FATHER (*Wounded, smoothly*). Oh, sir, you surely know that life is full of infinite absurdities which, brazenly enough, do not need to appear probable, because they're true.

DIRECTOR. What in God's name are you saying?

FATHER. I'm saying it can actually be considered madness, sir, to force oneself to do the opposite: that is, to give probability to things so they will seem true. But permit me to observe that, if this is madness, it is also the *raison d'être* of your profession.

(*The Actors become agitated and indignant.*)

DIRECTOR (*Rising and looking him over*). It is, is it? It seems to you an affair for madmen, our profession?

FATHER. Well, to make something seem true which is not true . . . without any need, sir: just for fun . . . Isn't it your job to give life on stage to creatures of fantasy?

DIRECTOR (*Immediately, making himself spokesman for the growing indignation of his Actors*). Let me tell you something, my good sir. The actor's profession is a very noble one. If, as things go nowadays, our new playwrights give us nothing but stupid plays, with puppets in them instead of men, it is our boast, I'd have you know, to have given life—on these very boards—to immortal works of art.

(*Satisfied, the Actors approve and applaud their* DIRECTOR.)

FATHER (*Interrupting and bearing down hard*). Exactly! That's just it. You have created living beings—*more* alive than those that breathe and wear clothes! Less real, perhaps; but more true! We agree completely!

(*The Actors look at each other, astounded.*)

DIRECTOR. What? You were saying just now . . .

FATHER. No, no, don't misunderstand me. You shouted that you hadn't time to waste on madmen. So I wanted to tell you that no one knows better than you that Nature employs the human imagination to carry her work of creation on to a higher plane!

DIRECTOR. All right, all right. But what are you getting at, exactly?

FATHER. Nothing, sir. I only wanted to show that one may be born to this life in many modes, in many forms: as tree, as rock, water or butterfly . . . or woman. And that . . . characters are born too.

DIRECTOR (*His amazement ironically feigned*). And you—with these companions of yours—were born a character?

FATHER. Right, sir. And alive, as you see.

(*The* DIRECTOR *and the Actors burst out laughing as at a joke.*)

FATHER (*Wounded*). I'm sorry to hear you laugh, because, I repeat, we carry a painful drama within us, as you all might deduce from the sight of that lady there, veiled in black.

(*As he says this, he gives his hand to the* MOTHER *to help her up the last steps and, still holding her by the hand, he leads her with a certain tragic solemnity to the other side of the stage, which is suddenly bathed in fantastic light. The* LITTLE GIRL *and the* BOY *follow the* MOTHER; *then the* SON, *who stands on one side at the back; then the* STEPDAUGHTER *who also detaches herself from the others—downstage and leaning against the proscenium arch. At first astonished at this development, then overcome with admiration, the Actors now burst into applause as at a show performed for their benefit.*)

DIRECTOR (*Bowled over at first, then indignant*). Oh, stop this! Silence please! (*Then, turning to the Characters*) And you, leave! Get out of here! (*To the* STAGE MANAGER) For God's sake, get them out!

STAGE MANAGER (*Stepping forward but then stopping, as if held back by a strange dismay*). Go! Go!

FATHER (*To the* DIRECTOR). No, look, we, um—

DIRECTOR (*Shouting*). I tell you we've got to work!

LEADING MAN. It's not right to fool around like this . . .

FATHER (*Resolute, stepping forward*). I'm amazed at your incredulity! You're accustomed to seeing the created characters of an author spring to life, aren't you, right here on this stage, the one confronting the other? Perhaps the trouble is there's no script *there* (*Pointing to the* PROMPTER'*s box*) with us in it?

STEPDAUGHTER (*Going right up to the* DIRECTOR, *smiling, coquettish*). Believe me, we really are six characters, sir. Very interesting ones at that. But lost. Adrift.

FATHER (*Brushing her aside*). Very well: lost, adrift. (*Going right on*) In the sense, that is, that the author who created us, made us live, did not wish, or simply and materially was not able, to place us in the world of art. And that was a real crime, sir, because whoever has the luck to be born a living character can also laugh at death. He will never die! The man will die, the writer, the instrument of creation; the creature will never die! And to have eternal life it doesn't even take extraordinary gifts, nor the performance of miracles. Who was Sancho Panza? Who was Don Abbondio?* But they live forever because, as live germs, they have the luck to find a fertile matrix, an imagination which knew how to raise and nourish them, make them live through all eternity!

DIRECTOR. That's all well and good. But what do you people want here?

FATHER. We want to live, sir.

DIRECTOR (*Ironically*). Through all eternity?

FATHER. No, sir. But for a moment at least. In you.

AN ACTOR. Well, well, well!

LEADING LADY. They want to live in us.

JUVENILE LEAD (*Pointing to the* STEPDAUGHTER). Well, I've no objection, so long as I get that one.

FATHER. Now look, look. The play is still in the making. (*To the* DIRECTOR) But if you wish, and your actors wish, we can make it right away. Acting in concert.

LEADING MAN (*Annoyed*). Concert? We don't put on concerts! We do plays, dramas, comedies!

FATHER. Very good. That's why we came.

DIRECTOR. Well, where's the script?

FATHER. Inside us, sir. (*The Actors laugh.*) The drama is inside us. It *is* us.

---

* A humble priest in Manzoni's *The Betrothed.*

And we're impatient to perform it. According to the dictates of the passion within us.

STEPDAUGHTER (*Scornful, with treacherous grace, deliberate impudence*). My passion—if you only knew, sir! My passion—for him! (*She points to the* FATHER *and makes as if to embrace him but then breaks into a strident laugh.*)

FATHER (*An angry interjection*). You keep out of this now. And please don't laugh that way!

STEPDAUGHTER. No? Then, ladies and gentlemen, permit me. A two months' orphan, I shall dance and sing for you all. Watch how! (*She mischievously starts to sing "Beware of Chu Chin Chow" by Dave Stamper, reduced to fox trot or slow one step by Francis Salabert: the first verse, accompanied by a step or two of dancing.* While she sings and dances, the Actors, especially the young ones, as if drawn by some strange fascination, move towards her and half raise their hands as if to take hold of her. She runs away and when the Actors burst into applause she just stands there, remote, abstracted, while the* DIRECTOR *protests.*)

ACTORS AND ACTRESSES (*Laughing and clapping*). Brava! Fine! Splendid!

DIRECTOR (*Annoyed*). Silence! What do you think this is, a night spot? (Taking the FATHER *a step or two to one side, with a certain amount of consternation*) Tell me something. Is she crazy?

FATHER. Crazy? Of course not. It's much worse than that.

STEPDAUGHTER (*Running over at once to the* DIRECTOR). Worse! Worse! Not crazy but worse! Just listen: I'll play it for you right now, this drama, and at a certain point you'll see me—when this dear little thing—(*She takes the* LITTLE GIRL *who is beside the* MOTHER *by the hand and leads her to the* DIRECTOR.)—isn't she darling? (*Takes her in her arms and kisses her.*) Sweetie! Sweetie! (*Puts her down again and adds with almost involuntary emotion.*) Well, when God suddenly takes this little sweetheart away from her poor mother, and that idiot there—(*Thrusting the* BOY *forward, rudely seizing him by a sleeve.*) does the stupidest of things, like the nitwit that he is, (*With a shove she drives him back towards the* MOTHER.) then you will see me take to my heels. Yes, ladies and gentlemen, take to my heels! I can hardly wait for that moment. For after what happened between him and me—(*She points to the* FATHER *with a horrible*

---

* Pirandello gives four lines of the song in French, and hitherto the English translators have followed him. However, the song is an American one, music by Dave Stamper, lyrics by Gene Buck, from the Ziegfeld Follies, 1917. Here are the words:

In a fairy book a Chinese crook
Has won such wondrous fame
But nowadays he appears in plays
And Chu Chin Chow's his name.
With his forty thieves he now achieves
A great success each night.
Just lend an ear and listen here
And I will put you right:
    Beware of Chu Chin Chow!
    Take care, he's coming now!
    He's a robber from the Orient
    And he's filled with Chinese sentiment.
    At night when lights are low
    He wanders to and fro.
    He's the master of his art.
    He can steal a girlie's heart.
    Love he'll plunder, he's a wonder:
    Chu Chin Chow!
Mister Chu Chin Chow you must allow
Has a manner all his own
For he does not woo as others do
He's never quite alone.
With his forty jugs he carries hugs
And kisses to bestow.
'Tis in the sand he'll win your hand,
This Chinese Romeo.
    Beware of Chu Chin Chow, etc.

(Copyright 1917 by T. B. Harms and Francis, Day and Hunter.)

wink.) something very intimate, you understand—I can't stay in such company any longer, witnessing the anguish of our mother on account of that fool there—(*She points to the* SON.) just look at him, look at him!—how indifferent, how frozen, because he is the legitimate son, that's what he is, full of contempt for me, for him, (*the* BOY) and for that little creature, (*The* LITTLE GIRL) because we three are bastards, d'you see? bastards. (*Goes to the* MOTHER *and embraces her.*) And this poor mother, the common mother of us all, he—well, he doesn't want to acknowledge her as *his* mother too, and he looks down on her, that's what he does, looks on her as only the mother of us three bastards, the wretch! (*She says this rapidly in a state of extreme excitement. Her voice swells to the word: "bastards!" and descends again to the final "wretch," almost spitting it out.*)

MOTHER (*To the* DIRECTOR, *with infinite anguish*). In the name of these two small children, sir, I implore you . . . (*She grows faint and sways.*) Oh, heavens . . .

FATHER (*Rushing over to support her with almost all the Actors who are astonished and scared*). Please! Please, a chair, a chair for this poor widow!

ACTORS (*Rushing over*).—Is it true then?—She's *really* fainting?

DIRECTOR. A chair!

(*One of the Actors proffers a chair. The others stand around, ready to help. The* MOTHER, *seated, tries to stop the* FATHER *from lifting the veil that hides her face.*)

FATHER (*To the* DIRECTOR). Look at her, look at her . . .

MOTHER. Heavens, no, stop it!

FATHER. Let them see you. (*He lifts her veil.*)

MOTHER (*Rising and covering her face with her hands, desperate*). Oh, sir, please stop this man from carrying out his plan. It's horrible for me!

DIRECTOR (*Surprised, stunned*). I don't know where we're at! What's this all about? (*To the* FATHER) Is this your wife?

FATHER (*At once*). Yes, sir, my wife.

DIRECTOR. Then how is she a widow, if you're alive?

(*The Actors relieve their astonishment in a loud burst of laughter.*)

FATHER (*Wounded, with bitter resentment*). Don't laugh! Don't laugh like that! Please! Just that is her drama, sir. She had another man. Another man who should be here!

MOTHER (*With a shout*). No! No!

STEPDAUGHTER. He had the good luck to die. Two months ago, as I told you. We're still in mourning, as you see.

FATHER. But he's absent, you see, not just because he's dead. He's absent—take a look at her, sir, and you will understand at once!—Her drama wasn't in the love of two men for whom she was incapable of feeling anything—except maybe a little gratitude (not to me, but to him)—She is not a woman, she is a mother!—And her drama—a powerful one, very powerful—is in fact all in those four children which she bore to her two men.

MOTHER. *My* men? Have you the gall to say I wanted two men? It was him, sir. He forced the other man on me. Compelled—yes, compelled—me to go off with him!

STEPDAUGHTER (*Cutting in, roused*). It's not true!

MOTHER (*Astounded*). How d'you mean, not true?

STEPDAUGHTER. It's not true! It's not true!

MOTHER. And what can you know about it?

STEPDAUGHTER. It's not true. (*To the* DIRECTOR) Don't believe it. Know why

she says it? For his sake. (*Pointing to the* SON) His indifference tortures her, destroys her. She wants him to believe that, if she abandoned him when he was two, it was because he (*The* FATHER) compelled her to.

MOTHER (*With violence*). He did compel me, he did compel me, as God is my witness! (*To the* DIRECTOR) Ask him if that isn't true. (*Her husband*) Make him tell him. (*The* SON) She couldn't know anything about it.

STEPDAUGHTER. With my father, while he lived, I know you were always happy and content. Deny it if you can.

MOTHER. I don't deny it, I don't . . .

STEPDAUGHTER. He loved you, he cared for you! (*To the* BOY, *with rage*) Isn't that so? Say it! Why don't you speak, you dope?

MOTHER. Leave the poor boy alone. Why d'you want to make me out ungrateful, daughter? I have no wish to offend your father! I told him (*The* FATHER) I didn't abandon my son and my home for my own pleasure. It wasn't my fault.

FATHER. That's true, sir. It was mine. (*Pause.*)

LEADING MAN (*To his companions*). What a show!

LEADING LADY. And *they* put it on—for us.

JUVENILE LEAD. Quite a change!

DIRECTOR (*Who is now beginning to get very interested*). Let's listen to this, let's listen! (*And saying this, he goes down one of the stairways into the auditorium, and stands in front of the stage, as if to receive a spectator's impression of the show.*)

SON (*Without moving from his position, cold, quiet, ironic*). Oh yes, you can now listen to the philosophy lecture. He will tell you about the Demon of Experiment.

FATHER. You are a cynical idiot, as I've told you a hundred times. (*To the* DIRECTOR, *now in the auditorium*) He mocks me, sir, on account of that phrase I found to excuse myself with.

SON (*Contemptuously*). Phrases!

FATHER. Phrases! Phrases! As if they were not a comfort to everyone: in the face of some unexplained fact, in the face of an evil that eats into us, to find a word that says nothing but at least quiets us down!

STEPDAUGHTER. Quiets our guilt feelings too. That above all.

FATHER. Our guilt feelings? Not so. I have never quieted my guilt feelings with words alone.

STEPDAUGHTER. It took a little money as well, didn't it, it took a little dough! The hundred lire he was going to pay me, ladies and gentlemen!

(*Movement of horror among the Actors.*)

SON (*With contempt towards the* STEPDAUGHTER). That's filthy.

STEPDAUGHTER. Filthy? The dough was there. In a small pale blue envelope on the mahogany table in the room behind the shop. Madam Pace's (*pronounce: Pah-chay*) shop. One of those Madams who lure us poor girls from good families into their *ateliers* under the pretext of selling *Robes et Manteaux.*

SON. And with those hundred lire he was going to pay she has bought the right to tyrannize over us all. Only it so happens—I'd have you know—that he never actually incurred the debt.

STEPDAUGHTER. Oh, oh, but we were really going to it, I assure you! (*She bursts out laughing.*)

MOTHER (*Rising in protest*). Shame, daughter! Shame!

STEPDAUGHTER (*Quickly*). Shame? It's my revenge! I am frantic, sir, frantic to live it, live that scene! The room . . . here's the shopwindow with the coats in it; there's the bed-sofa; the mirror; a screen; and in front of the window the little mahogany table with the 100 lire in the pale blue envelope. I can see it. I could take it. But you men should turn away now: I'm almost naked. I don't blush any more. It's he that blushes now. (*Points to the* FATHER.) But I assure you he was very pale, very pale, at that moment. (*To the* DIRECTOR) You must believe me, sir.

DIRECTOR. You lost me some time ago.

FATHER. Of course! Getting it thrown at you like that! Restore a little order, sir, and let *me* speak. And never mind this ferocious girl. She's trying to heap opprobrium on me by withholding the relevant explanations!

STEPDAUGHTER. This is no place for longwinded narratives!

FATHER. I said—explanations.

STEPDAUGHTER. Oh, certainly. Those that suit your turn.

(*At this point, the* DIRECTOR *returns to the stage to restore order.*)

FATHER. But that's the whole root of the evil. Words. Each of us has, inside him, a world of things—to everyone, his world of things. And how can we understand each other, sir, if, in the words I speak, I put the sense and value of things as they are inside me, whereas the man who hears them inevitably receives them in the sense and with the value they have for him, the sense and value of the world inside him? We think we understand each other but we never do. Consider: the compassion, all the compassion I feel for this woman (*The* MOTHER) has been received by her as the most ferocious of cruelties!

MOTHER. You ran me out of the house.

FATHER. Hear that? Ran her out. It *seemed to her* that I ran her out.

MOTHER. You can talk; I can't . . . But, look, sir, after he married me . . . and who knows why he did? I was poor, of humble birth . . .

FATHER. And that's why. I married you for your . . . humility. I loved you for it, believing . . . (*He breaks off, seeing her gestured denials; seeing the impossibility of making himself understood by her, he opens his arms wide in a gesture of despair, and turns to the* DIRECTOR.) See that? She says No. It's scarifying, isn't it, sir, scarifying, this deafness of hers, this mental deafness! She has a heart, oh yes, where her children are concerned! But she's deaf, deaf in the brain, deaf, sir, to the point of desperation!

STEPDAUGHTER (*To the* DIRECTOR). All right, but now make him tell you what his intelligence has ever done for us.

FATHER. If we could only foresee all the evil that can result from the good we believe we're doing!

(*At this point, the* LEADING LADY, *who has been on hot coals seeing the* LEADING MAN *flirt with the* STEPDAUGHTER, *steps forward and asks of the* DIRECTOR:)

LEADING LADY. Excuse me, is the rehearsal continuing?

DIRECTOR. Yes, of course! But let me listen a moment.

JUVENILE LEAD. This is something quite new.

INGENUE. Very interesting!

LEADING LADY. If that sort of thing interests you. (*And she darts a look at the* LEADING MAN.)

DIRECTOR (*To the* FATHER). But you must give us *clear* explanations. (*He goes and sits down.*)

FATHER. Right. Yes. Listen. There was a man working for me. A poor man. As my secretary. Very devoted to me. Understood *her* (*The* MOTHER) very well. There was mutual understanding between them. Nothing wrong in it. They thought no harm at all. Nothing off color about it. No, no, he knew his place, as she did. They didn't do anything wrong. Didn't even think it.

STEPDAUGHTER. So he thought it *for* them. And did it.

FATHER. It's not true! I wanted to do them some good. And myself too, oh yes, I admit. I'd got to this point, sir: I couldn't say a word to either of them but they would exchange a significant look. The one would consult the eyes of the other, asking how what I had said should be taken, if they didn't want to put me in a rage. That sufficed, you will understand, to keep me continually in a rage, in a state of unbearable exasperation.

DIRECTOR. Excuse me, why didn't you fire him, this secretary?

FATHER. Good question! That's what I did do, sir. But then I had to see that poor woman remain in my house, a lost soul. Like an animal without a master that one takes pity on and carries home.

MOTHER. No, no, it's—

FATHER (*At once, turning to her to get it in first*). Your son? Right?

MOTHER. He'd already snatched my son from me.

FATHER. But not from cruelty. Just so he'd grow up strong and healthy. In touch with the soil.

STEPDAUGHTER (*Pointing at the latter, ironic*). And just look at him!

FATHER (*At once*). Uh? Is it also my fault if he then grew up this way? I sent him to a wetnurse, sir, in the country, a peasant woman. I didn't find her (*The* MOTHER) strong enough, despite her humble origin. I'd married her for similar reasons, as I said. All nonsense maybe, but there we are. I always had these confounded aspirations towards a certain solidity, towards what is morally sound. (*Here the* STEPDAUGHTER *bursts out laughing.*) Make her stop that! It's unbearable!

DIRECTOR. Stop it. I can't hear, for Heaven's sake!

(*Suddenly, again, as the* DIRECTOR *rebukes her, she is withdrawn and remote, her laughter cut off in the middle. The* DIRECTOR *goes down again from the stage to get an impression of the scene.*)

FATHER. I couldn't bear to be with that woman any more. (*Points to the* MOTHER) Not so much, believe me, because she irritated me, and even made me feel physically ill, as because of the pain —a veritable anguish—that I felt on her account.

MOTHER. And he sent me away!

FATHER. Well provided for. And to that man. Yes, sir. So she could be free of me.

MOTHER. And so *he* could be free.

FATHER. That, too. I admit it. And much evil resulted. But I intended good. And more for her than for me, I swear it! (*He folds his arms across his chest. Then, suddenly, turning to the* MOTHER) I never lost sight of you, never lost sight of you till, from one day to the next, unbeknown to me, he carried you off to another town. He noticed I was interested in her, you see, but that was silly, because my interest was absolutely pure, absolutely without ulterior motive. The interest I took in her new family, as it grew up, had an unbelievable tenderness to it. Even she should bear witness to that! (*He points to the* STEPDAUGHTER.)

STEPDAUGHTER. Oh, very much so! I was a little sweetie. Pigtails over my shoulders. Panties coming down a little bit below my skirt. A little sweetie. He would see me coming out of school, at the gate. He would come and see me as I grew up . . .

FATHER. This is outrageous. You're betraying me!

STEPDAUGHTER. I'm not! What do you mean?

FATHER. Outrageous. Outrageous. (*Immediately, still excited, he continues in a tone of explanation, to the* DIRECTOR.) My house, sir, when she had left it, at once seemed empty. (*Points to the* MOTHER) She was an incubus. But she filled my house for me. Left alone, I wandered through these rooms like a fly without a head. This fellow here (*The* SON) was raised away from home. Somehow, when he got back, he didn't seem mine any more. Without a mother between me and him, he grew up on his own, apart, without any relationship to me, emotional or intellectual. And then —strange, sir, but true—first I grew curious, then I was gradually attracted toward *her* family, which I had brought into being. The thought of *this* family began to fill the void around me. I had to—really had to—believe she was at peace, absorbed in the simplest cares of life, lucky to be away and far removed from the complicated torments of my spirit. And to have proof of this, I would go and see that little girl at the school gate.

STEPDAUGHTER. Correct! He followed me home, smiled at me and, when I was home, waved to me, like this! I would open my eyes wide and look at him suspiciously. I didn't know who it was. I told mother. And she guessed right away it was him. (*The* MOTHER *nods.*) At first she didn't want to send me back to school for several days. When I did go, I saw him again at the gate—the clown!—with a brown paper bag in his hand. He came up to me, caressed me, and took from the bag a lovely big Florentine straw hat with a ring of little May roses round it—for me!

DIRECTOR. You're making too long a story of this.

SON (*Contemptuously*). Story is right! Fiction! Literature!

FATHER. Literature? This is life, sir. Passion!

DIRECTOR. Maybe! But not actable!

FATHER. I agree. This is all preliminary. I wouldn't *want* you to act it. As you see, in fact, she (*The* STEPDAUGHTER) is no longer that little girl with pigtails—

STEPDAUGHTER. —and the panties showing below her skirt!

FATHER. The drama comes now, sir. Novel, complex—

STEPDAUGHTER (*Gloomy, fierce, steps forward*). —What my father's death meant for us was—

FATHER (*Not giving her time to continue*). —poverty, sir. They returned, unbeknown to me. She's so thick headed. (*Pointing to the* MOTHER) It's true she can hardly write herself, but she could have had her daughter write, or her son, telling me they were in need!

MOTHER. But, sir, how could I have guessed he felt the way he did?

FATHER. Which is just where you always went wrong. You could never guess how I felt about anything!

MOTHER. After so many years of separation, with all that had happened . . .

FATHER. And is it my fault if that fellow carried you off as he did? (*Turning to the* DIRECTOR) From one day to the next, as I say. He'd found some job someplace. I couldn't even trace them. Necessarily, then, my interest dwindled, with the years. The drama breaks out, sir, unforeseen and violent, at their return. When I, alas, was impelled by the misery of my still living flesh . . . Oh, and what misery that is for a man who is alone, who has not wanted to form debasing relationships, not yet old enough to do without a woman, and no longer young enough to go and look for one without shame! Misery? It's horror, horror, because no woman can give him love any more.—Knowing this, one should go without! Well, sir, on the outside, when other people are watching, each man is clothed in dignity: but, on the inside, he knows what unconfessable things are going on within him. One gives way, gives way to temptation, to rise again, right afterwards, of course, in a great hurry to put our dignity together again, complete, solid, a stone on a grave that hides and buries from our eyes every sign of our shame and even the very memory of it! It's like that with everybody. Only the courage to say it is lacking—to say certain things.

STEPDAUGHTER. The courage to do them, though—everybody's got that.

FATHER. Everybody. But in secret. That's why it takes more courage to say them. A man only has to say them and it's all over: he's labeled a cynic. But, sir, he isn't! He's just like everybody else. Better! He's better because he's not afraid to reveal, by the light of intelligence, the red stain of shame, there, in the human beast, which closes its eyes to it. Woman —yes, woman—what is she like, actually? She looks at us, inviting, tantalizing. You take hold of her. She's no sooner in your arms than she shuts her eyes. It is the sign of her submission. The sign with which she tells the man: Blind yourself for I am blind.

STEPDAUGHTER. How about when she no longer keeps them shut? When she no longer feels the need to hide the red stain of shame from herself by closing her eyes, and instead, her eyes dry now and impassive, sees the shame of the man, who has blinded himself even without love? They make me vomit, all those intellectual elaborations, this philosophy that begins by revealing the beast and then goes on to excuse it and save its soul . . . I can't bear to hear about it! Because when a man feels obliged to *reduce* life this way, reduce it all to "the beast," throwing overboard every vestige of the truly human, every aspiration after chastity, all feelings of purity, of the ideal, of duties, of modesty, of shame, then nothing is more contemptible, more nauseating than his wretched guilt feelings! Crocodile tears!

DIRECTOR. Let's get to the facts, to the facts! This is just discussion.

FATHER. Very well. But a fact is like a sack. When it's empty, it won't stand up. To make it stand up you must first pour into it the reasons and feelings by which it exists. I couldn't know that—when that man died and they returned here in poverty—she went out to work as a dressmaker to support the children, nor that the person she went to work for was that . . . that Madam Pace!

STEPDAUGHTER. A highclass dressmaker, if you'd all like to know! To all appearances, she serves fine ladies, but then she arranges things so that the fine ladies serve *her* . . . without prejudice to ladies not so fine!

MOTHER. Believe me, sir, I never had the slightest suspicion that that old witch hired me because she had her eye on my daughter . . .

STEPDAUGHTER. Poor momma! Do you know, sir, what the woman did when I brought her my mother's work? She would point out to me the material she'd ruined by giving it to my mother to sew. And she deducted for that, she deducted. And so, you understand, *I* paid, while that poor creature thought she was making sacrifices for me and those two by sewing, even at night, Madam Pace's material!

(*Indignant movements and exclamations from the Actors.*)

DIRECTOR (*Without pause*). And there, one day, you met—

STEPDAUGHTER (*Pointing to the* FATHER). —him, him, yes sir! An old client! Now there's a scene for you to put on! Superb!

FATHER. Interrupted by her—the mother—

STEPDAUGHTER (*Without pause, treacherously*). —almost in time!—

FATHER (*Shouting*). No, no, *in* time! Because, luckily, I recognized the girl in time. And I took them all back, sir, into my home. Now try to visualize my situation and hers, the one confronting the other—she as you see her now, myself unable to look her in the face any more.

STEPDAUGHTER. It's too absurd! But—afterwards—was it possible for me to be a modest little miss, virtuous and well-bred, in accordance with those confounded aspirations towards a certain solidity, towards what is morally sound?

FATHER. And therein lies the drama, sir, as far as I'm concerned: in my awareness that each of us thinks of himself as *one* but that, well, it's not true, each of us is many, oh so many, sir, according to the possibilities of being that are in us. We are one thing for this person, another for that! Already *two* utterly different things! And with it all, the illusion of being always one thing for all men, and always this one thing in every single action. It's not true! Not true! We realize as much when, by some unfortunate chance, in one or another of our acts, we find ourselves suspended, hooked. We see, I mean, that we are not wholly in that act, and that therefore it would be abominably unjust to judge us by that act alone, to hold us suspended, hooked, in the pillory, our whole life long, as if our life were summed up in that act! Now do you understand this girl's treachery? She surprised me in a place, in an act, in which she should never have had to know me—I couldn't be that way for her. And she wants to give me a reality such as I could never had expected I would have to assume for her, the reality of a fleeting moment, a shameful one, in my life! This, sir, this is what I feel most strongly. And you will see that the drama will derive tremendous value from this. But now add the situation of the others! His . . . (*He points to the* SON.)

SON (*Shrugging contemptuously*). Leave me out of this! It's none of my business.

FATHER. What? None of your business?

SON. None. And I *want* to be left out. I wasn't made to be one of you, and you know it.

STEPDAUGHTER. We're common, aren't we?—And he's so refined.—But from time to time I give him a hard, contemptuous look, and he looks down at the ground. You may have noticed that, sir. He looks down at the ground. For he knows the wrong he's done me.

SON (*Hardly looking at her*). Me?

STEPDAUGHTER. You! You! I'm on the streets because of you! (*A movement of horror from the Actors*) Did you or did you not, by your attitude, deny us—I won't say the intimacy of home but even the hospitality which puts guests at their ease? We were the intruders, coming to invade the kingdom of your legitimacy! I'd like to have you see, sir, certain little scenes between just him and me! He says I tyrannized over them all. But it was entirely because of his attitude that I started to exploit the situation he calls filthy, a situation which had brought me into his home with my mother, who is also *his* mother, *as its mistress!*

SON (*Coming slowly forward*). They can't lose, sir, three against one, an easy game. But figure to yourself a son, sitting quietly at home, who one fine day sees a young woman arrive, an impudent type with her nose in the air, asking for his father, with whom she has heaven knows what business; and then he sees her return, in the same style, accompanied by that little girl over there; and finally he sees her treat his father—who can say why?—in a very ambiguous and cool manner, demanding money, in a tone that takes for granted that he *has* to give it, has to, is obligated—

FATHER. —but I *am* obligated: it's for your mother!

SON. How would I know? When, sir, (*To the* DIRECTOR) have I ever seen her? When have I ever heard her spoken of. One day I see her arrive with her, (*The* STEPDAUGHTER) with that boy, with that little girl. They say to me: "It's your mother too, know that?" I manage to figure out from her carryings-on (*Pointing at the* STEPDAUGHTER) why they arrived in our home from one day to the next . . . What I'm feeling and experiencing I can't put into words, and wouldn't want to. I wouldn't want to confess it, even to myself. It cannot therefore result in any action on my part. You can see that. Believe me, sir, I'm a character that, dramatically speaking, remains unrealized. I'm out of place in their company. So please leave me out of it all!

FATHER. What? But it's just because you're so—

SON (*In violent exasperation*).—I'm so what? How would *you* know? When did you ever care about me?

FATHER. *Touché! Touché!* But isn't even that a dramatic situation? This withdrawnness of yours, so cruel to me, and to your mother who, on her return home is seeing you almost for the first time, a grown man she doesn't recognize, though she knows you're her son . . . (*Pointing out the* MOTHER *to the* DIRECTOR) Just look at her, she's crying.

STEPDAUGHTER (*Angrily, stamping her foot*). Like the fool she is!

FATHER (*Pointing her out to the* DIRECTOR). And she can't abide him, you know. (*Again referring to the* SON)—He says it's none of his business. The truth is he's almost the pivot of the action. Look at that little boy, clinging to his mother all the time, scared, humiliated . . . It's all because of *him*. (*The* SON) Perhaps the most painful situation of all is that little boy's: he feels alien, more than all the others, and the poor little thing is so mortified, so anguished at being taken into our home—out of charity, as it were . . . (*Confidentially*) He's just like his father: humble, doesn't say anything . . .

DIRECTOR. He won't fit anyway. You've no idea what a nuisance children are on stage.

FATHER. But he wouldn't be a nuisance for long. Nor would the little girl, no, she's the first to go . . .*

DIRECTOR. Very good, yes! The whole thing interests me very much indeed. I have a hunch, a definite hunch, that there's material here for a fine play!

STEPDAUGHTER. (*Trying to inject herself*). With a character like me in it!

FATHER (*Pushing her to one side in his anxiety to know what the* DIRECTOR *will decide*). You be quiet!

DIRECTOR (*Going right on, ignoring the interruption*). Yes, it's new stuff . . .

FATHER. Very new!

DIRECTOR. You had some gall, though, to come and throw it at me this way . . .

FATHER. Well, you see, sir, born as we are to the stage . . .

DIRECTOR. You're amateurs, are you?

FATHER. No. I say: "born to the stage" because . . .

* The first edition had the Father continue as follows:—"Because, finally, the drama is all in this: when the mother reenters my home, the family she had elsewhere, which was being, as it were, superimposed on the first one, comes to an end, it's alien, it can't grow in this soil. The little girl dies, the little boy comes to a tragic end, the older girl flees. And so, after all the torment, there remain—we three—myself, the mother, the son. And when the alien family is gone, we too find ourselves alien—the one to the other. We find ourselves utterly desolated. As he (pointing to the Son) scornfully said, it's the revenge of the Demon of Experiment which, alas, I carry inside me, a demon that makes me seek an impossible good, which is what happens when absolute faith is lacking—the faith that enables us humbly to accept life as it is—instead, in our pride, we try to take it over, creating for other persons a reality we consider to be in their line; but sir, it isn't; each of us has his own reality within him, to be respected before God, even when it harms us."

DIRECTOR. Oh, come on, you must have done some acting!

FATHER. No, no, sir, only as every man acts the part assigned to him—by himself or others—in this life. In me you see passion itself, which—in almost all people, as it rises—invariably becomes a bit theatrical . . .

DIRECTOR. Well, never mind! Never mind about that!—You see, my dear sir, without the author . . . I could direct you to an author . . .

FATHER. No, no, look: you be the author!

DIRECTOR. Me? What are you talking about?

FATHER. Yes, you. You. Why not?

DIRECTOR. Because I've never been an author, that's why not!

FATHER. Couldn't you be one now, hm? There's nothing to it. Everyone's doing it. And your job is made all the easier by the fact that you have us—here—alive—right in front of your nose!

DIRECTOR. It wouldn't be enough.

FATHER. Not enough? Seeing us live our own drama . . .

DIRECTOR. I know, but you always need someone to write it!

FATHER. No. Just someone to take it down, maybe, since you have us here—in action—scene by scene. It'll be enough if we piece together a rough sketch for you, then you can rehearse it.

DIRECTOR (*Tempted, goes up on stage again*). Well, I'm almost, almost tempted . . . Just for kicks . . . We could actually rehearse . . .

FATHER. Of course you could! What scenes you'll see emerge! I can list them for you right away.

DIRECTOR. I'm tempted . . . I'm tempted . . . Let's give it a try . . . Come to my office. (*Turns to the Actors*) Take a break, will you? But don't go away. We'll be back in fifteen or twenty minutes. (*To the* FATHER) Let's see what we can do . . . Maybe we can get something very extraordinary out of all this . . .

FATHER. We certainly can. Wouldn't it be better to take *them* along? (*He points to the Characters.*)

DIRECTOR. Yes, let them all come. (*Starts going off, then comes back to address the Actors*) Now don't forget. Everyone on time. Fifteen minutes.

(DIRECTOR *and Six Characters cross the stage and disappear. The Actors stay there and look at one another in amazement.*)

LEADING MAN. Is he serious? What's he going to do?

JUVENILE. This is outright insanity.

A THIRD ACTOR. We have to improvise a drama right off the bat?

JUVENILE LEAD. That's right. Like *Commedia dell'Arte.*

LEADING LADY. Well, if he thinks *I'm* going to lend myself to that sort of thing . . .

INGENUE. Count me out.

A FOURTH ACTOR (*Alluding to the Characters*). I'd like to know who those people are.

THE THIRD ACTOR. Who would they be? Madmen or crooks!

JUVENILE LEAD. And he's going to pay attention to them?

INGENUE. Carried away by vanity! Wants to be an author now . . .

LEADING MAN. It's out of this world. If this is what the theater is coming to, my friends . . .

A FIFTH ACTOR. I think it's rather fun.

THE THIRD ACTOR. Well! We shall see. We shall see. (*And chatting thus among themselves, the Actors leave the stage, some using the little door at the back, others returning to their dressing rooms.*)

The curtain remains raised. The performance is interrupted by a twenty-minute intermission.

*Bells ring. The performance is resumed.**

From dressing rooms, from the door, and also from the house, the Actors, the STAGE MANAGER, *the* TECHNICIAN, *the* PROMPTER, *the* PROPERTY MAN *return to the stage; at the same time the* DIRECTOR *and the Six Characters emerge from the office.*

As soon as the house lights are out, the stage lighting is as before.

DIRECTOR. Let's go, everybody! Is everyone here? Quiet! We're beginning. (*Calls the* TECHNICIAN *by name.*)

TECHNICIAN. Here!

DIRECTOR. Set the stage for the parlor scene. Two wings and a backdrop with a door in it will do, quickly please!

(*The* TECHNICIAN *at once runs to do the job, and does it while the* DIRECTOR *works things out with the* STAGE MANAGER, *the* PROPERTY MAN, *the* PROMPTER, *and the Actors. This indication of a set consists of two wings, a drop with a door in it, all in pink and gold stripes.*)

DIRECTOR (*To the* PROPERTY MAN). See if we have some sort of bed-sofa in the prop room.

PROPERTY MAN. Yes, sir, there's the green one.

STEPDAUGHTER. No, no, not green! It was yellow, flowered, plush, and very big. Extremely comfortable.

PROPERTY MAN. Well, we have nothing like that.

DIRECTOR. But it doesn't matter. Bring the one you have.

STEPDAUGHTER. Doesn't matter? Madam Pace's famous *chaise longue!*

DIRECTOR. This is just for rehearsal. Please don't meddle! (*To the* STAGE MANAGER) See if we have a display case—long and rather narrow.

STEPDAUGHTER. The table, the little mahogany table for the pale blue envelope!

STAGE MANAGER (*To the* DIRECTOR). There's the small one. Gilded.

DIRECTOR. All right. Get that one.

FATHER. A large mirror.

STEPDAUGHTER. And the screen. A screen, please, or what'll I do?

STAGE MANAGER. Yes, ma'am, we have lots of screens, don't worry.

DIRECTOR (*To the* STEPDAUGHTER). A few coat hangers?

STEPDAUGHTER. A great many, yes.

DIRECTOR (*To the* STAGE MANAGER). See how many we've got, and have them brought on.

STAGE MANAGER. Right, sir, I'll see to it.

(*The* STAGE MANAGER *also hurries to do his job and while the* DIRECTOR *goes on talking with the* PROMPTER *and then with the Characters and the Actors, has the furniture carried on by stage hands and arranges it as he thinks fit.*)

DIRECTOR (*To the* PROMPTER). Meanwhile you can get into position. Look: this is the outline of the scenes, act by act. (*He gives him several sheets of paper.*) You'll have to be a bit of a virtuoso today.

---

* In the first edition, a passage follows most of which is found at a later point of the revised text. But this interesting speech of the Son was dropped: "Perform this! . . . As if there were any reason! But he (the Father) has found the meaning. As if everyone couldn't find the meaning of anything that happens in this life, *his* meaning, corresponding to *his* presuppositions! (Pause) He complains, this man, of having been discovered *where* he shouldn't have been and doing *what* he shouldn't have been doing—caught in an act which should have remained hidden, outside that reality which he should have sustained for other people. And I? Hasn't he acted in such a way as to force me to discover what no son should ever discover? That father and mother are alive and are man and woman, for each other, outside that reality of father and mother which we give them. For, as soon as this reality is uncovered, our life is no longer tied to that man and that woman except at a single point—one which will only shame them, should we see it!"

PROMPTER. Shorthand?

DIRECTOR (*Pleasantly surprised*). Oh, good! You know shorthand?

PROMPTER. I may not know prompting, but shorthand . . . (*Turning to a stage hand*) Get me some paper from my room—quite a lot—all you can find!

(*The stage hand runs off and returns a little later with a wad of paper which he gives to the* PROMPTER.)

DIRECTOR (*Going right on, to the* PROMPTER). Follow the scenes line by line as we play them, and try to pin down the speeches, at least the most important ones. (*Then, turning to the Actors*) Clear the stage please, everyone! Yes, come over to this side and pay close attention. (*He indicates the left.*)

LEADING LADY. Excuse me but—

DIRECTOR (*Forestalling*). There'll be no improvising, don't fret.

LEADING MAN. Then what are we to do?

DIRECTOR. Nothing. For now, just stop, look, and listen. Afterwards you'll be given written parts. Right now we'll rehearse. As best we can. With them doing the rehearsing for us. (*He points to the Characters.*)

FATHER (*Amid all the confusion on stage, as if he'd fallen from the clouds*). *We're* rehearsing? How d'you mean?

DIRECTOR. Yes, for them. You rehearse for them. (*Indicates the Actors.*)

FATHER. But if we are the characters . . .

DIRECTOR. All right, you're characters, but, my dear sir, characters don't perform here, actors perform here. The characters are there, in the script—(*He points to the* PROMPTER'S *box.*) when there *is* a script!

FATHER. Exactly! Since there isn't, and you gentlemen have the luck to have them right here, alive in front of you, those characters . . .

DIRECTOR. Oh, great! Want to do it all yourselves? Appear before the public, do the acting yourselves?

FATHER. Of course. Just as we are.

DIRECTOR (*Ironically*). I'll bet you'd put on a splendid show!

LEADING MAN. Then what's the use of staying?

DIRECTOR (*Without irony, to the Characters*). Don't run away with the idea that you can act! That's laughable . . . (*And in fact the Actors laugh.*) Hear that? They're laughing. (*Coming back to the point*) I was forgetting. I must cast the show. It's quite easy. It casts itself. (*To the* SECOND ACTRESS) You, ma'am, will play the Mother. (*To the* FATHER) You'll have to find her a name.

FATHER. Amalia, sir.

DIRECTOR. But that's this lady's real name. We wouldn't want to call her by her real name!

FATHER. Why not? If that is her name . . . But of course, if it's to be this lady . . . (*He indicates the* SECOND ACTRESS *with a vague gesture.*) To me *she* (*The* MOTHER) is Amalia. But suit yourself . . . (*He is getting more and more confused.*) I don't know what to tell you . . . I'm beginning to . . . oh, I don't know . . . to find my own words ringing false, they sound different somehow.

DIRECTOR. Don't bother about that, just don't bother about it. We can always find the right sound. As for the name, if you say Amalia, Amalia it shall be; or we'll find another. For now, we'll designate the characters thus: (*To the* JUVENILE LEAD) You're the Son. (*To the* LEADING LADY) You, ma'am, are of course the Stepdaughter.

STEPDAUGHTER (*Excitedly*). What, what? That one there is me? (*She bursts out laughing.*)

DIRECTOR (*Mad*). What is there to laugh at?

LEADING LADY (*Aroused*). No one has ever dared laugh at me! I insist on respect—or I quit!

STEPDAUGHTER. But, excuse me, I'm not laughing at you.

DIRECTOR (*To the* STEPDAUGHTER). You should consider yourself honored to be played by . . .

LEADING LADY (*Without pause, contemptuously*). —"That one there!"

STEPDAUGHTER. But I wasn't speaking of you, believe me. I was speaking of me. I don't see me in you, that's all. I don't know why . . . I guess you're just not like me!

FATHER. That's it, exactly, my dear sir! What is *expressed* in us . . .

DIRECTOR. Expression, expression! You think that's your business? Not at all!

FATHER. Well, but what *we* express . . .

DIRECTOR. But you don't. You don't express. You provide us with raw material. The actors give it body and face, voice and gesture. They've given expression to much loftier material, let me tell you. Yours is on such a small scale that, if it stands up on stage at all, the credit, believe me, should all go to my actors.

FATHER. I don't dare contradict you, sir, but it's terribly painful for us who are as you see us—with these bodies, these faces—

DIRECTOR (*Cutting in, out of patience*). —that's where make-up comes in, my dear sir, for whatever concerns the face, the remedy is make-up!

FATHER. Yes. But the voice, gesture—

DIRECTOR. Oh, for Heaven's sake! You can't exist here! Here the actor acts you, and that's that!

FATHER. I understand, sir. But now perhaps I begin to guess also why our author who saw us, alive as we are, did not want to put us on stage. I don't want to offend your actors. God forbid! But I feel that seeing myself acted . . . I don't know by whom . . .

LEADING MAN (*Rising with dignity and coming over, followed by the gay young Actresses who laugh*). By me, if you've no objection.

FATHER (*Humble, smooth*). I'm very honored, sir. (*He bows.*) But however much art and willpower the gentleman puts into absorbing me into himself . . . (*He is bewildered now.*)

LEADING MAN. Finish. Finish.

(*The Actresses laugh.*)

FATHER. Well, the performance he will give, even forcing himself with make-up to resemble me, well, with that figure (*All the Actors laugh.*) he can hardly play me as I am. I shall rather be—even apart from the face—what he interprets me to be, as he feels I am—if he feels I am anything—and not as I feel myself inside myself. And it seems to me that whoever is called upon to judge us should take this into account.

DIRECTOR. So now you're thinking of what the critics will say? And I was still listening! Let the critics say what they want. We will concentrate on putting on your play! (*He walks away a little, and looks around.*) Come on, come on. Is the set ready? (*To the Actors and the Characters*) Don't clutter up the stage, I want to be able to see! (*He goes down from the stage.*) Let's not lose any more time! (*To the* STEPDAUGHTER) Does the set seem pretty good to you?

STEPDAUGHTER. Oh! But I can't recognize it!

DIRECTOR. Oh my God, don't tell me we should reconstruct Madam Pace's back room for you! (*To the* FATHER) Didn't you say a parlor with flowered wallpaper?

FATHER. Yes, sir. White.

DIRECTOR. It's not white. Stripes. But it doesn't matter. As for furniture we're in pretty good shape. That little table—bring it forward a bit! (*Stage hands do this. To the* PROPERTY MAN) Meanwhile you get an envelope, possibly a light blue one, and give it to the gentleman. (*Indicating the* FATHER)

PROPERTY MAN. A letter envelope?

DIRECTOR AND FATHER. Yes, a letter envelope.

PROPERTY MAN. I'll be right back. (*He exits.*)

DIRECTOR. Come on, come on. It's the young lady's scene first. (*The* LEADING LADY *comes forward.*) No, no, wait. I said the young lady. (*Indicating the* STEPDAUGHTER) You will just watch—

STEPDAUGHTER (*Adding, without pause*). —watch me live it!

LEADING LADY (*Resenting this*). I'll know how to live it too, don't worry, once I put myself in the role!

DIRECTOR (*Raising his hands to his head*). Please! No more chatter! Now, scene one. The Young Lady with Madam Pace. Oh, and how about this Madam Pace? (*Bewildered, looking around him, he climbs back on stage.*)

FATHER. She isn't with us, sir.

DIRECTOR. Then what do we do?

FATHER. But she's alive. She's alive too.

DIRECTOR. Fine. But where?

FATHER. I'll tell you. (*Turning to the Actresses*) If you ladies will do me the favor of giving me your hats for a moment.

THE ACTRESSES (*Surprised a little, laughing a little, in chorus*). —What?—Our hats?—What does he say?—Why?—Oh, dear!

DIRECTOR. What are you going to do with the ladies' hats?

(*The Actors laugh.*)

FATHER. Oh, nothing. Just put them on these coathooks for a minute. And would some of you be so kind as to take your coats off too?

ACTORS (*As before*). Their coats too?—And then?—He's nuts!

AN ACTRESS OR TWO (*As above*). —But why?—Just the coats?

FATHER. Just so they can be hung there for a moment. Do me this favor. Will you?

ACTRESSES (*Taking their hats off, and one or two of them their coats, too, continuing to laugh, and going to hang the hats here and there on the coathooks*). —Well, why not?—There!—This is getting to be really funny!—Are we to put them on display?

FATHER. Exactly! That's just right, ma'am: on display!

DIRECTOR. May one inquire *why* you are doing this?

FATHER. Yes, sir. If we set the stage better, who knows but she may come to us, drawn by the objects of her trade . . . (*Inviting them to look toward the entrance at the back*) Look! Look!

(*The entrance at the back opens, and* MADAM PACE *walks a few paces downstage, a hag of enormous fatness with a pompous wig of carrot-colored wool and a fiery red rose on one side of it,* à l'espagnole, *heavily made up, dressed with gauche elegance in garish red silk, a feathered fan in one hand and the other hand raised to hold a lighted cigarette between two fingers. At the sight of this apparition, the* DIRECTOR *and the Actors at once dash off the stage with a yell of terror, rushing down the stairs and making as if to flee up the aisle. The* STEPDAUGHTER, *on the other hand, runs to* MADAM PACE—*deferentially, as to her boss.*)

STEPDAUGHTER (*Running to her*). Here she is, here she is!

FATHER (*Beaming*). It's she! What did I tell you? Here she is!

DIRECTOR (*Overcoming his first astonishment, and incensed now*). What tricks are these?

(*The next four speeches are more or less simultaneous.*)

LEADING MAN. What goes on around here?

JUVENILE LEAD. Where on earth did she come from?

INGENUE. They must have been holding her in reserve.

LEADING LADY. Hocus pocus! Hocus pocus!

FATHER (*Dominating these protests*). Excuse me, though! Why, actually, would you want to destroy this prodigy in the name of vulgar truth, this miracle of a reality that is born of the stage itself—called into being by the stage, drawn here by the stage, and shaped by the stage—and which has more right to live on the stage than you have because it is much truer? Which of you actresses will later re-create Madam Pace? This lady *is* Madam Pace. You must admit that the actress who re-creates her will be less true than this lady—who is Madam Pace. Look: my daughter recognized her, and went right over to her. Stand and watch the scene!

(*Hesitantly, the* DIRECTOR *and the Actors climb back on stage. But the scene between the* STEPDAUGHTER *and* MADAM PACE *has begun during the protest of the Actors and the* FATHER'*s answer: sotto voce, very quietly, in short naturally—as would never be possible on a stage. When, called to order by the* FATHER, *the Actors turn again to watch, they hear* MADAM PACE, *who has just placed her hand under the* STEPDAUGHTER'*s chin in order to raise her head, talk unintelligibly. After trying to hear for a moment, they just give up.*)

DIRECTOR. Well?

LEADING MAN. What's she saying?

LEADING LADY. One can't hear a thing.

JUVENILE LEAD. Louder!

STEPDAUGHTER (*Leaving* MADAM PACE, *who smiles a priceless smile, and walking down towards the Actors*). Louder, huh? How d'you mean: louder? These aren't things that can be said louder. *I* was able to say them loudly—to shame him—(*Indicating the* FATHER) that was my revenge. For Madam, it's different, my friends: it would mean—jail.

DIRECTOR. Oh my God! It's like that, is it? But, my dear young lady, in the theater one must be heard. And even we couldn't hear you, right here on the stage. How about an audience out front? There's a scene to be done. And anyway you *can* speak loudly—it's just between yourselves, we won't be standing here listening like now. Pretend you're alone. In a room. The back room of the shop. No one can hear you. (*The* STEPDAUGHTER *charmingly and with a mischievous smile tells him No with a repeated movement of the finger.*) Why not?

STEPDAUGHTER (*Sotto voce, mysteriously*). There's someone who'll hear if she (MADAM PACE) speaks loudly.

DIRECTOR (*In consternation*). Is someone else going to pop up now?

(*The Actors make as if to quit the stage again.*)

FATHER. No, no, sir. She means me. I'm to be there—behind the door—waiting. And Madam knows. So if you'll excuse me. I must be ready for my entrance. (*He starts to move.*)

DIRECTOR. (*Stopping him*). No, wait. We must respect the exigencies of the theater. Before you get ready—

STEPDAUGHTER (*Interrupting him*). Let's get on with it! I tell you I'm dying with desire to live it, to live that scene! If he's ready, I'm more than ready!

DIRECTOR (*Shouting*). But first we have to get that scene out of you and her! (*Indicating* MADAM PACE) Do you follow me?

STEPDAUGHTER. Oh dear, oh dear, she was telling me things you already know

—that my mother's work had been badly done once again, the material is ruined, and I'm going to have to bear with her if I want her to go on helping us in our misery.

MADAM PACE (*Coming forward with a great air of importance*). Si, si, senor, porque yo no want profit. No advantage, no.

DIRECTOR (*Almost scared*). What, what? She talks like *that?!*

(*All the Actors loudly burst out laughing.*)

STEPDAUGHTER (*Also laughing*). Yes, sir, she talks like that—half way between Spanish and English—very funny, isn't it?

MADAM PACE. Now that is not good manners, no, that you laugh at me! Yo hablo the English as good I can, senor!

DIRECTOR. And it *is* good! Yes! Do talk that way, ma'am! It's a sure-fire effect! There couldn't be anything better to, um, soften the crudity of the situation! Do talk that way! It's fine!

STEPDAUGHTER. Fine! Of course! To have certain propositions put to you in a lingo like that. Sure fire, isn't it? Because, sir, it seems almost a joke. When I hear there's "an old senor" who wants to "have good time conmigo," I start to laugh—don't I, Madam Pace?

MADAM PACE. Old, viejo, no. Viejito—leetle beet old, si, darling? Better like that: if he no give you fun, he bring you prudencia.

MOTHER (*Jumping up, to the stupefaction and consternation of all the Actors, who had been taking no notice of her, and who now respond to her shouts with a start and, smiling, try to restrain her, because she has grabbed* MADAM PACE'*s wig and thrown it on the floor*). Witch! Witch! Murderess! My daughter!

STEPDAUGHTER (*Running over to restrain her* MOTHER). No, no, momma, no, please!

FATHER (*Running over too at the same time*). Calm down, calm down! Sit here.

MOTHER. Then send that woman away!

STEPDAUGHTER (*To the* DIRECTOR, *who also has run over*). It's not possible, not possible that my mother should be here!

FATHER (*Also to the* DIRECTOR.) They can't be together. That's why, you see, the woman wasn't with us when we came. Their being together would spoil it, you understand.

DIRECTOR. It doesn't matter, doesn't matter at all. This is just a preliminary sketch. Everything helps. However confusing the elements, I'll piece them together somehow. (*Turning to the* MOTHER *and sitting her down again in her place*) Come along, come along, ma'am, calm down: sit down again.

STEPDAUGHTER (*Who meanwhile has moved center stage again. Turning to* MADAM PACE). All right, let's go!

MADAM PACE. Ah, no! No thank you! Yo aqui no do nada with your mother present.

STEPDAUGHTER. Oh, come on! Bring in that old senor who wants to have good time conmigo! (*Turning imperiously to all the others*) Yes, we've got to have it, this scene!—Come on, let's go! (*To* MADAM PACE) You may leave.

MADAM PACE. Ah si, I go, I go, go seguramente . . . (*She makes her exit furiously, putting her wig back on, and looking haughtily at the Actors who applaud mockingly.*)

STEPDAUGHTER (*To the* FATHER). And you can make your entrance. No need to go out and come in again. Come here. Pretend, you're already in. Right. Now I'm here with bowed head, modest, huh? Let's go! Speak up! With a different voice, the voice of someone just in off the street: "Hello, miss."

DIRECTOR (*By this time out front again*). Now look: are you directing this, or am I? (*To the* FATHER *who looks un-*

decided and perplexed.) Do it, yes. Go to the back. Don't leave the stage, though. And then come forward.

(*The* FATHER *does it, almost dismayed. Very pale; but already clothed in the reality of his created life, he smiles as he approaches from the back, as if still alien to the drama which will break upon him. The Actors now pay attention to the scene which is beginning.*)

DIRECTOR (*Softly, in haste, to the* PROMPTER *in the box*). And you, be ready now, ready to write!

THE SCENE

FATHER (*Coming forward, with a different voice*). Hello, miss.

STEPDAUGHTER (*With bowed head and contained disgust*). Hello.

FATHER (*Scrutinizing her under her hat which almost hides her face and noting that she is very young, exclaims, almost to himself, a little out of complaisance and a little out of fear of compromising himself in a risky adventure*). Oh . . . —Well, I was thinking, it wouldn't be the first time, hm? The first time you came here.

STEPDAUGHTER (*As above*). No, sir.

FATHER. You've been here other times? (*And when the* STEPDAUGHTER *nods*) More than one? (*He waits a moment for her to answer, then again scrutinizes her under her hat; smiles; then says*) Well then, hm . . . it shouldn't any longer be so . . . May I take this hat off for you?

STEPDAUGHTER (*Without pause, to forestall him, not now containing her disgust*). No, sir, *I* will take it off! (*And she does so in haste, convulsed.*)

(*The* MOTHER, *watching the scene with the* SON *and with the two others, smaller and more her own, who are close to her all the time, forming a group at the opposite side of the stage from the Actors, is on tenterhooks as she follows the words and actions of* FATHER *and* STEPDAUGHTER *with varied expression: grief, disdain, anxiety, horror, now hiding her face, now emitting a moan.*)

MOTHER. Oh God! My God!

FATHER (*Is momentarily turned to stone by the moaning; then he reassumes the previous tone*). Now give it to me: I'll hang it up for you. (*He takes the hat from her hands.*) But I could wish for a little hat worthier of such a dear, lovely little head! Would you like to help me choose one? From the many Madam has?—You wouldn't?

INGENUE (*Interrupting*). Oh now, come on, those are *our* hats!

DIRECTOR (*Without pause, very angry*). Silence, for Heaven's sake, don't try to be funny!—This is the stage. (*Turning back to the* STEPDAUGHTER) Would you begin again, please?

STEPDAUGHTER (*Beginning again*). No, thank you, sir.

FATHER. Oh, come on now, don't say no. Accept one from me. To please me . . . There are some lovely ones you know. And we would make Madam happy. Why else does she put them on display?

STEPDAUGHTER. No, no, sir, look: I wouldn't even be able to wear it.

FATHER. You mean because of what the family would think when they saw you come home with a new hat on? Think nothing of it. Know how to handle that? What to tell them at home?

STEPDAUGHTER (*Breaking out, at the end of her rope*). But that's not why, sir. I couldn't wear it because I'm . . . as you see me. You might surely have noticed! (*Points to her black attire.*)

FATHER. In mourning, yes. Excuse me. It's true: I do see it. I beg your pardon. I'm absolutely mortified, believe me.

STEPDAUGHTER (*Forcing herself and plucking up courage to conquer her contempt and nausea*). Enough! Enough!

It's for me to thank you, it is not for you to be mortified or afflicted. Please pay no more attention to what I said. Even for me, you understand . . . (*She forces herself to smile and adds*) I need to forget I am dressed like this.

DIRECTOR (*Interrupting, addressing himself to the* PROMPTER *in his box, and going up on stage again*). Wait! Wait! Don't write. Leave that last sentence out, leave it out! (*Turning to the* FATHER *and* STEPDAUGHTER) It's going very well indeed. (*Then to the* FATHER *alone*) This is where you go into the part we prepared. (*To the Actors*) Enchanting, that little hat scene, don't you agree?

STEPDAUGHTER. Oh but the best is just coming. Why aren't we continuing?

DIRECTOR. Patience one moment. (*Again addressing himself to the Actors*) Needs rather delicate handling, of course . . .

LEADING MAN. —With a certain *ease*—

LEADING LADY. Obviously. But there's nothing to it. (*To the* LEADING MAN) We can rehearse it at once, can't we?

LEADING MAN. As far as I'm . . . Very well, I'll go out and make my entrance. (*And he does go out by the back door, ready to re-enter.*)

DIRECTOR (*To the* LEADING LADY). And so, look, your scene with that Madam Pace is over. I'll write it up later. You are standing . . . Hey, where are you going?

LEADING LADY. Wait. I'm putting my hat back on . . . (*She does so, taking the hat from the hook.*)

DIRECTOR. Oh yes, good.—Now, you're standing here with your head bowed.

STEPDAUGHTER (*Amused*). But she's not wearing black!

LEADING LADY. I *shall* wear black! And I'll carry it better than you!

DIRECTOR (*To the* STEPDAUGHTER). Keep quiet, please! Just watch. You can learn something. (*Claps his hands*) Get going, get going! The entrance! (*And he goes back out front to get an impression of the stage.*)

(*The door at the back opens, and the* LEADING MAN *comes forward, with the relaxed, waggish manner of an elderly Don Juan. From the first speeches, the performance of the scene by the Actors is quite a different thing, without, however, having any element of parody in it—rather, it seems corrected, set to rights. Naturally, the* STEPDAUGHTER *and the* FATHER, *being quite unable to recognize themselves in this* LEADING LADY and LEADING MAN *but hearing them speak their own words express in various ways, now with gestures, now with smiles, now with open protests, their surprise, their wonderment, their suffering, etc., as will be seen forthwith.*

The PROMPTER'S *voice is clearly heard from the box.**)

LEADING MAN. Hello, miss.

FATHER (*Without pause, unable to contain himself*). No, no!

(*The* STEPDAUGHTER *seeing how the* LEADING MAN *makes his entrance has burst out laughing.*)

DIRECTOR (*Coming from the proscenium, furious*). Silence here! And stop that laughing at once! We can't go ahead till it stops.

STEPDAUGHTER (*Coming from the proscenium*). How can I help it? This lady (*The* LEADING LADY) just stands there. If she's supposed to be me, let me tell you that if anyone said hello to me in that manner and that tone of voice, I'd burst out laughing just as I actually did!

FATHER (*Coming forward a little too*). That's right . . . the manner, the tone . . .

DIRECTOR. Manner! Tone! Stand to

---

* In Italian rehearsals, traditionally, the prompter reads all the lines a few seconds ahead of the actors until the latter have completely memorized their roles, if indeed they ever do.

one side now, and let me see the rehearsal.

LEADING MAN (*Coming forward*). If I'm to play an old man entering a house of ill—

DIRECTOR. Oh, pay no attention, please. Just begin again. It was going fine. (*Waiting for the Actor to resume*) Now then . . .

LEADING MAN. Hello, miss.

LEADING LADY. Hello.

LEADING MAN (*Recreating the* FATHER'*s gesture of scrutinizing her under her hat, but then expressing very distinctly first the complaisance and then the fear*). Oh . . . Well . . . I was thinking it wouldn't be the first time, I hope . . .

FATHER (*Unable to help correcting him*). Not "I hope." "Would it?" "Would it?"

DIRECTOR. He says: "would it?" A question.

LEADING MAN (*Pointing to the* PROMPTER). I heard: "I hope."

DIRECTOR. Same thing! "Would it." Or: "I hope." Continue, continue.—Now, maybe a bit less affected . . . Look, I'll do it for you. Watch me . . . (*Returns to the stage, then repeats the bit since the entrance*)—Hello, miss.

LEADING LADY. Hello.

DIRECTOR. Oh, well . . . I was thinking . . . (*Turning to the* LEADING MAN *to have him note how he has looked at the* LEADING LADY *under her hat*) Surprise . . . fear and complaisance. (*Then, going on, and turning to the* LEADING LADY) It wouldn't be the first time, would it? The first time you came here. (*Again turning to the* LEADING MAN *with an inquiring look*) Clear? (*To the* LEADING LADY) Then you say: No, sir. (*Back to the* LEADING MAN) How shall I put it? Plasticity! (*Goes back out front.*)

LEADING LADY. No, sir.

LEADING MAN. You came here other times? More than one?

DIRECTOR. No, no, wait. (*Indicating the* LEADING LADY) First let her nod. "You came here other times?"

(*The* LEADING LADY *raises her head a little, closes her eyes painfully as if in disgust, then nods twice at the word "Down" from the* DIRECTOR.)

STEPDAUGHTER (*Involuntarily*). Oh, my God! (*And she at once puts her hand on her mouth to keep the laughter in.*)

DIRECTOR (*Turning round*). What is it?

STEPDAUGHTER (*Without pause*). Nothing, nothing.

DIRECTOR (*To the* LEADING MAN). That's your cue. Go straight on.

LEADING MAN. More than one? Well then, hm . . . it shouldn't any longer be so . . . May I take this little hat off for you?

(*The* LEADING MAN *says this last speech in such a tone and accompanies it with such a gesture that the* STEPDAUGHTER, *her hands on her mouth, much as she wants to hold herself in, cannot contain her laughter, which comes bursting out through her fingers irresistibly and very loud.*)

LEADING LADY (*Returning to her place, enraged*). Now look, I'm not going to be made a clown of by that person!

LEADING MAN. Nor am I. Let's stop.

DIRECTOR (*To the* STEPDAUGHTER, *roaring*). Stop it! Stop it!

STEPDAUGHTER. Yes, yes. Forgive me, forgive me . . .

DIRECTOR. You have no manners! You're presumptuous! So there!

FATHER (*Seeking to intervene*). That's true, yes, that's true, sir, but forgive . . .

DIRECTOR (*On stage again*). Forgive nothing! It's disgusting!

FATHER. Yes, sir. But believe me, it has such a strange effect—

DIRECTOR. Strange? Strange? What's strange about it?

FATHER. I admire your actors, sir, I really admire them, this gentleman (LEADING MAN) and that lady (LEADING

LADY) but assuredly . . . well, they're not us . . .

DIRECTOR. So what? How *could* they be you, if they're the actors?

FATHER. Exactly, the actors! And they play our parts well, both of them. But of course, to us, they seem something else—that tries to be the same but simply isn't!

DIRECTOR. How d'you mean: isn't? What is it then?

FATHER. Something that . . . becomes theirs. And stops being ours.

DIRECTOR. Necessarily! I explained that to you!

FATHER. Yes. I understand, I do under—

DIRECTOR. Then that will be enough! (*Turning to the Actors.*) We'll be rehearsing by ourselves as we usually do. Rehearsing with authors present has always been hell, in my experience. There's no satisfying them. (*Turning to the* FATHER *and the* STEPDAUGHTER.) Come along then. Let's resume. And let's hope you find it possible not to laugh this time.

STEPDAUGHTER. Oh, no, I won't be laughing this time around. My big moment comes up now. Don't worry!

DIRECTOR. Very well, when she says: "Please pay no more attention to what I said . . . Even for me—you understand . . ." (*Turning to the* FATHER). You'll have to cut right in with: "I understand, oh yes, I understand . . ." and ask her right away—

STEPDAUGHTER (*Interrupting*). Oh? Ask me what?

DIRECTOR. —why she is in mourning.

STEPDAUGHTER. No, no, look: when I told him I needed to forget I was dressed like this, do you know what his answer was? "Oh, good! Then let's take that little dress right off, shall we?"

DIRECTOR. Great! Terrific!. It'll knock 'em right out of their seats!

STEPDAUGHTER. But it's the truth.

DIRECTOR. Truth, is it? Well, well, well. This is the theater! Our motto is: truth up to a certain point!

STEPDAUGHTER. Then what would you propose?

DIRECTOR. You'll see. You'll see it. Just leave me alone.

STEPDAUGHTER. Certainly not. From my nausea—from all the reasons one more cruel than another why I am what I am, why I am "that one there"—you'd like to cook up some romantic, sentimental concoction, wouldn't you? He asks me why I'm in mourning, and I tell him, through my tears, that Papa died two months ago! No, my dear sir! He has to say what he did say: "Then let's take that little dress right off, shall we?" And I, with my two-months mourning in my heart, went back there—you see? behind that screen—and—my fingers quivering with shame, with loathing—I took off my dress, took off my corset . . .

DIRECTOR (*Running his hands through his hair*). Good God, what are you saying?

STEPDAUGHTER (*Shouting frantically*). The truth, sir, the truth!

DIRECTOR. Well, yes, of course, that must be the truth . . . and I quite understand your horror, young lady. Would you try to understand that all that is impossible *on the stage?*

STEPDAUGHTER. Impossible? Then, thanks very much, I'm leaving.

DIRECTOR. No, no, look . . .

STEPDAUGHTER. I'm leaving, I'm leaving! You went in that room, you two, didn't you, and figured out "what is possible on the stage"? Thanks very much. I see it all. He wants to skip to the point where he can act out his (*Exaggerating*) spiritual travail! But I want to play *my* drama. Mine!

DIRECTOR (*Annoyed, and shrugging haughtily*). Oh well, *your* drama. This is not just your drama, if I may say so. How about the drama of the others? His drama, (*The* FATHER) hers? (*The*

MOTHER) We can't let one character hog the limelight, just taking the whole stage over, and overshadowing all the others! Everything must be placed within the frame of one harmonious picture! We must perform only what is performable! I know as well as you do that each of us has a whole life of his own inside him and would like to bring it all out. But the difficult thing is this: to bring out only as much as is needed—in relation to the others—and in this to *imply* all the rest, *suggest* what remains inside! Oh, it would be nice if every character could come down to the footlights and tell the audience just what is brewing inside him—in a fine monologue or, if you will, a lecture! (*Good-natured, conciliatory.*) Miss, you will have to *contain yourself*. And it will be in your interest. It could make a bad impression—let me warn you—this tearing fury, this desperate disgust—since, if I may say so, you confessed having been with others at Madam Pace's—before him—more than once!

STEPDAUGHTER (*Lowering her head, pausing to recollect, a deeper note in her voice*). It's true. But to me the others are also *him,* all of them equally!

DIRECTOR (*Not getting it*). The others? How d'you mean?

STEPDAUGHTER. People "go wrong." And wrong follows on the heels of wrong. Who is responsible, if not whoever it was who first brought them down? Isn't that always the case? And for me that is him. Even before I was born. Look at him, and see if it isn't so.

DIRECTOR. Very good. And if he has so much to feel guilty about, can't you appreciate how it must weigh him down? So let's at least permit him to act it out.

STEPDAUGHTER. And how, may I ask, how could he act out all that "noble" guilt, all those so "moral" torments, if you propose to spare him the horror of one day finding in his arms—after having bade her take off the black clothes that marked her recent loss—a woman now, and already gone wrong—that little girl, sir, that little girl whom he used to go watch coming out of school?

(*She says these last words in a voice trembling with emotion. The* MOTHER, *hearing her say this, overcome with uncontrollable anguish, which comes out first in suffocated moans and subsequently bursts out in bitter weeping. The emotion takes hold of everyone. Long pause.*)

STEPDAUGHTER (*As soon as the* MOTHER *gives signs of calming down, somber, determined*). We're just among ourselves now. Still unknown to the public. Tomorrow you will make of us the show you have in mind. You will put it together in your way. But would you like to really see—our drama? Have it explode—the real thing?

DIRECTOR. Of course. Nothing I'd like better. And I'll use as much of it as I possibly can!

STEPDAUGHTER. Very well. Have this Mother here go out.

MOTHER (*Ceasing to weep, with a loud cry*). No, no! Don't allow this, don't allow it!

DIRECTOR. I only want to take a look, ma'am.

MOTHER. I can't, I just can't!

DIRECTOR. But if it's already happened? Excuse me but I just don't get it.

MOTHER. No, no, it's happening now. It's always happening. My torment is not a pretense! I am alive and present—always, in every moment of my torment—it keeps renewing itself, it too is alive and always present. But those two little ones over there—have you heard them speak? They cannot speak, sir, not any more! They still keep clinging to me—to keep my torment alive and present. For themselves they don't exist, don't exist any longer. And she, (*The* STEPDAUGHTER) she just fled, ran away from me, she's lost, lost . . . If I see her before me now, it's for the same reason: to renew the torment, keep it always alive and present forever—the torment I've suffered on her account too—forever!

FATHER (*Solemn*). The eternal moment, sir, as I told you. She (*The* STEPDAUGHTER) is here to catch me, fix me, hold me there in the pillory, hanging there forever, hooked, in that single fleeting shameful moment of my life! She cannot give it up. And, actually, sir, *you* cannot spare me.

DIRECTOR. But I didn't say I wouldn't use that. On the contrary, it will be the nucleus of the whole first act. To the point where she (*The* MOTHER) surprises you.

FATHER. Yes, exactly. Because that is the sentence passed upon me: all our passion which has to culminate in her (*The* MOTHER'*s*) final cry!

STEPDAUGHTER. It still rings in my ears. It's driven me out of my mind, that cry!—You can present me as you wish, sir, it doesn't matter. Even dressed. As long as at least my arms—just my arms—are bare. Because it was like this. (*She goes to the* FATHER *and rests her head on his chest.*) I was standing like this with my head on his chest and my arms round his neck like this. Then I saw something throbbing right here on my arm. A vein. Then, as if it was just this living vein that disgusted me, I jammed my eyes shut, like this, d'you see? and buried my head on his chest. (*Turning to the* MOTHER) Scream, scream, mamma! (*Buries her head on the* FATHER'*s chest and with her shoulders raised as if to avoid hearing the scream she adds in a voice stifled with torment.*) Scream as you screamed then!

MOTHER (*Rushing forward to part them*). No! My daughter! My daughter! (*Having pulled her from him*) Brute! Brute! It's my daughter, don't you see—my daughter!

DIRECTOR (*The outburst having sent him reeling to the footlights, while the Actors show dismay*). Fine! Splendid! And now: curtain, curtain!

FATHER (*Running to him, convulsed*). Right! Yes! Because that, sir, is how it actually was!

DIRECTOR (*In admiration and conviction*). Yes, yes, of course! Curtain! Curtain!

(*Hearing this repeated cry of the* DIRECTOR, *the* TECHNICIAN *lets down the curtain, trapping the* DIRECTOR *and the* FATHER *between curtain and footlights.*)

DIRECTOR (*Looking up, with raised arms*). What an idiot! I say Curtain, meaning that's how the act should end, and they let down the actual curtain! (HE *lifts a corner of the curtain so he can get back on stage. To the* FATHER) Yes, yes, fine, splendid! Absolutely sure fire! Has to end that way. I can vouch for the first act. (*Goes behind the curtain with the* FATHER.)

(*When the curtain rises we see that the stage hands have struck that first "indication of a set," and have put on stage in its stead a small garden fountain. On one side of the stage, the Actors are sitting in a row, and on the other are the Characters. The* DIRECTOR *is standing in the middle of the stage, in the act of meditating with one hand, fist clenched, on his mouth.*)

DIRECTOR (*Shrugging after a short pause*). Yes, well then, let's get to the second act. Just leave it to me as we agreed beforehand and everything will be all right.

STEPDAUGHTER. Our entrance into his house (*The* FATHER) in spite of him. (*The* SON).

DIRECTOR (*Losing patience*). Very well. But leave it all to me, I say.

STEPDAUGHTER. In spite of him. Just let that be clear.

MOTHER (*Shaking her head from her corner*). For all the good that's come out of it . . .

STEPDAUGHTER (*Turning quickly on her*). It doesn't matter. The more damage to us, the more guilt feelings for him.

DIRECTOR (*Still out of patience*). I understand, I understand. All this will be taken into account, especially at the beginning. Rest assured.

MOTHER (*Supplicatingly*). Do make them understand, I beg you, sir, for my conscience sake, for I tried in every possible way—

STEPDAUGHTER. (*Continuing her* MOTHER*'s speech, contemptuously*). To placate me, to advise me not to give him trouble. (*To the* DIRECTOR) Do what she wants, do it because it's true. I enjoy the whole thing very much because, look: the more she plays the suppliant and tries to gain entrance into his heart, the more he holds himself aloof: he's an absentee! How I relish this!

DIRECTOR. We want to get going—on the second act, don't we?

STEPDAUGHTER. I won't say another word. But to play it all in the garden, as you want to, won't be possible.

DIRECTOR. Why won't it be possible?

STEPDAUGHTER. Because he (*The* SON) stays shut up in his room, on his own. Then again we need the house for the part about this poor bewildered little boy, as I told you.

DIRECTOR. Quite right. But on the other hand, we can't change the scenery in view of the audience three or four times in one act, nor can we stick up signs—

LEADING MAN. They used to at one time . . .

DIRECTOR. Yes, when the audiences were about as mature as that little girl.

LEADING LADY. They got the illusion more easily.

FATHER (*Suddenly, rising*). The illusion, please don't say illusion! Don't use that word! It's especially cruel to us.

DIRECTOR (*Astonished*). And why, if I may ask?

FATHER. Oh yes, cruel, cruel! You should understand that.

DIRECTOR. What word would you have us use anyway? The illusion of creating here for our spectators—

LEADING MAN. —By our performance—

DIRECTOR. —the illusion of a reality.

FATHER. I understand, sir, but perhaps you do not understand us. Because, you see, for you and for your actors all this—quite rightly—is a game—

LEADING LADY (*Indignantly interrupting*). Game! We are not children, sir. We act in earnest.

FATHER. I don't deny it. I just mean the game of your art which, as this gentleman rightly says, must provide a perfect illusion of reality.

DIRECTOR. Yes, exactly.

FATHER. But consider this. We, (*He quickly indicates himself and the other five Characters*) we have no reality outside this illusion.

DIRECTOR (*Astonished, looking at his Actors who remain bewildered and lost*). And that means?

FATHER (*After observing them briefly, with a pale smile*). Just that, ladies and gentlemen. How should we have any other reality? What for you is an illusion, to be created, is for us our unique reality. (*Short pause. He takes several short steps toward the* DIRECTOR, *and adds*) But not for us alone, of course. Think a moment. (*He looks into his eyes.*) Can you tell me who you are? (*And he stands there pointing his first finger at him.*)

DIRECTOR (*Upset, with a half-smile*). How do you mean, who I am? I am I.

FATHER. And if I told you that wasn't true because you are me?

DIRECTOR. I would reply that you are out of your mind. (*The Actors laugh.*)

FATHER. You are right to laugh: because this is a game. (*To the* DIRECTOR) And you can object that it's only in a game that that gentleman there, (LEAD-

ING MAN) who is himself, must be me, who am *my*self. I've caught you in a trap, do you see that?

(*Actors start laughing again.*)

DIRECTOR (*Annoyed*). You said all this before. Why repeat it?

FATHER. I won't—I didn't intend to say that. I'm inviting you to emerge from this game. (*He looks at the* LEADING LADY *as if to forestall what she might say.*) This game of art which you are accustomed to play here with your actors. Let me again ask quite seriously: Who are you?

DIRECTOR (*Turning to the Actors, amazed and at the same time irritated*). The gall of this fellow! Calls himself a character and comes here to ask me who I am!

FATHER (*Dignified, but not haughty*). A character, sir, can always ask a man who he is. Because a character really has his own life, marked with his own characteristics, by virtue of which he is always someone. Whereas, a man—I'm not speaking of you now—*a man* can be no one.

DIRECTOR. Oh sure. But you are asking me! And I am the manager, understand?

FATHER (*Quite softly with mellifluous modesty*). Only in order to know, sir, if you as you now are see yourself . . . for example, at a distance in time. Do you see the man you once were, with all the illusions you had then, with everything, inside you and outside, as it seemed then—as it was then for you!—Well sir, thinking back to those illusions which you don't have any more, to all those things which no longer seem to be what at one time they were for you, don't you feel, not just the boards of this stage, but the very earth beneath slipping away from you? For will not all that you feel yourself to be now, your whole reality of today, as it is now, inevitably seem an illusion tomorrow?

DIRECTOR (*Who has not followed exactly, but has been staggered by the plausibilities of the argument*). Well, well, what do you want to prove?

FATHER. Oh nothing sir. I just wanted to make you see that if *we* (*Pointing again at himself and the other Characters*) have no reality outside of illusion, it would be well if you should distrust your reality because, though you breathe it and touch it today, it is destined like that of yesterday to stand revealed to you tomorrow as illusion.

DIRECTOR (*Deciding to mock him*). Oh splendid! And you'll be telling me next that you and this play that you have come to perform for me are truer and more real than I am.

FATHER (*Quite seriously*). There can be no doubt of that, sir.

DIRECTOR. Really?

FATHER. I thought you had understood that from the start.

DIRECTOR. More real than me?

FATHER. If your reality can change overnight . . .

DIRECTOR. Of course it can, it changes all the time, like everyone else's.

FATHER (*With a cry*). But ours does not, sir. You see, that is the difference. It does not change, it cannot ever change or be otherwise because it is already fixed, it is what is, just that, forever—a terrible thing, sir!—an immutable reality. You should shudder to come near us.*

---

* In the first edition, the following passage occurs here:

FATHER. If you are truly conscious that your reality, on the other hand, your reality in time is an ephemeral and extremely fleeting illusion which you unconsciously invent, today in this day and tomorrow in some other way according to cases, according to conditions and will and feelings which you invent with the intellect which shows them to you today in one way and tomorrow . . . who knows how: illusions of reality as acted out in that fatuous comedy of life which does not end, which can not ever end because,

DIRECTOR (*Suddenly struck by a new idea, he steps in front of the* FATHER). I should like to know, however, when anyone ever saw a character get out of his part and set about expounding and explicating it, delivering lectures on it. Can you tell me? I have never seen anything like that.

FATHER. You have never seen it, sir, because authors generally hide the travail of their creations. When characters are alive and turn up, living, before their author, all that author does is follow the words and gestures which they propose to him. He has to want them to be as they themselves want to be. Woe betide him if he doesn't! When a character is born, he at once acquires such an independence, even of his own author, that the whole world can imagine him in innumerable situations other than those the author thought to place him in. At times he acquires a meaning that the author never dreamt of giving him.

DIRECTOR. Certainly, I know that.

FATHER. Then why all this astonishment at us? Imagine what a misfortune it is for a character such as I described to you—given life in the imagination of an author who then wished to deny him life—and tell me frankly: isn't such a character, given life and left without life, isn't he right to set about doing just what we are doing now as we stand here before you, after having done just the same—for a very long time, believe me—before *him,* trying to persuade him, trying to push him . . . I would appear before him sometimes, sometimes she (*Looks at* STEPDAUGHTER) would go to him, sometimes that poor mother . . .

STEPDAUGHTER (*Coming forward as if in a trance*). It's true. I too went there, sir, to tempt him, many times, in the melancholy of that study of his, at the twilight hour, when he would sit stretched out in his armchair, unable to make up his mind to switch the light on,

---

if tomorrow it should end, then good bye, all is finished.

DIRECTOR. In the name of God, I wish you at least would stop your philosophizing and let's see if we might end this play which you people have brought me! Too much reasoning, too much reasoning, my dear sir.—You know you almost seem to me a . . . (*He interrupts and looks him over from top to toe*) . . . exactly, yes: You introduced yourself here as a—let's put it this way—as a character created by an author who decided not to make a play out of you. Correct?

FATHER. That's the simple truth, sir.

DIRECTOR. Cut it out. None of us believes you. Such things can't be seriously believed, you must know that. You know what I rather think is going on? I think that you are adopting the manner of a certain author whom I particularly detest—let me admit that—although, unfortunately, I've had to put on some of his works. I happen to have been rehearsing one of them when you all came. (*Turning to the Actors*) Think what we gained by the exchange! From the frying pan into the fire!

FATHER. I don't know, sir, what author you may be alluding to, but believe me, I feel, I feel what I think. And only those who do not think about what they feel would say I am just reasoning: they are blind to their own feelings. I know, I know that many consider such self-blinding much more human, but the opposite is true, sir, for man never reasons so much—on or off the point—as when he suffers. He wants to see the cause of his sufferings, he wants to know who is giving them to him, if this is just or unjust. When, on the other hand, he is enjoying himself, he just accepts the enjoyment and stops reasoning—as if to enjoy oneself were a right. Only the animals suffer without reasoning, sir. Yet put on stage a man who reasons in the midst of his suffering, and everyone will object. But let him suffer like an animal and everyone will say: "Oh, yes, he is human."

DIRECTOR. And in the meanwhile you go on reasoning, huh?

FATHER. Because I suffer, sir. I am not reasoning, I am crying aloud the why and wherefore of my suffering.

and letting the evening shadows invade the room, knowing that these shadows were alive with us and that we were coming to tempt him . . . (*As if she saw herself still in that study and felt only annoyance at the presence of all of these Actors*) Oh, if only you would all go away! Leave us alone! My mother there with her son—I with this little girl—the boy there always alone—then I with him —(*The* FATHER) then I by myself, I by myself . . . in those shadows. (*Suddenly she jumps up as if she wished to take hold of herself in the vision she has of herself lighting up the shadows and alive.*) Ah my life! What scenes, what scenes we went there to propose to him: I, I tempted him more than the others.

FATHER. Right, but perhaps that was the trouble: you insisted too much. You thought you could seduce him.

STEPDAUGHTER. Nonsense. He wanted me that way. (*She comes up to the* DIRECTOR *to tell him as in confidence.*) If you ask me, sir, it was because he was so depressed, or because he despised the theater the public knows and wants . . .

DIRECTOR. Let's continue. Let's continue, for Heaven's sake. Enough theories, I'd like some facts. Give me some facts.

STEPDAUGHTER. It seems to me that we have already given you more facts than you can handle—with our entry into his (*The* FATHER'*s*) house! You said you couldn't change the scene every five minutes or start hanging signs.

DIRECTOR. Nor can we, of course not, we have to combine the scenes and group them in one simultaneous close-knit action. Not your idea at all. You'd like to see your brother come home from school and wander through the house like a ghost, hiding behind the doors, and brooding on a plan which—how did you put it—?

STEPDAUGHTER. —shrivels him up, sir, completely shrivels him up, sir.

DIRECTOR. "Shrivels!" What a word! All right then: his growth was stunted except for his eyes. Is that what you said?

STEPDAUGHTER. Yes, sir. Just look at him. (*She points him out next to the* MOTHER.)

DIRECTOR. Good girl. And then at the same time you want this little girl to be playing in the garden, dead to the world. Now, the boy in the house, the girl in the garden, is that possible?

STEPDAUGHTER. Happy in the sunshine! Yes, that is my only reward, her pleasure, her joy in that garden! After the misery, the squalor of a horrible room where we slept, all four of us, she with me: just think, of the horror of my contaminated body next to hers! She held me tight, oh so tight with her loving innocent little arms! In the garden she would run and take my hand as soon as she saw me. She did not see the big flowers, she ran around looking for the teeny ones and wanted to show them to me, oh the joy of it!

(*Saying this and tortured by the memory she breaks into prolonged desperate sobbing, dropping her head onto her arms which are spread out on the work table. Everyone is overcome by her emotion. The* DIRECTOR *goes to her almost paternally and says to comfort her*)

DIRECTOR. We'll do the garden. We'll do the garden, don't worry, and you'll be very happy about it. We'll bring all the scenes together in the garden. (*Calling a stagehand by name*) Hey, drop me a couple of trees, will you, two small cypress trees, here in front of the fountain.

(*Two small cypress trees are seen descending from the flies. A stagehand runs on to secure them with nails and a couple of braces.*)

DIRECTOR (*To the* STEPDAUGHTER). Something to go on with anyway. Gives us an idea. (*Again calling the stagehand by name*) Hey, give me a bit of sky.

STAGEHAND (*From above*). What?

DIRECTOR. Bit of sky, a back-cloth, to go behind that fountain. (*A white backdrop is seen descending from the flies.*) Not white, I said sky. It doesn't matter, leave it, I'll take care of it. (*Shouting*) Hey, Electrician, put these lights out. Let's have a bit of atmosphere, lunar atmosphere, blue background, and give me a blue spot on that back-cloth. That's right. That's enough. (*At his command a mysterious lunar scene is created which induces the Actors to talk and move as they would on an evening in the garden beneath the moon.*) (*To* STEPDAUGHTER) You see? And now instead of hiding behind doors in the house the boy could move around here in the garden and hide behind trees. But it will be difficult, you know, to find a little girl to play the scene where she shows you the flowers. (*Turning to the* BOY). Come down this way a bit. Let's see how this can be worked out. (*And when the* BOY *doesn't move*) Come on, come on. (*Then dragging him forward he tries to make him hold his head up but it falls down again every time.*) Oh dear, another problem, this boy . . . What *is* it? . . . My God, he'll have to say something . . . (*He goes up to him, puts a hand on his shoulder and leads him behind one of the tree drops.*) Come on. Come on. Let me see. You can hide a bit here . . . Like this . . . You can stick your head out a bit to look . . . (*He goes to one side to see the effect. The* BOY *has scarcely run through the actions when the Actors are deeply affected; and* THEY *remain quite overwhelmed.*) Ah! Fine! Splendid! (*He turns again to the* STEPDAUGHTER.) If the little girl surprises him, looking out and runs over to him don't you think she might drag a few words out of him too?

STEPDAUGHTER (*Jumping to her feet*). Don't expect him to speak while *he's* here. (*She points to the* SON.) You have to send *him* away first.

SON (*Going resolutely toward one of the two stairways*). Suits me. Glad to go. Nothing I want more.

DIRECTOR (*Immediately calling him*). No. Where are you going? Wait.

(*The* MOTHER *rises, deeply moved, in anguish at the thought that he is really going. She instinctively raises her arms as if to halt him, yet without moving away from her position.*)

SON (*Arriving at the footlights, where the* DIRECTOR *stops him*). I have absolutely nothing to do here. So let me go please. Just let me go.

DIRECTOR. How do you mean, you have nothing to do?

STEPDAUGHTER (*Placidly, with irony*). Don't hold him! He won't go.

FATHER. He has to play the terrible scene in the garden with his mother.

SON (*Unhesitating, resolute, proud*). I play nothing. I said so from the start. (*To the* DIRECTOR) Let me go.

STEPDAUGHTER (*Running to the* DIRECTOR *to get him to lower his arms so that he is no longer holding the* SON *back*). Let him go. (*Then turning to the* SON *as soon as the* DIRECTOR *has let him go*) Very well, go. (*The* SON *is all set to move toward the stairs but, as if held by some occult power, he cannot go down the steps. While the Actors are both astounded and deeply troubled, he moves slowly across the footlights straight to the other stairway. But having arrived there he remains poised for the descent but unable to descend. The* STEPDAUGHTER *who has followed him with her eyes in an attitude of defiance bursts out laughing.*) He can't, you see. He can't. He has to stay here, has to. Bound by a chain, indissolubly. But if I who do take flight, sir, when that happens which has to happen, and precisely because of the hatred I feel for him, precisely so as not to see him again—very well, if *I* am still here and can bear the sight of him and his company—you can imagine whether *he* can go away. He who really must, must remain here with that fine father of his and that mother there who no longer has any other children. (*Turning again to the* MOTHER) Come on, Mother, come on. (*Turning again to the* DIRECTOR *and pointing to the* MOTHER) Look, she got up to hold him back. (*To the* MOTHER, *as if exerting a magical power over her*) Come. Come . . . (*Then to the* DIRECTOR) You can imagine how little she wants to display her love in front of your actors. But so great is her desire to get at him that—look, you see—she is even prepared to live her scene.

(*In fact the* MOTHER *has approached and no sooner has the* STEPDAUGHTER *spoken her last words than she spreads her arms to signify consent.*)

SON (*Without pause*). But *I* am not, *I* am not. If I can not go I will stay here, but I repeat: I will play nothing.

FATHER (*To the* DIRECTOR, *enraged*). You can force him, sir.

SON. No one can force me.

FATHER. I will force you.

STEPDAUGHTER. Wait, wait. First the little girl must be at the fountain. (*She runs to take the* LITTLE GIRL, *drops on her knees in front of her, takes her little face in her hands.*) My poor little darling, you look bewildered with those lovely big eyes of yours. Who knows where you think you are? We are on a stage my dear. What is a stage? It is a place where you play at being serious, a place for play-acting, where we will now play-act. But seriously! For real! You too . . . (*She embraces her, presses her to her bosom and rocks her a little*). Oh, little darling, little darling, what an ugly play you will enact! What a horrible thing has been planned for you, the garden, the fountain . . . All pretense, of course, that's the trouble, my sweet, everything is make-believe here, but perhaps for you, my child, a make-believe fountain is nicer than a real one for playing in, hmm? It will be a game for the others, but not for you, alas, because you are real, my darling, and are actually playing in a fountain that is real, beautiful, big, green with many bamboo plants reflected in it and giving it shade. Many, many ducklings can swim in it, breaking the shade to bits. You want to take hold of one of these ducklings . . . (*With a shout that fills everyone with dismay*) No! No, my Rosetta! Your mother is not looking after you because of that beast of a son. A thousand devils are loose in my head . . . and *he* . . . (*She leaves the* LITTLE GIRL *and turns with her usual hostility to the* BOY). And what are you doing here, always looking like a beggar child? It will be your fault too if this little girl drowns—with all your standing around like that. As if I hadn't paid for everybody when I got you all into this house. (*Grabbing one of his arms to force him to take a hand out of his pocket*) What have you got there? What are you hiding? Let's see this hand. (*Tears his hand out of his pocket, and to the horror of everyone discovers that it holds a small revolver. She looks at it for a moment as if satisfied and then says*) Ah! Where did you get that and how? (*And as the* BOY *in his confusion, with his eyes staring and vacant all the time, does not answer her*) Idiot, if I were you I wouldn't have killed myself, I would have killed one of those two—or both of them—the father and the son! (*She hides him behind the small cypress tree from which he had been looking out, and she takes the* LITTLE GIRL *and hides her in the fountain, having her lie down in it in such a way as to be quite hidden. Finally, the* STEPDAUGHTER *goes down on her knees with her face in her hands which are resting on the rim of the fountain.*)

DIRECTOR. Splendid! (*Turning to the* SON) And at the same time . . .

SON (*With contempt*). And at the same time, nothing. It is not true, sir.

There was never any scene between me and her. (*He points to the* MOTHER.) Let her tell you herself how it was.

(*Meanwhile the* SECOND ACTRESS *and the* JUVENILE LEAD *have detached themselves from the group of Actors. The former has started to observe the* MOTHER, *who is opposite her, very closely. And the other has started to observe the* SON. *Both are planning how they will recreate the roles.*)

MOTHER. Yes, it is true, sir. I had gone to his room.

SON. My room, did you hear that? Not the garden.

DIRECTOR. That is of no importance. We have to rearrange the action, I told you that.

SON (*Noticing that the* JUVENILE LEAD *is observing him*). What do *you* want?

JUVENILE LEAD. Nothing. I am observing you.

SON (*Turning to the other side where the* SECOND ACTRESS *is*). Ah, and here we have you to re-create the role, eh? (*He points to the* MOTHER.)

DIRECTOR. Exactly, exactly. You should be grateful, it seems to me, for the attention they are giving you.

SON. Oh yes, thank you. But you still haven't understood that you cannot do this drama. We are not inside you, not in the least, and your actors are looking at us from the outside. Do you think it's possible for us to live before a mirror which, not content to freeze us in the fixed image it provides of our expression, also throws back at us an unrecognizable grimace purporting to be ourselves?

FATHER. That is true. That is true. You must see that.

DIRECTOR (*To the* JUVENILE LEAD *and the* SECOND ACTRESS). Very well, get away from here.

SON. No good. I won't cooperate.

DIRECTOR. Just be quiet a minute and let me hear your mother. (*To the* MOTHER) Well? You went into his room?

MOTHER. Yes sir, into his room. I was at the end of my tether. I wanted to pour out all of the anguish which was oppressing me. But as soon as he saw me come in—

SON. —There was no scene. I went away. I went away so there would be no scene. Because I have never made scenes, never, understand?

MOTHER. That's true. That's how it was. Yes.

DIRECTOR. But now there's got to be a scene between you and him. It is indispensable.

MOTHER. As for me, sir, I am ready. If only you could find some way to have me speak to him for one moment, to have me say what is in my heart.

FATHER (*Going right up to the* SON, *very violent*). You will do it! For your mother! For your mother!

SON (*More decisively than ever*). I will do nothing!

FATHER (*Grabbing him by the chest and shaking him*). By God, you will obey! Can't you hear how she is talking to you? Aren't you her son?

SON (*Grabbing his* FATHER). No! No! Once and for all let's have done with it!

(*General agitation. The* MOTHER *terrified, tries to get between them to separate them.*)

MOTHER (*As before*). Please, please!

FATHER (*Without letting go of the* SON). You must obey, you must obey!

SON (*Wrestling with his* FATHER *and in the end throwing him to the ground beside the little stairway, to the horror of everyone*). What's this frenzy that's taken hold of you? To show your shame and ours to everyone? Have you no restraint? I won't cooperate, I won't cooperate! And that is how I interpret the wishes of the man who did not choose to put us on stage.

DIRECTOR. But you came here.

SON (*Pointing to his* FATHER). *He* came here—not me!

DIRECTOR. But aren't you here too?

SON. It was he who wanted to come, dragging the rest of us with him, and then getting together with you to plot not only what really happened, but also—as if that did not suffice—*what did not happen.*

DIRECTOR. Then tell me. Tell me what did happen. Just tell me. You came out of your room without saying a thing?

SON (*After a moment of hesitation*). Without saying a thing. In order not to make a scene.

DIRECTOR (*Driving him on*). Very well, and then, what did you do then?

SON (*While everyone looks on in anguished attention, he moves a few steps on the front part of the stage*). Nothing . . . crossing the garden . . . (*He stops, gloomy, withdrawn*).

DIRECTOR (*Always driving him on to speak, impressed by his reticence*). Very well, crossing the garden?

SON (*Desperate, hiding his face with one arm*). Why do you want to make me say it, sir? It is horrible.

(*The* MOTHER *trembles all over, and stifles groans, looking toward the fountain.*)

DIRECTOR (*Softly, noticing this look of hers, turning to the* SON, *with growing apprehension*). The little girl?

SON (*Looking out into the auditorium*). Over there—in the fountain . . .

FATHER (*On the ground, pointing compassionately toward the* MOTHER). And she followed him, sir.

DIRECTOR (*To the* SON, *anxiously*). And then you . . .

SON (*Slowly, looking straight ahead all the time*). I ran out. I started to fish her out . . . but all of a sudden I stopped. Behind those trees I saw something that froze me: the boy, the boy was standing there, quite still. There was madness in the eyes. He was looking at his drowned sister in the fountain. (*The* STEP-DAUGHTER, *who has been bent over the fountain, hiding the* LITTLE GIRL, *is sobbing desperately, like an echo from the bottom. Pause*) I started to approach and then . . .

(*From behind the trees where the* BOY *has been hiding, a revolver shot rings out.*)

MOTHER (*Running up with a tormented shout, accompanied by the* SON *and all the Actors in a general tumult*). Son! My son! (*And then amid the hubbub and the disconnected shouts of the others*) Help! Help!

DIRECTOR (*Amid the shouting, trying to clear a space while the* BOY *is lifted by his head and feet and carried away behind the backcloth*) Is he wounded, is he wounded, really?

(*Everyone except the* DIRECTOR *and the* FATHER, *who has remained on the ground beside the steps, has disappeared behind the backcloth which has served for a sky, where they can still be heard for a while whispering anxiously. Then from one side and the other of this curtain, the Actors come back on stage.*)

LEADING ACTRESS (*Re-entering from the right, very much upset*). He's dead! Poor boy! He's dead! What a terrible thing!

LEADING ACTOR (*Re-entering from the left, laughing*). How do you mean, dead? Fiction, fiction, one doesn't believe such things.

OTHER ACTORS (*On the right*). Fiction? Reality! Reality! He is dead!

OTHER ACTORS (*On the left*). No! Fiction! Fiction!

FATHER (*Rising, and crying out to them*). Fiction indeed! Reality, reality, gentlemen, reality! (*Desperate, he too disappears at the back.*)

DIRECTOR (*At the end of his rope*). Fiction! Reality! To hell with all of you! Lights, lights, lights! (*At a single stroke the whole stage and auditorium is flooded with very bright light. The* DIRECTOR *breathes again, as if freed from an incubus and they all look each other in the eyes, bewildered and lost.*) Things like this don't happen to me, they've made me lose a whole day. (*He looks at his watch.*) Go, you can all go. What could we do now anyway? It is too late to pick up the rehearsal where we left off. See you this evening. (*As soon as the Actors have gone he talks to the* ELECTRICIAN *by name.*) Hey, Electrician, lights out. (*He has hardly said the words when the theater is plunged for a moment into complete darkness.*) Hey, for God's sake, leave me at least one light! I like to see where I am going!

(*Immediately, from behind the backcloth, as if the wrong switch had been pulled, a green light comes on which projects the silhouettes, clear-cut and large, of the Characters, minus the* BOY *and the* LITTLE GIRL. *Seeing the silhouettes, the* DIRECTOR, *terrified, rushes from the stage. At the same time the light behind the backcloth goes out and the stage is again lit in nocturnal blue as before.*

Slowly, from the right side of the curtain, the SON *comes forward first, followed by the* MOTHER *with her arms stretched out towards him; then from the left side, the* FATHER. *They stop in the middle of the stage and stay there as if in a trance. Last of all from the right, the* STEPDAUGHTER *comes out and runs towards the two stairways. She stops on the first step, to look for a moment at the other three, and then breaks into a harsh laugh before throwing herself down the steps; she runs down the aisle between the rows of seats; she stops one more time and again laughs, looking at the three who are still on stage; she disappears from the auditorium, and from the lobby her laughter is still heard. Shortly thereafter the curtain falls.*)

THE LIFE AND WORKS OF LUIGI PIRANDELLO

By ERIC BENTLEY

LUIGI PIRANDELLO was born on June 28, 1867, near Agrigento in southern Sicily. As he himself put it, "I am the son of Chaos, and not allegorically but literally, because I was born in a country spot, called, by the people around, *Cavasu,* a dialectical corruption of the authentic, ancient Greek word, *cháos.*" Pirandello's father was a sulphur-mine owner who had fought for Garibaldi in 1860 and 1862 and who, in 1863, had married the sister of one of his comrades in arms. Until he was nineteen, it looked as if Pirandello might spend his whole lifetime within the circle of family interests: he was to enter his father's line of business and he became engaged to his cousin Lina. But in 1886, when he returned from school in Palermo to his native Agrigento, he went back again to Palermo almost at once, and enrolled in literature courses at the university. Although his engagement lasted another three years, he was soon writing Lina sentiments which, far from expressing confidence in their relationship, voiced agonized doubts as to the possibility of any relationship at all. These letters later came to be considered characteristically Pirandellian and some commentators lightheartedly considered them a vintage product of the 1920s:

> Meditation is the black abyss, populated by dark phantoms, watched over by desperate dejection. No ray of light ever pierces it: the desire for one only sinks you ever deeper in the dense shadows. . . . It is an insatiable thirst, an obstinate fury: but there's nothing to drink but the blackness, and the silent immensity freezes you. We are like the poor spiders which, in order to live, need to weave their subtle web in some corner, we are like the poor snails which, in order to live, need to carry their frail shells on their backs, or like the poor mollusks which crave their conches at the bottom of the sea. We are spiders, snails, mollusks of a nobler race, to be sure, we wouldn't want a web, a shell, a conch, to be sure, but we would want a little world, oh yes, both to live in it and to live by it. An ideal, a feeling, a habit, an occupation—that's the little world, that's the shell of this giant snail or man as we call it. . . . I write and study to forget myself—to distract myself from despair. (From a letter to Lina, October 31, 1886. Published in 1961 in *Terzo programma,* n. 3.)

In 1887, Pirandello left the University of Palermo for the University of Rome, and in 1889, he went on to the Univer-

---

sity of Bonn in Germany, where he got his doctorate two years later with a dissertation on the dialect of his native Agrigento. In 1889 he also began publishing. Though his earliest literary career was that of a minor poet, by 1893 he was writing a novel, *L'esclusa* (*The Outcast*). In 1894, unable to fulfill his engagement to his cousin Lina, he married the daughter of one of his father's associates, Maria Antonietta Portulano. The couple had three children: Stefano, born in 1895, Lietta, born in 1897, and Fausto, born in 1899; Fausto was to become one of the notable Italian painters of the twentieth century. In 1897, Pirandello began to work at a girls' school in Rome, l'Istituto Superiore di Magistero, which post he was not to leave until 1922.

He would undoubtedly have left much earlier but for an economic disaster that hit him and his wife in 1903. In that year a landslide destroyed the mine in which both his father's fortune and his wife's dowry were tied up. The marriage had been an "economic" one from the beginning, and now it was shattered by an economic disaster. Maria Antonietta was stricken with paralysis of the legs when she got the news, and, although her legs recovered after six months, she became a victim of paranoid jealousy, and was insane for the rest of her life, though her husband delayed committing her to an institution until 1919 (where she lived until 1959). What was to be Pirandello's only really famous novel was the fruit of this family crisis, *Il fu Mattia Pascal* (*The Late Mattia Pascal,* 1904).

There were other novels: *Il turno* (*The Merry Go Round*), written in 1895, was published in 1902; *I vecchi e i giovani* (*The Old and the Young*) came out serially, 1906–1908; *Suo marito* (Her *Husband*), the only Pirandello novel that still has not been published in English, was out by 1911; *Si gira!* (*Shoot*) followed in 1915; *Uno, Nessuno e centomila* (*One, None, and a Hundred Thousand*) was published in 1926. But until well after World War I, Pirandello's reputation rested principally upon the many short stories he had been publishing since the early 1890s: *Amori senza amore* (*Loves Without Love,* 1894); *Beffe della morte e della vita* (*Jests of Death and Life*) and *Quand'ero matto* (*When I Was Crazy,* 1902); *Erma bifronte* (*Two-faced Erma,* 1906); *La vita nuda* (*Naked Life,* 1911); *Terzetti* (*Trios,* 1912); *Le due maschere* (*The Two Masks,* 1914); *La trappola* (*The Trap*) and *Erba del nostro orto* (*Grass in Our Garden,* 1915); *E domani, lunedì* (*Tomorrow Is Monday,* 1917); *Un cavallo nella luna* (*A Horse in the Moon,* 1918); *Berecche e la guerra* (*Berecche and the War*) and *Il carnevale dei morti* (*The Carnival of the Dead,* 1919). His playwriting also began in the 1890s. A one-act, *L'epilogo* (*The Epilogue*), later called *La morsa* (*The Vise*), was printed in 1898. In the following year he wrote a full-length play *Se non così* (*If Not Thus*), which was not staged until 1915. Indeed, it was not until the second decade of this century that Pirandello got over the modern writer's feeling of superiority to all things theatrical, a feeling he recaptured and exploited even later in *Sei personaggi in cerca d'autore* (*Six Characters in Search of an Author*).

His career as a practicing playwright really began in 1910, under some degree of suasion from the actor-manager Nino Martoglio, but it was not until the later war years that plays, one after the other, began to flow from Pirandello's pen: *Pensaci, Giacomino!* (*Think of That, Giacomino!,* 1916) *Così è* (*se vi pare*) (*Right You Are*); *Il berretto a sonagli* (*Cap and Bells*), and *Il piacere dell'onestà* (*The Pleasure of Honesty,* 1917); *Ma non é una cosa seria* (*But It's Not Serious*) and *Il giuoco delle parti* (*The Rules of the Game,* 1918); *L'uomo, la bestia, e la virtù* (*Man, Beast, and Virtue,* 1919); *Tutto per bene* (*All for the Best*), *Come prima, meglio di prima* (*Like the First Time Only Better*), and *La Signora Morli, una e due* (*Mrs. Morley One and Two,* 1920).

Pirandello was still a struggling playwright, however, when *Six Characters in Search of an Author* opened at the Teatro Valle in Rome on May 10, 1921. Of his previous plays only one—*Like the First Time Only Better,* which opened in Milan on March 24, 1920—had found full favor with its audience. *Six Characters,* at its opening in Rome, was a *succès de scandale,* and the author had to slip out of the theater to wild cries of "madhouse." But the Milan opening that fall—September 27 at the Teatro Manzoni—was a shot heard round the world. Though banned in London by the Lord Chamberlain, through the good offices of Bernard Shaw and others, *Six Characters* reached a public there in February 1922, under the auspices of a technically private club. By November it was playing at the Fulton Theater in New York and in 1923 it played Paris, Cracow, Prague, Amsterdam, Warsaw, Barcelona, and Athens; in 1924 it played Vienna, Berlin, Zagreb, and Tokyo.

Financially, Pirandello was at last able to abandon his uncongenial teaching post. For the last fourteen years of his life he pursued the career of an international theater man. His second most important play, *Enrico IV* (*The Emperor*) followed right on the heels of *Six Characters. The Emperor* also enjoyed a broad international success. Pirandello traveled with his plays to a number of the principal countries where they were performed—France, the United States, Argentina, Brazil, Germany—and, in Italy in 1925, became artistic director of a new Teatro d'Arte di Roma, for which he entertained very high hopes.

But only the years 1921–1925, if those, were a simple success story for Pirandello. Italy has a perennial and chronic problem with all attempts to found stable theaters, and even the small degree of stability achieved by the Mussolini regime (1922–1943) was not extended to Pirandello's effort: as usual the *Duce* offered more flowery language than *lire.* What is a profounder pity is that Pirandello did not prove able to sustain the high standard of *Six Characters* and *The Emperor* in his subsequent plays. Over the next decade a great many new plays were produced: *Vestire gli ignudi* (*Naked,* 1922); *La vita che ti diedi* (*The Life I Gave You,* 1923); *Ciascuno a suo mode* (*Each in His Own Way,* 1924); *Diana e la Tuda* (*Diana and Tuda*) and *L'amica delle moglie* (*The Wives' Friend,* 1927); *La nuova colonia* (*The New Colony,* 1928); *O di uno o di nessuno* (*About Either One or No One*) and *Lazzaro* (*Lazarus,* 1929); *Come tu mi vuoi* (*As You Desire Me*) and *Questa sera si recita a soggetto* (*Tonight We Improvise,* 1930); *Trovarsi* (*To Find Oneself,* 1932); *Quando si è qualcuno* (*When One Is Somebody,* 1933); *Non si sa come* (*No One Knows How,* 1935); *I giganti della montagna* (*Giants of the Mountain*) (unfinished, but posthumously produced in 1937).

These plays are not without interest for students of Pirandello, but they have not unduly interested anyone else. *As You Desire Me* did become a Greta Garbo picture, but it was not a very good film, and no one has attempted another treatment since. There is Pirandello's own authority for regarding *Each in His Own Way* and *Tonight We Improvise* as making up a trilogy with *Six Characters* as part one, but the continuity is only thematic, and the second and third parts seem less an artistic outgrowth of the first than a discursive, at times garrulous, elaboration of it. For it is not just that Pirandello's later plays are less popular, but they are far less intense, and fatally attempt to make up in bigness of intellectual intention what they lack in realized emotion.

There are biographical reasons for this artistic decline and they have been worked out in some detail by Gaspare Giudice (*Luigi Pirandello,* 1963). Pirandello's great creative period of the early 1920s fell between the commitment of his wife Maria Antonietta to a sanatorium in 1919, and the marriage, and consequent departure from Italy of his daughter Lietta in 1921–1922. It was preceded by the death of Pirandello's mother in 1915, the wartime imprisonment of his son Stefano by the Austrians, and his own father's coming to live with him just after the war. The departure of Maria Antonietta also meant the return home of Lietta, who had been driven out by the virulence of her mother's paranoia. Now while it is not to be expected that these facts, as baldly rehearsed here, can prove very much, it may be useful to report that Signor Giudice is able to prove a good deal by a more extended exposition of them. He shows that Pirandello was an unusually personal, confessional, autobiographical writer from beginning to end and that the power of his writing is a matter of exactly which moment in his private life it springs from. Events of the second decade of this century led to a brief period of maximum creativity at the beginning of the third decade. No such period was to occur again.

There are two other topics in Pirandello's later life that can hardly be overlooked: Fascism and Marta Abba. Until Giudice's book came out, the story of Pirandello's membership in the Fascist party during the last dozen years of his life had never been fully told. There was understandable embarrassment among his family and friends, and even the present-day Italian editions of his writings have some remarkable political lacunae. Hardly to be overlooked is the fact that Pirandello is presumably the only winner of the Nobel Prize to destroy his gold medal. As his bibliographer, Manlio Lo Vecchio Musti, reported this event: "During the Ethiopian campaign, he gave to the country all the gold he had, including the medal of the Nobel Prize, a gesture that aroused in Sweden the indignation of the hypocrites and the imbeciles."

Pirandello's relationship with the Fascist party had its ups and downs. He is said to have torn up his membership card once in a fit of rage, and even to have vowed that he would never return to Italy. But he and Mussolini had exchanged compliments at the time he joined the party—a time when Italians of humane views were shocked by the murder of the anti-Fascist leader Giacomo Matteotti—and Pirandello's Fascism grew ever more outrageous with the years. It reached a climax with a speech he delivered to the Italian Academy in rapturous praise of the Abyssinian invasion in general, and Mussolini in particular (printed in *Quadrivio,* November 3, 1935; omitted from the collected works in Italian; first printed in English in *The Drama Review,* Summer 1969).

Although marital infidelity was always the charge leveled at Pirandello by his sick wife, and he was exposed to what she regarded as constant temptation at the girls' school where he taught, it is clear that his private life was unusually solitary. There seem to have been only two girls in the period before his marriage—his cousin Lina and a German girl he fell in love with in Bonn, Jenny Schulz-Lander; no women at all in the period of his marriage up to Maria Antonietta's being committed, and, after that, just one—Marta Abba. In 1925, Abba was a young, unknown actress whom Pirandello brought from Milan to his new Teatro d'Arte. She was soon playing leads in his plays, old and new. The leads in some of the new plays—*Diana and Tuda, The Wives' Friend, As You Desire Me,* above all *To Find One-self*—if not based on Abba's own personality, were at least shaped to fit it. Pirandello loved her, and left her the rights to nine of his last plays in his will. Yet she does not seem to have ever become his mistress. Reports of the singular chastity of the relationship reached Mussolini himself, and the only definitely anti-Fascist remark Pirandello was ever quoted as making was a comment on the *Duce*'s asking why he didn't sleep with Abba. "He is vulgar," said the Maestro. Perhaps Pirandello's letters to Abba, when they are published, will clarify the relationship. For the present the critic can only associate this romance with the romantic but overly abstract quality of most of the last plays, noting that when passionate feeling entered Pirandello's work its source seems always to have been his immediate family—his wife, his parents, his children. If Marta Abba was his Beatrice, this was a modern Dante swayed less by the ideal vision than by hates and fears, compulsions and anxieties and, if sometimes also by love, then by filial or paternal affection.

Outwardly, his life was quiet. In his last years he lived a good deal in hotel rooms all over the Western world, but the following brief account describes a larger span of his life:

> I very rarely go to the theater. By then, every evening, I am in bed. I get up in good time every morning and usually work till twelve. After lunch, usually, I get to my writing table at 2:30 and remain there till 5:30, but after the morning hours I don't do any more writing, unless it is urgently necessary; rather, I read or study. In the evening, after supper, I enjoy conversation with my small family, read the headlines and article titles in some paper or other; then to bed. As you see, there is nothing worthy of special mention about my life: it is all inside, in the work, and in my thoughts which . . . are not cheerful.

"O si scrive o si vive," he liked to say, "Either you write or you live," and he was not in doubt as to his own choice.

He died in his house, 15 via Antonio Bosio, Rome, on December 10, 1936. Born in "Chaos," he died in what, for a recent Nobel Prizewinner, was obscurity, for the papers at the time were full of the news of the abdication of King Edward VIII of England, and the death of the great Italian was lost in the back pages. He had fallen sick while watching the filming of *The Late Mattia Pascal.* This novel had given voice to the crisis that had ended his life as a relatively happy family man. It describes an effort to become someone else: Mattia Pascal becomes Adriano Meis. Is it possible that as Meis killed Pascal, Pascal now killed Pirandello? The thought may be extravagant, but it is not un-Pirandellian.

Although, as has been suggested above, *Six Characters in Search of an Author* was a precipitate from Pirandello's family situation at the time it was written, the idea had been in the author's mind and heart for some time. Nardelli, his interviewer-biographer, says it was written in three weeks. But that it was at least ten years forming will be plain to any reader of the short story, *"Tragedia di un personaggio"* ("Tragedy of a Character," 1911) and the two stories, *"Colloqui coi personaggi"* ("Conversations with Characters," 1915). Among posthumous materials that have come out in the collected works (Volume 6, 1960) is the following, from a letter to his son Stefano written in 1917:

> But I already have my head full of novelties! So many short stories. . . . And a queer thing, so sad, so very sad: SIX CHARACTERS IN SEARCH OF AN AUTHOR: novel-in-the-making. Maybe you understand. Six characters, caught in a terrible drama, who visit me hoping to get themselves put in a novel. An obsession. And I don't want to know about it. I tell them it's no use. What do I care about "them"? What do I care about anything? And they show me all their sores. And I send them packing . . . and in this way, finally, the novel-in-the-making turns out to be "made."

The same volume contains a fragment from this projected, but never completed, novel, which demonstrates that Madam Pace's establishment was an integral part of the scheme from an early date; also that the setting, a detail never given in the play, is (or at least was) Rome.

The ideas of the play can be found, for that matter, in many earlier Pirandello works. There are, essentially, three ideas to the work, according to the Maestro's own preface: "the deceit of mutual understanding irremediably founded on the empty abstraction of words; the multiple personality of everyone (corresponding to the possibilities of being to be found in each of us); and finally the inherent tragic conflict between life (which is always moving and changing) and form (which fixes it, immutable)."

Martin Esslin, in the *New York Times* of June 25, 1967, summed it up this way: "For Pirandello, more than any other playwright, has been responsible for a revolution in man's attitude to the world, in its way as significant as the revolution caused by Einstein's discovery of the concept of relativity. Pirandello has transformed the whole concept of *reality* in human relation." This is perhaps to put the matter too philosophically, as if Pirandello were a William James or an A. N. Whitehead, yet the word "attitude" suggests what is perhaps nearer the truth: that it is a matter of how we *confront* certain things, how we *feel* about them, what our *sense* of them is.

There is an indispensable clue within the text of *Six Characters* itself. A play is being rehearsed when the six characters arrive. It is not *Charley's Aunt,* as in one American production, or some bit of fashionable chaff as is implied in at least one printed summary. It is a play by Luigi Pirandello with a title that says everything: *Il giuoco delle parti* (*The Game of Role Playing*), which seems all too near the bone in the 1970's. A recent book by Robert Jay Lifton characterizes the younger generation in America today with the term "protean personality," while all during the 1960's individual behavior has more and more been judged as (to use the title of a best seller in the field) *Games People Play*. The director in *Six Characters* leads off with a summary of *The Game of Role Playing:* "You beat eggs. And you think you have nothing more on your hands than the beating of eggs? Guess again. You symbolize the shell of those eggs . . . the empty form of reason without the content of instinct, which is blind. You are reason, and your wife is instinct in the game of role playing. You play the part assigned you, and you're your own puppet—of your own free will." Now this is sound enough abstract summary of the sort that critics visit upon Pirandello, and which he was not always above visiting upon himself. But here it is ridiculed, satirized, distanced; that is, we are confronted with an attitude to it and the attitude is as important as its own object.

The action of *Six Characters* might be characterized as "what came of interrupting the rehearsal of *The Game of Role Playing.*" This action explores the aforementioned "attitude" in depth, that is, in drama or in conflicting passions. *Six Characters* is not a disquisition on role playing. It *is* role playing, concretely presented; and through the intensity of the author's passion, the virtuosity of his talent, and the synthesizing power of his genius, it amounts to a unified vision of life as role playing, and as such as an archetype of the twentieth-century imagination.

According to some accounts, the idea for *The Emperor* came to Pirandello when he was thumbing through an illustrated magazine and happened upon a picture of a cavalcade. One account specifies that it was the Roman Hunt Club riding to Villa Doria in medieval costume, but Arthur Livingston, a translator of Pirandello, in his *Essays on Modern Italian Literature* claims the Maestro gave a different version. *"Henry IV* [*The Emperor*] has its origin in an episode of Italy's movie world during the manufacture [sic] of a now famous play. An Italian actor, called upon to assume the role of Dante, threw himself so wholly into his work that he broke down under strain. Thereafter, as Pirandello says, he was unable to 'de-Dantify' himself, and is to this day living a placid life in an Italian insane asylum as the immortal poet of Beatrice."

Another translator of Pirandello's, Benjamin Crémieux, tells what books the Maestro consulted about the German Emperor Henry IV, namely, the appropriate volume in Wilhelm Oncken's *Allgemeine Geschichte* (a history of civilization in many volumes), and an early nineteenth-century life of Pope Gregory VII, also by a German scholar, Johannes Voigt. Having looked these books up, this writer cannot report that Pirandello drew upon them for more than he could have found in any textbook, or even in encyclopedia articles, though it is of interest that Oncken contains pictures of Henry's palace at Goslar and of the Abbey of Cluny.

More significant than Pirandello's reading on the theme is his choice of it. He had been a student at the University of Bonn, and undoubtedly German culture exercised a powerful influence on him, perhaps even a fascination. The philosophy which people call "Pirandellian" could be regarded as his own little digest of the German contribution to metaphysics from Kant on. If we have heard, in our time, of a Rome-Berlin Axis, we might speak, as students of Pirandello, of a Palermo-Bonn axis, for Pirandello spent much spiritual energy endeavoring to fuse within himself the Sicilian and popular elements with the European and intellectual elements. He naturally makes his Henry a spokesman for German idealism, or "Pirandellianism."

Pirandello is wise enough to put into the play itself any historical details he wishes his audiences to be aware of, but he does assume the spectator's prior knowledge of "Canossa." "We shall not go to Canossa," Bismarck had said in Pirandello's lifetime. For any educated European, Canossa is a permanent symbol of Papal supremacy and, its converse, of the subjection of the temporal to the ecclesiastical power. In the year 1077, eleven years after William the Conqueror set foot in England, the Holy Roman Emperor knelt two days in the snow at Canossa, doing obeisance to the Pope and begging his Holiness for an audience. His wife, Empress Bertha, knelt with him, and Bertha's mother Adelaide went with the Abbot of Cluny, another friendly witness, to plead with the Pope and his ally the Countess Matilda of Tuscany.

Such is the scene which has remained indelibly imprinted upon the memory of Europe. Or perhaps one should say upon the fantasy of Europe, for the incident did not actually signify—as it is often taken to—that in the Middle Ages emperors always took their orders from the Popes. There is evidence that this very emperor, Henry IV, knelt there not in sincere submission, but because it was the smart thing to do. In 1076, at Tribur, the German princes had proposed the deposition of Henry. In kneeling at Canossa, the latter was heading off the prospect of having to face his accusers. Pirandello draws on very little of this material, but does remind us that the pseudohumble Henry remained the Pope's fierce enemy and, in the year 1080, at Brixen, would declare Pope Gregory VII deposed. Pirandello was no doubt interested also in the insecurity of Henry's position—and the insecurity of a world in which not only the Pope but also the Emperor lived in daily danger of deposition.

If the Canossa symbol is clear, and the reference to Brixen at least understandable, all the history the reader need bother his head with concerns the situation of Henry in his childhood. Even at Canossa he is only twenty-six years old. He had succeeded to the throne as a child, and his mother, Agnes, had to be regent. But she had come under suspicion of adultery with Henry, Bishop of Augsburg. Pirandello adds a touch of his own in making one of Pope's henchmen, Peter Damiani, actually point an accusing finger at the pair. Agnes is removed as regent, and Henry IV himself rules—under the tutelage of others, and especially of Hanno, Bishop of Cologne. Later, Adalbert, Bishop of Bremen, becomes Henry's chief adviser, and Pirandello brings up the curtain at the point where Adalbert, as Henry supposedly believes, has been driven away by rival bishops.

Pirandello does not work out any point-for-point analogy between the eleventh-century story and his twentieth-century one (the reader to whom an historical reference here or there means nothing, need not feel he is missing clues). When Pirandello wishes his audience to know that Matilda of Tuscany corresponds to Matilda Spina he says so. He also lets it be known that while the historical Matilda of Tuscany was simply the enemy of the Emperor, "our" Henry harbors a secret love for her . . . and so on.

The play is, after all, about the twentieth century. It is, in particular, a study in insanity, and while we need not take Pirandello too literally as a pathologist, he stays, in essentials, close to well-known symptoms. Here are two sentences about insane delusions from Bernard Hart's standard introduction to the subject, *The Psychology of Insanity:* "Delusions may be of all kinds, but there are two types which call for special mention on account of their great frequency, *grandiose* and *persecutory*. . . . The two types are frequently combined; for example, a patient may maintain that he is the king but that an organized conspiracy exists to deprive him of his birthright."

Pirandello himself may not have been committed to the "absolute relativism" which is preached by his protagonists. His plays, in fact, imply objective standards, as perhaps plays have to. For example, they imply a clear distinction between delusion and non-delusion. Without such a distinction, it would be meaningless to say that Henry ceased being mad after twelve years. Similarly, in the play which professes in its title that a thing "*is* so if it seems so" to anyone, it is definitely implied that "seeming" may be an unreliable guide to truth, since the person to whom something seems thus and so may be crazy.

No major playwright has ever dealt chiefly in opinions per se. The playwright deals in experience—and therefore in opinions only insofar as they are not merely spoken or held, but experienced. The doubts about reality and identity with which *Six Characters* bristles are less a philosophical than a psychological matter, and Dr. Charles Kligerman in his essay "A Psychoanalytic Study of Pirandello's *Six Characters in Search of an Author*" (in the *Journal of the American Psychoanalytic Association*), has shown that even a narrowly clinical approach to that play can be illuminating. Some of the very same clinical "material" is present in *The Emperor,* notably the fantasy of a father embracing his daughter, and indeed the whole play can reasonably be taken as a realistically intended study of both neurotic and psychotic phenomena. If anyone seriously doubts this, let him reread the expository part of Act One, particularly what Belcredi and Matilda say about themselves and about Henry. The language may not be that of psychiatry in the second half of the twentieth century; but the content is close to, say, R. D. Laing's *The Divided Self* or Alexander Lowen's *Betrayal of the Body*.

It even makes sense to set aside the talk of "relativity" and conclude at the end that Henry *is* insane, that the unlucky experiment, though it went wrong, has produced the result that was feared and driven him back into insanity; the experiment, that is, plus the unfortunate turn taken by the conversation after it. What, after all, is going on? It is not possible to take the murder of Belcredi as one is invited to take the murder of Claudius in *Hamlet*, namely, as a just retribution willed by God. It is naked revenge at best, and committed in a peculiarly ignoble, unimperial way: would the medieval Emperor have run an unarmed man through—and, at that, through the belly? One should not see the ending of this play as "romantic" and of vague import, or as a rather forced illustration of a metaphysical thesis, but just as what it brutally seems—either immoral or insane, most probably the latter. In either case, Pirandello's *Hamlet*—and the play might be considered such—is a modern *Hamlet,* an anti-*Hamlet,* a savage and serious parody. It is not tragedy but tragicomedy, and it belongs to the modern and extreme form of this genre: tragic farce.

In its substance, *The Emperor* is not *merely* psychological; not, at any rate, in the limited terms of the psychoanalytic journals. To understand Pirandello, one would need a psychology with a psyche —a psychology which finds in the traditional terms "spirit" and "soul" a good deal more than can be reduced to the sexual mishaps of infancy or later. Pirandello writes of a sickness of the human creature that can scarcely be ascribed solely to the misadventures of the bedroom or the nursery. To diagnose this sickness one would need the instruments of disciplines other than the clinical; and even within the field of psychology, men of religious interests and deep intuition might offer more help in interpreting Pirandello than those who rely solely on current therapeutic science. St. Augustine, for instance, said: "Every disordered spirit is punishment to itself," which might stand as an adequate motto for *The Emperor*. Less summary, but even more suggestive by way of analogy and illustration, is this passage from William James: "One evening there fell upon me without warning a terrible fear of my own existence. There arose in my mind the image of an epileptic patient whom I had seen in the asylum, a blackhaired youth with greenish skin, looking absolutely nonhuman. That shape am I, I felt, potentially."

Eric Bentley, who has translated Pirandello into English, writes on drama for *The New York Times* and other publications.

THE 1934 PRIZE

By KJELL STRÖMBERG

RARELY in the history of the Nobel Prize for Literature has a candidate won the award the first time he was nominated. One such writer was Luigi Pirandello, the Italian dramatist, novelist, and short-story writer, who was proposed for the first time in 1934 and received the award in December of that year. His candidacy had been submitted by the literary division of the Royal Italian Academy, recently organized by Mussolini. The proposal submitting Pirandello's name was signed by Guglielmo Marconi, inventor of the wireless and winner for the Nobel Prize for Physics in 1909.

Pirandello's fame was of relatively recent origin, although in 1934 he had reached the respectable age of sixty-seven. His reputation was created by his resounding successes in a few little Parisian theaters—first at Charles Dullin's Atelier in 1922 with *The Pleasure of Honesty,* then at Jacques Hébertot's Comédie des Champs Elysées, where, in 1923, the Pitoëffs had astounded the Parisian public with his *Six Characters in Search of an Author*. This extraordinary play, hailed as a masterpiece by the critics, was immediately taken up by Max Reinhardt in Berlin and George Bernard Shaw in London; it soon circled the globe. His next play, *The Emperor,* an ingenious variation on the Hamlet theme, established Pirandello as a playwright of worldwide importance.

When Pirandello won so easily and so quickly in Stockholm, it was unlikely that his victory could be exclusively ascribed to his literary qualifications, which were undeniably admirable but insufficient to outstrip all possible competition on the first try. As it happened, in 1934 no truly dangerous rival was competing for the Prize. One gets the impression from the record that the various foreign academies and other groups qualified to make nominations had grown rather discouraged by the repeated defeats of the candidates whom they kept proposing year after year—candidates of the caliber of Valéry, Gorki, Wells, Croce, Unamuno, and many others, all of whom had been defeated the year before by Ivan Bunin, an honorable but comparatively unknown Russian novelist. Among the twenty-eight candidates proposed together with Pirandello, there were two newcomers who were later to win the award—Eugene O'Neill, the American dramatist, whose rising star already threatened to eclipse Pirandello's, and Roger Martin du Gard of France, author of the Thibault cycle, who had gained a wide audience in Sweden.

Both had been proposed by influential members of the Swedish Academy. Except for two brothers, Francisco and Ventura García Calderón, Peruvian poets proposed by their fellow countrymen, no other name of interest figured in the list of candidates, which was basically the same as for the preceding year.

In his report to the Nobel Committee, Per Hallström, than permanent secretary of the Academy and president of the committee, did not stint in his praise.

> Pirandello is a remarkable writer from many points of view, but what is most extraordinary is that he has succeeded in winning over the mass of the public and in channeling its interest to a theater crammed with philosophical speculation. To judge from the public in our own country, it is hard to imagine a more difficult proof of power, because if there is anything which the public detests it is abstract thought, anything that might upset it or cause it to question itself or the firm foundations of existence. It may be that the public is a little less inert, a little less fainthearted elsewhere, but the general tendency of the age is to resist being educated by subtle thought. To have succeeded in capturing and holding under his spell those ears which are stubborn and often rather long is an unchallengeable proof of genius, in spite of certain procedures worthy of a licensed magician, which no doubt noticeably facilitated his task.

For his colleagues Hallström's recommendation this time had the force of a command, and the Prize was awarded to the new magician of the Italian theater without much palavering. Another consideration may have been the fact that many of the members of the Swedish Academy, together with a good number of celebrities from all over the world, had been guests of the Royal Italian Academy on the occasion of a lavish international theater congress held in Rome with Pirandello presiding. This gave them an opportunity to appreciate the prestige and personal charm of the Sicilian. He was then at the peak of his fame. His plays were produced in all the capitals of Europe by the most famous directors, including Max Reinhardt, who, although exiled from Berlin, still ruled over his theatrical court in Vienna. Pirandello had also been honored on the other side of the ocean in Hollywood, where Greta Garbo had played the lead in a motion picture version based on *As You Desire Me*.

The only shadow in the picture was quickly dissipated when Pirandello settled his score with Mussolini. The dictator had obliged the Royal Opera of Rome to cancel an opera by Malipiero, *The Fable of the Prodigal Son,* with a libretto by Pirandello which was judged to be immoral, obscene, or at any rate not in keeping with the widely trumpeted "Fascist morality." Naturally, for the moment, the conflict subsided into a fair truce, if not a final armistice, when Italy was suddenly honored by a Nobel Prize through the award to the refractory playwright. As soon as he returned from Stockholm the new laureate was received in private audience by the *Duce* and later publicly acclaimed in one of the most important theaters of Rome. Pirandello took advantage of this occasion to submit a project to the dictator calling for the creation of a national theater to be housed in the splendid Teatro Argentina in Rome and with a repertory troupe made up of the best Italian actors—the sort of thing that had not been heard of since the theatrical troupes sponsored by the old royal and princely courts before the unification of Italy. In spite of the respectful attention which must have been given to Pirandello's proposals in view of his prestige after winning the Nobel Prize, this was never accomplished.

Pirandello's stay in Stockholm ended with a gala performance by the Royal Dramatic Theater of the play which had opened the gates of glory for him so many years before in Paris, *The Pleasure of Honesty*. Almost the entire Royal Family attended, and the evening ended in an explosion of applause, laurels, and embraces.

Translated by Dale McAdoo.

Henrik Pontoppidan

1917

"For his authentic descriptions
of present-day life in Denmark"

Illustrated by LEONOR FINI

BECAUSE OF WORLD WAR I, NO NOBEL
PRIZE CEREMONIES WERE HELD IN 1917

THE PROMISED LAND

By HENRIK PONTOPPIDAN

Translated from the Danish by Mrs. Edgar Lucas

BOOK ONE

CHAPTER I

A man was following the plough up and down the big fields north of Veilby. He was a tall man with a youthful figure, dressed in a patched sackcloth smock, red muffatees, and clumsy Wellington boots with the loops sticking up on both sides of the baggy knees of his trousers. He wore a faded beaver hat, under the wide brim of which his long hair, bleached by sun and rain, fell to the collar; a large light beard floated over his chest, and from time to time was blown over his shoulder. He had a thin face, a high arched forehead, and large, light, gentle eyes.

A flock of Royston crows were wheeling about a few yards above his head; every now and then, first one, then another would swoop down on to the newly turned furrows behind him, only hopping aside when he twitched the reins to make his slow, lumbering horses go faster.

This man was the parish priest of Veilby and Skibberup—Emanuel as he allowed himself to be called by his parishioners; "The Modern Apostle," as his less friendly disposed colleagues in the neighborhood maliciously dubbed him.

In spite of his dress and unkempt hair and beard, it was easy to see that he was no mere peasant. His figure was too supple, and the shoulders too sloping for that. His hands were certainly purple and swollen, but they were not so out of proportion as those of persons who have labored from the cradle. Nor was his face of a uniform dark leathery tint like a peasant's skin; it was patchy and freckled.

It was a cold raw morning in the beginning of March. Sheets of mist were every now and then driven over the land by gusts of west wind. At one moment the plain was enveloped in so thick a gray fog that one field could not be seen from the other; in the next, the wind would drive it away, only leaving thin wreaths of mist creeping over the furrows. Occasionally a pale sunbeam would slowly pierce the dark clouds and flicker over the fields.

At those moments, from the high-lying Parsonage fields, one could see the whole parish mapped out and stretching away to the distant church by the Fiord, which looked like a pale ghost in the mist. Somewhat nearer, between two hills, there was a peep of the foam-flecked

Fiord itself. In the west were the three hills of Skibberup, and a bright spot of red marked the tiled gables of the new Meeting House on the ridge of the hill.

Emanuel was too much absorbed in his thoughts to notice the shifting changes in the landscape. Even when he stopped a moment to breathe his horses, his glance wandered over the fields without seeing them. He had trodden these undulating hills for seven years; his eye was so much at home that sunshine gave way to shower without his observing the change. Towards mid-day he was roused by the voices of a little party approaching by the field path.

First came a sturdy little girl, four or five years old, who by the help of a rope over her shoulder, was dragging an old basket-carriage with a baby in it. With the effort of dragging the carriage through the deep mud, her hood had slipped off her wind-blown yellow hair, and she had to let go the rope every moment to pull up her red stockings which kept falling down over her wooden shoes. The carriage was pushed behind by another child, a boy, who had a knitted cap with flaps tied tightly down over his ears, and a bit of wadding which was stuffed into one flap, half covered his cheek.

An erect young peasant woman brought up the rear. She walked a little way behind the others on the very edge of the road; she had a little flowered shawl on her head, the corners of which fluttered in the wind. She walked along humming to herself, and sometimes singing aloud without lifting her eyes from the knitting in her brown hands.

It was Hansine and her three children, Emanuel's whole family.

When the little caravan had almost reached the end of the field where Emanuel was ploughing, the children let go the carriage and sat down on a stone by the roadside, whence they could see their father, who was working towards them from the other end of the field. Their faces were blue with cold and their noses were running. As they sat there in their worn old wooden shoes and patched clothes, they were just like any of the other village ragamuffins. It would certainly never have occurred to any one that they belonged to the palatial Parsonage, whose red roof and high poplar avenues rose above the slate roofs of the peasants' farms.

Emanuel waved his hat gaily to them from a considerable distance, and when he reached the end of the ridge he stopped his steaming horses, and called:

"Anything new, Hansine?"

Hansine had remained standing by the roadside, moving the carriage backwards and forwards with her foot,—the little one was impatient at the stopping of the carriage.

She counted her stitches on one needle, and then answered with her unsophisticated peasant accent:

"No, not that I know of. . . . Oh yes, the weaver was round, he said he wanted to talk to you."

"Indeed," said Emanuel, absently looking back at the field to measure what he had done. "What had he got on his mind?"

"Oh, he didn't say much. I was to tell you to go to the Parish Council Meeting at three o'clock."

"I suppose it's about the poor relief then," he threw in, "or perhaps the vestry. Didn't he say anything about it?"

"No, he said nothing, he just sat and stared about him a bit, and then went away."

"Oh, well, he's a queer fellow. . . . I say, Hansine!" he interrupted himself in a different voice, "Do you remember my talking about this new system of manuring that I read about in the farming paper? The more I think about it the better I like it. And it's much more natural isn't it, to put the manure fresh on to the fields and plough it in at once, rather than storing it up in great heaps till the strength has evaporated, besides poisoning the air all the time. Do you remember according to the paper, the land used to lose three millions a year by the old method? I can't imagine why nobody came to think of such a simple thing before. I believe these dungheaps were a simple outcome of the system of villenage. As the peasants always had to serve their lords before they could attend to their own affairs, they were obliged to put off their work day after day, and heap up their stuff till they could steal a few hours to look after their own affairs. As the origin of the heaping up was gradually forgotten, the peasants came to think it a matter of great importance to store it up. In short, these stinking heaps are relics of the days of serfdom, like so many other rotten things we are trying to free ourselves from today. Oh—it's a glorious time to live in, Hansine! To be a witness of enlightenment, and see by degrees how the dawning ideas of truth and justice, in great things and small, are breaking down the yoke of slavery, and preparing mankind for brighter and happier times!"

Hansine moved a needle, and answered by an absent smile. She knew how easily Emanuel's enthusiasm was roused by the new ideas of the day, and she was used to listening silently to the explanation of the great results he expected. "Well, it's time to unharness the horses," he said, after looking at a great silver watch, first holding it to his ear in true peasant fashion.

"Now, Laddie, can you come and give father a hand!"

The boy was still sitting on the stone by his sister. He was dreamily watching the crows as they flitted about the ploughed field a little way off, and did not hear his father call. He sat immoveable, resting the ear with the wadding over it on his hand, with the solemn expression children wear when they are recalling past sufferings.

He was rather small for his age, and though a year older, he was of a slighter build than his sister, who had the robust limbs and brightly colored cheeks and eyes of a village child. He was the image of Emanuel. He had the same high, intellectual forehead, and the same gentle expression; he had also inherited Emanuel's soft brown wavy hair, and large light eyes, which in the sunlight were almost colorless.

"Don't you hear, my boy? . . . Father is calling you," said Hansine, as he didn't move.

At the sound of his mother's voice he tore his hand away from his ear, with a poor little attempt at a smile which roused her attention.

"Does your ear still hurt, my boy?" she asked cautiously.

"No, not a bit," he said eagerly. "I don't feel anything now."

"Are you coming, then, Laddie?" Emanuel called again from the plough.

The urchin rose at once, and walked with measured steps over the furrows to the horses, and began to undo the traces —as gravely and conscientiously as a little carter.

This boy was the apple of Emanuel's eye, and the pride of the village; partly because of his unpeasant-like appearance, and also because of his extreme good temper. He was called after Hansine's old father, Anders Jörgen, but both at home and in village he was also called "Laddie,"—a name Emanuel had given him at his birth, and which pleased every one so much that his baptismal name was forgotten.

At the sight of the wadding over his ear, Emanuel exclaimed:

"What's that, my man? Has your ear been bad again?"

"Yes, a little," answered the boy softly, as if ashamed.

"It's very tiresome about that ear, but it's nothing much, is it?"

"No, it's quite gone now. I don't feel it at all."

"That's right, my boy; you must be a brave lad, and don't fuss about a trifle. Weaklings, you know, are no good in the world, don't you?"

"Yes."

"And then, you'll remember, we have to drive to the mill this afternoon. We two haven't time to be ill."

Hansine's knitting-needles moved faster than ever, and when the others ceased speaking she said:

"I do think it would be best for Laddie to stay at home today, Emanuel. He hasn't been a bit well all the morning."

"Well, but dear! . . . you hear it's all over now. And I'm sure the fresh air can only do him good. The fresh air is the Almighty's cure, as the old proverb says. . . . Laddie has been moping in the house, and that's made him rather white-faced. That's all!"

"All the same, I believe it would be better if we dealt more carefully with him, Emanuel. And I do wish you'd make up your mind to talk to the doctor about him. He's had this business with his ear for nigh on two years, and it can never be right to go on like that."

Emanuel did not answer at once. It was a subject they had often discussed before.

"Well, of course, Hansine . . . if you really wish it, I should never think of opposing it. But you know I've no particular faith in the doctoring business, and you know my opinion of Doctor Hassing. Besides, earache is such a common affair with children, and will go away of itself, if you only give nature time and rest to heal the damage. Your mother says just the same, and she has many years' experience. Catch hold of that rein my boy. I shall never believe that the Almighty would have created men so imperfect that they would always be wanting the doctor to set them to rights again, as soon as they were a little out of order. We've got some more of that oil which Maren Nilen had from old Grete on Stryn island. It did the boy good before; at any rate, let's wait till there's something really the matter, and not worry ourselves over a bit of a cold, eh? . . . Come here, then, little man." At his last words he took the boy under his arms and lifted him on to the back of the near horse.

Hansine was silent. In these little skirmishes about the children Emanuel always had the last word. He was too rapid in argument for her, and expressed himself so easily, besides having so many reasons for his opinion, that even if she did not agree with him, she was often reduced to silence by his fluency.

The fog again swept over the fields in soft wooly masses, as the little party wandered back to the village.

The boy rode in front with the horses, and Emanuel followed with the little carriage, which he jogged along with one hand, while he carried his daughter Sigrid on his shoulder. Her nickname was Dumpling. She took off his hat and waved it about with little shouts of delight to amuse the little one, who answered her back from the carriage.

Hansine followed a little way behind with her knitting.

She carried herself just as erect as in her maiden days, and moved with the same decided and measured gait. But the expression of her dark-complexioned face had changed somewhat; it was even more introspective and a little depressed. Naturally, her seven years of married life and the birth of three children had not left her former youthful bloom entirely untouched. Her cheeks were thinner, and her serious eyes were even more deep-set.

But she was still an uncommonly pretty woman; and according to peasant standards, she wore her twenty-five years with unusual honor, and it was not surprising that in Skibberup, her native place, they were very proud of her. There were certainly some, who not able to reconcile themselves to her reserve, which they attributed to pride—secretly deplored Emanuel's choice when he chose a bride from among the congregation.

When Emanuel and his children passed through the arched gateway of the Parsonage, Niels, the farm laborer, was sitting on the edge of the big watering-trough under the pump, busily studying the *People's News,* which was spread out on his knee. He was a dark-haired fellow of twenty or so, of middle height, square-shouldered and broad-backed, with a turn-up nose, red cheeks, and an incipient beard.

The big courtyard where in Archdeacon Tönnesen's time, order and tranquillity always reigned, befitting its position as belonging to the church, now looked like all the other peasants' yards. Implements of every kind and bundles of hay were thrown all over the place hugger-mugger. Several doors stood open, and a continual lowing of cattle waiting for their mid-day hay, all bore witness to the press of work. Here and there the brine from pickled herrings was thrown on the uneven pavement to kill the weeds, and the chickens were scratching about outside the brew-house in a heap of kitchen refuse.

"What's that you're so deep in, Niels? Is there anything new in the papers?" asked Emanuel, when he had put down Sigrid and lifted Laddie off the horse.

The man looked up from his paper and answered by an uncommonly broad grin.

"Oh, ho, Mr. Philosopher! Have you been on the war-path again? Who has your lance been turned against today then, Niels, come let me see!' said he, when he had slipped the harness off the horses.

The man moved a little and stretched out the paper which Emanuel began to read while the little boy led the horses to the trough to drink.

"Where is it? . . . Oh, here! 'High schools and moral responsibilities.' Yes, yes the beginning isn't bad . . . really very good . . . yes, indeed! there you're right. Well you're no coward, Niels! . . ."

The man watched the changes in his master's face from his seat at the corner of the trough, and every time Emanuel nodded assentingly or made exclamations of approval, his little black eyes, which were almost buried in his cheeks, sparkled.

"That article does you honor," said Emanuel at last, as he smilingly gave him the paper back. "You are regularly cultivating yourself to become an author. Yes, yes, only beware of drowning yourself in the ink-pot, my friend. Ink is a dangerous poison at times to play with."

He was interrupted by Hansine, who had taken the path through the garden, and who now appeared on the stone steps to call them to dinner.

"Then we must be quick and get the mares in, my boy," he said to Laddie.

"I say, Niels . . . just go and call old Sören, he's hoeing turnips in the field."

CHAPTER II

About three in the afternoon a quiet man was sitting in the window of the well-known parlor of Jensen, chairman of the Parish Council. He was tall, thin and pale, dressed in a home-made suit of the roughest kind of dark homespun, with a high collar and tight sleeves. Outside his coat he had one of those black quilted chest preservers, which are hardly ever seen in these days. He wore tight celluloid wristbands, which seemed to have squeezed all the blood into his gigantic hands.

He was stooping forward resting his arms on his legs with his hands tucked in between his knees. His head was rather flat, and in proportion to the length of his body, remarkably small. His hair and beard were a grizzled red, his face was distorted and besprinkled with light freckles.

There was something almost uncanny about the absolute immobility of the man, and the dull gaze with which he stared straight before him out of his half-shut eyes, an effect which was intensified by the dim light creeping in through the thickly bedewed windows, and the stillness in which the house was wrapped. With his flat head, distorted mouth, and swollen eyelids, he looked like a lynx on the watch, looking out from his lair in the primeval forest, over the limitless steppes.

It was Hansen the weaver.

This best parlor, which had formerly been the scene of so many gay carouses, had entirely changed its character in the last few years. The polished mahogany chairs still stood in a row against the wall, and the gilt clock ticked in aristocratic seclusion on the chiffonier between two lightly draped plaster shepherdesses. But in the place of the card table between the windows, where many a jolly night had been spent with cards and toddy in the company of Aggerbölle the vet., Villing the shopkeeper, the late octogenarian schoolmaster, Mortensen, and their host; a huge writing table now stood laden with papers. There were bookshelves against the other wall crammed with account books, registers, and bundles of newspapers, which gave to the room a serious, office-like look.

It was in reality something of the kind, and a corresponding change had also come over Jensen himself.

The stormy political risings which were brought about by the enlightenment of the peasant class, and which in the last few years had spread all over the country, had at last roused his slumbering conscience and called him forth to do battle for the independence of his class. As he was undoubtedly the richest peasant in the parish, and known for more liberality than was usual in a peasant, he very soon came to take a prominent part in the district; and as in addition, he possessed an innate talent for public life, and showed that he had "the gift of the gab," he had gradually forced himself up, to be the acknowledged political leader in the neighborhood, whose name might be constantly seen in the papers, as that of "the well-known peasant leader, Hans Jensen of Veilby."

He had not, however, reached this leading position, without passing by the original instigator of the revolt among the congregation, namely, Hansen the weaver. Several people when they first saw the sudden rise of Jensen, had feared that the headstrong weaver would not tamely submit to be set aside in so gross a manner; but to the universal surprise on this occasion, the weaver took it with quite unaccustomed calm. Still greater was the astonishment when it was discovered that it was the weaver himself who had helped Jensen to take part in public life, as—with great solemnity—he pointed out to him, that in his independent position, he was actually bound to give his services to the constituency, when the old Bishop, the present member, retired—an event which was to be expected before long.

It almost looked now, when the dangers were over, and the "People's Cause" was triumphing, as if the weaver were voluntarily allowing the others to reap the honors and rewards which were the fruit of his years of labor. With an amount of unselfishness which called forth the wondering appreciation of the congregation, he drew himself year by year further into his shell, and even declined the smallest of the honorary posts which were liberally offered him in recognition of his services. He only took upon himself the humblest duties of a veteran in the furtherance of the cause. He voluntarily acted as general messenger, and helped the various committees with their accounts and correspondence; he also continued faithful—with even increased vigilance—to his detective duties among the congregation, by constantly popping up with his distorted smile where he was least expected.

It was almost half-past three before all the members summoned were assembled. They were the so-called "Select Committee," six in number, chosen by the congregation, whose special duties were to watch over their political interests, to arrange electoral meetings, bring down speakers, control the lists of electors, and conduct business with the other democratic centers.

After they had all arrived, Jensen came in from an adjoining room—in white shirt sleeves, an apple-green plush waistcoat, a gold chain, and a starched front which had bulged out over his waistcoat during his midday nap. He went round shaking hands with each and saying, "Good-day, and welcome": they then, at his invitation, took their seats round an oval table in the middle of the room. They all seemed to be in an unusually solemn frame of mind. The weaver had been questioned before Jensen came in as to the purpose of the meeting; and by his vague answers it had been gathered that it would be unusually important.

As chairman of the committee the host took his seat at the head of the table. His heavily-built figure, curly hair, and clean shaven chin looked quite stately in this position. Certainly his long, drooping nose was as purple as ever and his face as red—vexatious reminiscences of his past; but to make up for it, his bearing, his movements, and his manner of conducting business had gained that easy suavity which comes with habit in public life.

Emanuel, who had exchanged his working smock for a light gray coat, sat on his right—and beyond him a fat little Veilby peasant with bushy eyebrows and chubby red cheeks. On his left were two young, fair-haired Skibberup farmers, and Nielsen the tall carpenter, whose dark Viking beard had grown several inches longer in the course of years, and now almost reached his waist. The weaver sat at the foot of the table in his capacity of secretary.

"Then we're all assembled," said the president in his searching voice, glancing round the table. "We have a very important communication to make to you, friends. . . . Yes, please, Hansen begin!"

The last words were addressed to the weaver, who now drew a large sheet of paper from his tail pocket and carefully unfolded it, after which, in a slow, monotonous voice he read the following manifesto:—

"Confidential.

"We have received from the leading men of our party, instructions to discuss, among the various democratic committees, a number of reports of disquieting political rumors which have lately found their way into several of the newspapers. In consideration of the gravity of the times, and the importance of the matter, it has been thought right to bring this information before the notice of the local committees without delay. The gist of the matter is, that it is within the bounds of possibility that plots are being hatched in both houses between the government and the conservative party, which are calculated to cause serious anger and anxiety to every free man. Of course nothing is yet certainly known, as all these negotiations are carried on with the utmost secrecy; but signs are not wanting, in the sudden unwillingness of ministers to yield in parliamentary debates, even in trifles. If other significant traits are taken into consideration, it seems not impossible that the government are really concerting with the conservative party to oppose the 'People,' and to combat the growing influence of the masses on the government of the State, by an arbitrary repeal of the universal Franchise. Every man in the land who is true to the cause of freedom will know how to judge of such a proceeding. We therefore call upon all committees to assemble, and—as a support to our members in the House—to send out a powerful intimation of the unalterable purpose of the People to fight to the uttermost against the conduct of those in power. As to the best way of dealing with the matter, we leave that to the discretion of each committee; only, in accordance with the opinion of our friends in parliament, we advise, that opportunity should be given to members of the party to pass a resolution to give our members continued and powerful support in the battle for the uncurtailed freedom and rights of the People.

"A similar appeal is being sent to all committees, and it is hoped that such a protest, such a thousand-voiced warning to our opponents, coming from every quarter of the country, may yet bring them to their senses, and induce them to abandon their nefarious intentions.

"Long live freedom and right! Long live the memory of our never to be forgotten lamented King, Frederick, giver of the constitution! Beloved of the people!

"P.V.B.—Johansen, Advocate."

The contents of this paper roused the utmost excitement among the committee. Even before the conclusion Emanuel burst out quite pale with emotion.

"But that is sedition! . . . It is treason to the country!"

"Yes, there you're right . . . no honorable man can call it any thing else," chimed in Jensen. And with a wave of the hand and voice that recalled the platform, he continued, "But it shows us friends that we acted perfectly rightly, in showing a rigid front to such a party, whose only aim is to clamor for power, even if they can only get it by playing fast and loose with the welfare and future of their country. Such people are no longer our countrymen . . . they are Denmark's foes!"

"Hear, hear," came from the depths of the carpenter's beard like a hollow echo.

"Never . . . never will the Danish people submit to such infamy!" continued Emanuel, quite beside himself. "I propose that we call together the party this very evening and inform them what is at stake. There is no time to waste. We will rise as one man and show that we will defend our honor and our rights to the uttermost."

"Softly Emanuel—softly," said the president, laying his hand soothingly on his arm. "Before everything we must beware of going too far! only be calm, that will lead you furthest in politics! we must not forget that at present we do not know anything definite, and you mustn't put your gun to the shoulder before you see the bear, says an old proverb.

"For my part, I have a suspicion that it may be nothing but rumor which the friends of the government have set afloat to frighten our men in the house, and perhaps a bit of a trial balloon sent up to test the feeling in the country! We must remember that that's the way things are done in politics!" continued he, grandiloquently and waving his hand. "What we have to do first and foremost, is to scrutinize our opponents' tactics. Don't let's forget that, friends!"

"But if they're not empty rumors . . . if they act on their threats in earnest—send the parliament home, and put might in the place of right, . . . what then? . . . what then?"

The president looked firmly at Emanuel for a moment. Then he said slowly, with great self confidence, letting his hand drop heavily on the table:

"If that should happen—which God forbid—then three hundred thousand countrymen will rise and say, 'Now it is enough! now we must fight to the death the question, who is to be master, you or ourselves . . . am I not right?' "

At his last words he turned to the Skibberup men, who all answered with a loud "hear, hear," while the fat little Veilby man nodded approvingly.

"I now propose—that we call a meeting for Sunday evening next: I will willingly take upon myself the task of explaining the situation, after which we will bring forward the proposed resolution. Moreover, I am of opinion that we shall do well to keep this information private, so as not to alarm the party too much—and perhaps even unnecessarily. The honorable head committee evidently thought so too. I do not doubt that our opponents will lose their taste for entering on new engagements, when they hear the voice of the people through our meetings. Don't you agree with me friends?"

Four of the members expressed their approval, and Emanuel was at last infected with their courage, and became calmer. He was not in the habit of speaking on political subjects, and he had in fact only been elected on the political council on account of his great services in other ways. He had great difficulty in taking any interest in the parliamentary debates or the newspapers, to say nothing of the "tactics" of which the president and the other members thought so much.

He never could bring himself to doubt that right—as in the psalm—in "God's good time would conquer," and he had no faith in the efficacy of even the cleverest devices, either to hasten or delay it.

On the proposal of one of the Skibberup farmers, it was decided to give even more importance to the meeting, by inviting two strangers to speak. For a moment they even contemplated asking no less a person than their own member, the old Bishop. But though in the course of recent stormy debates, he had shown that he still wore the red garibaldi shirt of his youth under his velvet robes and diplomatist's coat, he had hitherto never allowed himself to be persuaded to leave what he called his "Archimedian" standpoint, outside both parties. So this idea was soon abandoned as fruitless. They thought they might induce a couple of other democratic members to come, and sent a message to headquarters at once. The president offered both to fetch the guests from the station in his carriage, and to give them a dinner, which offer won murmurs of approval.

When the hour for the meeting had been settled, and Hansen had entered the minutes, the president closed the meeting.

"Well, we've got that pig killed," he said gaily, as he rose. "And I think we want a bite and a sup after it, gentlemen."

This was his way of alluding to the "little refreshment" which was inevitable in this house, and had been prepared in the adjoining room. The door was thrown open by a portly peasant woman with a gold embroidered cap, a hooked nose, and a treble chin, who was the president's housekeeper.

The table was set out as usual, with

rich and heavy viands under the lamp, the yellow light of which struggled with the last rays of a red sunset. The table looked doubly inviting in the variegated light, and the company took their seats with appetites sharpened by the long sitting.

Even Emanuel got into quite a lively frame of mind at last. He looked round at these broadshouldered men who, in spite of all that threatened their future—sat there quiet and composed—perfectly secure as to the right of their cause. He was filled anew with admiration for the unfailing equanimity with which these people always met their fate.

Never had he even for a moment seen them lose their composure. Even under the hardest blows of fate they maintained a salutary calm, a manly self-control, such as he had great difficulty in himself acquiring.

The dishes were emptied with great energy, and new ones brought in by "big Sidse," who had managed Jensen's house since the death of his wife. This corpulent female was stealthily watched by the weaver all the time; he hardly spoke a word during the meal, but left both food and drink almost untouched. When his neighbor wanted to pour him out a glass of brandy, he put his hand over the glass with a feline smile—he had lately become a total abstainer, and in spite of Jensen's chaff, would not be induced to deviate from his usual rule, even in honor of the day.

Emanuel on the other hand, drank his "Snaps" with the others, as he usually did on these occasions . . . not because he cared for the brandy but he was unwilling to do differently from his company. As far as that went, he could follow, with an easy conscience, the customs even of the Veilby peasants, for they had become much more moderate in the last few years. He had on the whole taken up a good many peasant customs, sometimes knowingly, and at others, unconsciously. He had even got over his own dislike to tobacco; and when the meal was over and coffee on the table, and Jensen sent the cigars round, he drew a wooden pipe from his pocket and filled it from a packet of "smoking mixture" which he always carried.

At this point the weaver rose. With the excuse that he had someone to see before night, he shook hands all round and retired through the kitchen.

Out there he remained standing in the middle of the paved floor with his head on one side, and fixed the housekeeper with a glance from his half-shut eyes which made this mass of flesh tremble in every limb.

"Good Lord, Hansen . . . why d'ye stare at a body like that?" she said, ready to cry, and in alarm held a teacloth before her face.

The weaver quietly put his hat on and left without a word.

It was dark outside. The wind had dropped, and it was quite calm. A few large snowflakes were falling which melted as soon as they reached the ground. The snow came faster and then changed to a drizzle, as the weaver walked home with his hands behind him, along the solitary path over the hills to Skibberup. Every now and then a smile crossed his face, and his red eyes had the expression they always wore when he was ruminating over his plan of campaign in private.

CHAPTER III

It was a dark night and pouring with rain when Emanuel reached the Parsonage, and mounted the steps to the front door with a stranger.

Inside the lordly entrance hall, where at one time the mahogany pegs were adorned by Archdeacon Tönnesen's big bearskin coat and Miss Ragnhild's garden hat, and where tidy matting used to cover the black and white marble pavement in front of the door, a simple stable lantern was now burning. The mahogany pegs were now filled with a miscellaneous collection of common men's caps and women's many colored head squares, and on the tiles were a whole pile of dirty wooden shoes of all kinds, from the big clumsy laborer's with iron bands and a wisp of straw inside, to small women's shoes with leather toes lined with red flannel. The usual visitors who assembled two or three times a week after their work was done to be edified by conversation, reading and singing, had already arrived, and were sitting in rows along the walls of the large drawing and dining rooms which were poorly lighted by a single petroleum lamp.

Nothing remained in the large rooms, except the smoke-blackened cornices and the frescoes over the doors, to recall the "Salon" where Miss Ragnhild used to display her extravagant costumes among soft carpets, damask curtains, and inlaid furniture. Round the four naked walls a simple wooden bench ran, above which the blue distemper was worn off to the height of a man's shoulders. The four high windows, two on each side of the garden door—which in winter was blocked up—were covered at the top with a small red cotton valance. Under one window stood a white, scoured oaken table at the upper end of which the bench had taken the form of a kind of high seat. Besides this there were a few rush-bottom chairs and—as in the home of Hansine's childhood—one old-fashioned arm-chair by the stove and a green-painted corner cupboard by the kitchen door. A six-branched pewter chandelier hung from the middle of the ceiling.

This room—the "great room" or "hall," as the people called it, because in its stern simplicity it was the outcome of Emanuel's passion for antiquity—was, in fact, the living room of the family. All the other rooms except the former morning room, which was now the family bedroom, were empty and uninhabited, or were used for storing up seed, wool, or feeding stuffs. Emanuel had indeed inherited for his own use the room which in the Archdeacon's time had been known and feared as the "study," but the whole of its furniture consisted of a couple of dusty bookshelves, and an American cloth sofa. He very rarely occupied it except for the half hour after dinner when he took a little nap. His sermons and lectures were always thought out while following the plough or on his wanderings among the sick and the poor; for, as he said, he had turned his back on bookshelves since he had discovered that finer lessons of wisdom could be learned of the birds in the air, or the cows in the byre, than of all the learned books in the world.

. . . On this particular evening there were about fifty people of both sexes and all ages assembled. The young girls were all in a row, along the short wall, looking like a garland of flowers, the dark heads and the fair heads alike bent over pieces of fine crochet work which they could hardly hold in their stiff red fingers. Notwithstanding the bad light there was an air of great cheerfulness and comfort.

The married women had their fixed seats on the wall nearest the stove, where they labored steadily at huge pieces of knitting, talking meanwhile to their neighbors about housekeeping and dairy work, in the usual lachrymose voices which peasant women always adopt in company. Hansine had her accustomed seat in the arm-chair and was spinning at her wheel. She was dressed just like the others in a common linsey dress and a checked cotton apron; on her head she had a tight little black cap, and her dark brown hair was smoothed down in two stiffly formed bands above the temples, after the fashion of the district. She did not take much part in the conversation of the others, and there was often something absent in the glance with which she looked up from her yarn, when the door opened and some old laborer came in, in shirt sleeves, or a couple of round-cheeked girls stepped in with a nod and a broad grin.

The young men were gathered round the long oak table in the window. They were in the full light of the lamp which stood on the table next to a large jar of water with a wooden lid. The loudest gossip proceeded from this part of the room and the blue smoke from their pipes curled thickly round their heads of shaggy hair. In a place apart in the darkest corner of the room, two persons were sitting whose appearance and behavior plainly showed that it was not usual for them to be there. They were greeted by Emanuel on his entrance with special cordiality, he shaking hands with them and saying how glad he was to see them. They were two miserable-looking creatures, whose dripping rags had formed pools of water on the floor round their feet. One was as tall and thin as a well pole; the other, short, stout, and bald, with a lump as big as an egg over his eye. Both of them sat with their hands on their knees looking at the ground with embarrassed faces; but now and then, when they thought themselves unobserved, they would steal a sidelong glance at each other with a suppressed smile.

They were both well-known persons in the neighborhood—"Beery Svend" and "Brandy Pér"—who belonged to the fixed number of *mauvais sujets* in the parish. They belonged to the party who waited outside Villing's shop every morning till it opened, with bottles hidden under their garments. They lived, with others of their kind, in a collection of mud hovels on the outskirts of the village. One was a wooden-shoe maker, the other a thatcher; but their most important source of income was stealing potatoes from the peasants' pits, and shearing the tethered sheep on dark nights; and there were many who suspected them of having darker crimes on their consciences.

These circumstances were not unknown to Emanuel. In fact he had not been long in the country before his eyes were sufficiently opened to see that even there, poverty breeds misery and spiritual debasement. From the very first he had made great efforts, supported by the congregation, to win the confidence of the lost and strayed, and by mildness and indulgence, to smooth the way for them back to the paths of virtue. He had spared no personal pains to attain this end, and it was one of his greatest disappointments that in all these years he had not succeeded in getting over the hostility these people had shown towards all efforts to help them.

So he was doubly delighted every time—as in this case—he fancied he could see any signs of reconciliation. He did not remember at the moment that, as Chairman of the Poor Relief Committee, he had recently renewed an allowance to both these persons, and it never occurred to him that their presence tonight might be looked upon as a sort of receipt for assistance given.

There was another unaccustomed guest tonight, and that was Aggerbölle the veterinary. He sat smiling at one end of the bench next to the shuttered garden door, with his arms crossed over his broad chest, oblivious of the fact that in this position he mercilessly displayed a great rent in his coat under the arm. His hair and beard were quite white, and stuck out unclipped on every side, his eyes were like staring glass balls and the hairless part of his face was covered with boils.

It is difficult to say which of these people made the most deplorable impression—the two thieves. or this man so strangely tossed about by fate. Certainly the vet. wore elastic-sided leather shoes, cuffs and collar; he even had a *pince-nez* stuck into the breast of his buttoned-up frock coat. But the heartrending shabbiness of his clothes and the whole of his stiffly-held figure displayed such deep and hopeless degradation that it might rouse the pity of a pauper even.

In spite of all his efforts to appear at his ease in this company, he only succeeded indifferently in hiding a suppressed bitterness. It was not by his good will that he was there at all. His presence among the "Dunderheads," as in his hatred and contempt he had dubbed these modern "intellectual" peasants, was due to one of those mischances by which, as it seemed, his implacable fate pursued him through life. After being shut up all the dull day in his tumble-down house among the deserted fields in contemplation of his miserable, hopelessly ruined home, because for certain good reasons he dared not meet the baker who was in the neighborhood with his cart that day, he had at last ventured out about nightfall. With the excuse of having to see a patient, and after tenderly kissing his children, and taking the heart-rending farewell of his wife, without which he never left home even for an hour, he took the road to his old friend and sympathizer Villing, to seek a little consolation there, and, if possible, to obtain what he was fond of calling "a little oblivion." But it unfortunately happened that he met Emanuel just outside the Parsonage gates, and he patted him on the shoulder in delighted surprise, and exclaimed: "It is really good of you, dear friend, to come and see us at last. We have missed you for a long time. You're heartily welcome."

On the verge of despair after the long day, Aggerbölle was screwing up his courage to say that he was on the way to a patient, when Emanuel mentioned that he had just come from a meeting at Jensen's. The thought that the weaver was probably also of the party cooled his ardor, and, under the cirumstances, he thought he would have to give up all thought of escape. He sat there now with a convulsive smile, trembling with rage, which made all his boils stand out blue. Of all the humiliations imposed upon him by his poverty, none seemed so pitiless and degrading as this. He asked himself if all justice had disappeared from the world, since he was forced to put up with sitting here like a schoolboy on a bench, with cow-herds, milk-maids, and stinking stable lads. Or was it merely a delirious dream that he was the son of a district judge, and a man who had taken a degree; and that these self-same "Dunderheads," who now coerced him as well as the whole country, once used to stand before him, hat in hand, and looked upon it as an honor if he invited them into his room. . . . The conversation round the walls had gradually dropped, and finally there was a dead silence. They were all waiting for Emanuel, or some one else, to tell a story or read something.

Niels, the Parsonage man, seized this opportunity to try and attract Emanuel's attention to himself, by drawing the newspaper a little way out of his breast pocket, just far enough to show a little corner. Sometimes, if there was a dearth of entertainment, they would read a good article out of one of the papers, which would give a subject for discussion.

Emanuel did not, however, notice his efforts. After having moved about for a time from bench to bench among the guests, joining in their conversations here and there, he took his place on the high seat with his pipe, and fell into a fit of deep abstraction. The meeting at Jensen's was still surging through his mind, and his thoughts were fixed on the future in gloomy apprehension.

"Aren't we going to do anything at all tonight?" came a pert voice from the girls' bench at last.

The impatient exclamation, and the laughter which followed it, roused Emanuel from his reverie. He looked and said, with a smile:

"You're right, Abelone! Let us start something! . . . Haven't you anything to tell us tonight, Anton?" he said, turning to a brown-bearded clerical-looking little man in a white tie and skullcap, who was sitting with his hands folded over the bowl of his pipe, leaning back in an old basket chair at the other end of the table. This man was the new parish schoolmaster, the well-known Anton Antonsen, formerly a private teacher, who had been nominated by the Parish Council as Mortensen's successor. In answer to Emanuel, he first pressed his thick lips together, and sent out the tobacco smoke from the corners of his mouth in little puffs like the smoke of powder from the mouth of a cannon. Then he laid his head on one side with a sly smile, and said in broad dialect:

"Naa, naa, a won't trouble ye tonight."

His droll little person in connection with a certain dry humor made him an exhilarating element, whose little jocular speeches, proverbs, and humorous readings had become almost indispensable at every festival in the countryside.

"Oh, I say, Anton," said a man who had not yet stopped laughing, "Ye might read us a bit tonight. It's ever so long since ye've given us ought. Ye're forgetting that ye owe us that tale about Stine, how she went to the High School."

"Ay, ay, let's have it! Out wi' it, Anton!" cried several voices at once.

The schoolmaster shut one eye and looked round with a smile, which broadened as the clamor increased.

"Weel, weel, then, bairns," he said at last, when even the women by the stove joined in the request, "if there's naebody else wi' ought to say, a'm sure a'll not hould back. A wunnot hae it on ma conscience that Stine shouldn't get to the High School!"

"But shan't we hae a song first," cried the same pert voice from the girls' bench. It belonged to pretty Abelone, the Parsonage servant, a strapping girl of twenty, with black ribbons in her flaxen hair and a large rose in her bosom, and the bright leather belt indispensable to a pupil of the High School.

"Yes, let's have a song," agreed Emanuel. "Let it be a national air! I'm sure we want one in these times. What shall it be?"

"Thou Heroes grave by the ocean shore," proposed one.

"Yes, that'll do; we all know it by heart. You lead off, Abelone."

The room became quite silent as soon as the song came to an end. The youths settled themselves with their arms on the table, and the girls dropped their work, or else stuffed it into the pockets under their aprons, and then folded their hands in their laps, so as to give all their attention to Anton while he was reading.

As a reader and reciter the schoolmaster stood alone, and could only be compared to the old High School director at Sandinge. But while the latter, in telling his folklore tales and sagas, almost took the roof off with his own breathless excitement and his peculiar piping voice, which echoed through the lecture-hall like a war trumpet, and conjured up before them the giants, the dwarfs, and the valkyrie maidens of the sagas in so lifelike a manner that the whole brilliant Asgard race might have been passing before them, the schoolmaster's strength lay in his plain, moralizing stories of everyday life which had become so much the fashion. He imitated the characters—especially the comic ones—in so masterly a style, and used his comical little figure to make his personifications life-like, in a way quite new there.

He had contributed largely by these means to the introduction of works by modern writers, and had to a great extent driven out the old romantic poetry from these evening assemblages. Emanuel at first tried to wake the interest of the people, but had never thoroughly succeeded in doing so. He had not been able to understand his friends' want of appreciation of those old poems, instinct with life, to which he owed so many hours of happiness in his childhood. But as he gradually became more and more taken up with everyday life and its struggles, he began to see that these purposeless, fantastic tales of nightingales, fairies, and moonshine, were in fact too far removed from the feelings and ideas of the people of today. Besides, his eyes had been opened to the heathen spirit in which the passions of men and women were portrayed and, as a rule, glorified by the old poets. Time after time he had been struck by the immodesty with which the personal charm of the women was enlarged upon . . . and it probably was a similar feeling which caused the coldness of the Friends towards them, and the bashfulness with which they discussed them. . . . In the works of the modern writers these sober, realistic pictures, often written by men themselves of the people . . . and especially in the social dramas of the great Norwegian writers, they lived over again their own daily struggles and moods. In them he also found the moral earnestness, the popular point of view, the craving for truth and justice, which touched their deepest heartstrings.

CHAPTER IV

The same evening Villing and his wife were sitting in their warm, cozy little parlor behind the shop. A tall lamp with a red paper shade was burning on the center table and shedding a cheerful glow on the mistress as she sat on the sofa, knitting; while Villing was in the armchair on the other side of the table, reading the newspaper aloud.

All was empty and silent in the shop. The lamp was turned down, and smelling horribly as it hung from the ceiling among currycombs, and hanks of string. Behind a large cask of brandy in the darkest corner sat the specter-like shop-boy, who was regularly renewed from the capital every second or third year; but who nevertheless was always the same thin, timid cadaverous creature who for nearly twenty years had been seen wildly dashing about Villing's shop. At this moment he had fallen asleep with his head against the wall, his mouth wide open, and his hands stuck deep down into his pockets, as if in the fervent hope that he would never have to take them out again.

For the last couple of hours no one had disturbed him either in his dreams. Villing's shop which formerly was always full of customers, now stood empty the greater part of the day. By the redistribution of the parish, the big Co-operative Store at Skibberup had by degrees only left him the farthing trade of the village poor, a small coal business, and the sale of corn brandy and Bavarian beer.

It did not however look as if these bad years had weighed very heavily either on Villing or his wife. His own little broad-headed figure with the yellow whiskers, had rather gained in rosy fleshiness; certainly his wife had been obliged to take to spectacles when she worked, but her face retained its soft resigned expression, as if she too had found rest in the belief in what her husband usually called "The superiority of professional training," and "ultimate conquest."

The paper which Villing was reading was a Copenhagen conservative journal, whose minute details of events in the capital had long been the favorite, and indeed the only reading of the couple. For many years they had, from measures of precaution, not subscribed to the paper, but had it secretly sent by a business friend in the form of packing paper. Tonight they were having a special treat, the account of a brilliant court ball, at which all the grandeur and magnificence of the capital had been assembled. Villing, who at these readings never omitted the solemn and vibrating voice with which illiterate people show their reverence for print, had seized the opportunity to employ all his declamatory talent. Holding one whisker tightly, he rolled out the sentences descriptive of uniforms, stars, medals, brilliant gowns, and jewelry, with the greatest gusto.

"Her gracious majesty the Queen, who was unusually animated, and looked younger than ever, wore a white lace petticoat and a train of richest mauve brocade, five yards long, opal ornaments and a pale mauve aigret in her hair," he read. "Think of that, Sine, a mauve brocade train, five yards long, if we only reckon twelve yards of the usual width—at—let us say 45 kr. a yard, that makes 540 kr. for the stuff alone!"

Mrs. Villing, who was resting her cheek on one knitting needle, and in this position looked over the rim of her spectacles, fixing her eyes on the ceiling, added:

"And fifteen yards of lace at 25 kr. a yard, makes 375 kr."

"915 kr. altogether then."

"At least."

"For the stuff alone! you may call that splendor indeed. But let's have some more. 'Her royal highness the Crown Princess wore blue satin, the train brocaded with silver lilies.—Silver lilies, do you hear?—On her head she had a diadem of brilliants, and the same precious stones on neck and arms. A great sensation was made by her ear-rings, which consisted of one diamond each, as big as a sparrow's egg!—— Did you ever hear anything like it, Sine! Diamonds as big as sparrows' eggs! It's as much as to say that you have a country house, nay, a whole village hanging at each ear. That must be a wonderful feeling, don't you think so?"

Here he stopped and raised his head to listen. Merry voices were heard on the other side of the pond, as a party of girls went singing through the village.

"I suppose the Ranters' meeting is over for tonight," he said, and looked at the clock. It's high time too, past nine o'clock. Now let's get on, I hope we shan't be disturbed again."—

At this moment the cracked bell over the shop door began to ring. Villing hurriedly shut up his paper, ready to pop it into the drawer in an instant.

Mumbling voices were heard in the shop, and the jingling of bottles; then the bell rang again, and the door was shut.

"Elias!" shouted Villing with his stentorian voice, holding the paper behind his back.

The shopboy's ghostlike face appeared at the half open door, with his hair hanging about his sleepy eyes.

"Who was that?"

"It was Beery Svend and Brandy Pér . . . they came for a pint."

"All right, you can shut up for tonight and go to bed, but don't forget to put the candle out boy!—goodnight!"

As soon as the door was shut, Villing took up the paper again, but no sooner had he begun to read than the shop bell began to jangle again. This time the door was torn open noisily, the counter flap thrown up, and a man admitted. Villing turned pale and had hardly time to throw his paper into a drawer before the door was opened.

"Oh, it's you," he said with a sigh of relief when he saw Aggerbölle's broad figure dripping with rain. "We hadn't expected you. . . . How in the world do you come to be out at this time of night?"

"I? . . . oh, I've been seeing a patient," mumbled Aggerbölle, looking about for a place to put his hat and stick down.

"It's villainous weather! Downright hellish weather! Not fit to drive a creature out in. And the mud! One's not fit to go into a decent person's house. But I thought I'd just look in."

"It was very kind of you to come and see us, Aggerbölle," said Mrs. Villing, with a warning glance at her husband, who didn't take the least pains to hide his ill-temper at the visit—"You know we are so much alone now, and we are always glad to see you. We were just talking about you when you came in. Sit down and tell us how you all are in this bad weather."

Aggerbölle appeared not to hear this, but took a chair by the table, and with a gloomy and absent air continued to mutter curses at the weather, nervously groping about in his right hand trouser pocket as if his thoughts were busy with something there.

At last he pulled out his hand and threw down a 2 kr. piece on the table.

"If you'll give the hot water and a cigar, Villing, I'll give the brandy. We want something strong on a night like this I think."

The shopkeeper and his wife exchanged questioning glances, and there was a moment's pause. Then Mrs. Villing rose and went into the kitchen, while Villing with a dexterous twist took up the coin with one hand and whipped it into the other and thence into his purse.

Aggerbölle's eyes followed the piece of money with a reluctant glance till Villing's leather purse closed upon it. Then he looked silently at the floor.

"Well, how are you getting on, old fellow?" said Villing, leaning forward and slapping him on the knees in a friendly way.

"How am I getting on?" asked the vet. as he straightened himself up with a start as if he wanted to get out of the way of the other's touch. "Confoundedly, of course! How should it be otherwise?"

"Ah well, we business people have our troubles too. Prices go down everywhere . . . what is it to come to? I was just saying to my wife the other day, how tiresome it is that one has to pay ready money for everything. One would be glad to help a friend in difficulties, or tide a good customer over temporary embarrassment—help in deed as well as in word. But what is one to do when a fellow can hardly scrape through himself. I don't at the moment know how I shall pull through at quarter day. And it's very hard at my age with twenty years of honorable work to look back on. I'm cleaned out, absolutely cleaned out!"

Aggerbölle, to whom this speech was not new, mumbled some unintelligible words in his beard, and cast impatient glances at the kitchen door.

At last Mrs. Villing appeared with a tray; Aggerbölle seized a glass, just covered the bottom with water, filled it up with brandy, and without waiting for any clinking of glasses, or drinking of healths carried it to his lips with a shaking hand and half emptied it. Then he bit the end off a cigar which Villing in the meantime had given him, lighted it at the lamp, and puffing at it, threw himself back in his chair with his arms crossed, in his favorite position.

"Well," he burst out, rendered talkative at once by the spirit. "Is there anything new?"

"Anything new? Let me see!" said Villing, stirring his mixture. "Oh, the latest is that there has been a meeting of the Parish Council today."

"Do you call that new? Devil a bit! It seems to me they have a meeting every day, ... when they don't have two! The beasts of peasants have nothing else to do in these days. They send their milk to the co-operative dairies, and the pigs to the common slaughter-houses. . . . So they've plenty of time to do the consequential. By God, it was a different matter in the old times, old fellow, eh?"

"It was the Select Committee, I believe."

"Select Committee!" burst out Aggerbölle. "Are we to be dragged to another political farce? It's not more than a week since we had a meeting here! . . . Isn't it just what I was saying?" he continued, grinding his teeth and clenching his fist. "It's enough to worry the liver out of one's body to think of all the 'Dunderheads' have done in the country. It's not enough that they've murdered—yes, I say murdered the last traces of good old Danish joviality, ... but you have to sit and listen to all their damned braying into the bargain. What would old Didrik Jacobsen have said to it? D'ye remember old Didrik, Villing? Ah, he was a fine old blade. And his big Christmas feasts with the good old-fashioned roast legs of pork weighing three stone a-piece, with red cabbage, snaps, old Christmas ale, followed by first-rate coffee punch to console one for all the disappointments and troubles in life. And then Shrovetide, when one didn't close an eye for five nights running! Those were the times to live in, I say!"

Villing and his wife exchanged mournful glances. These words of Aggerbölle's roused tender memories in their minds too. It was in their shop that most of the good things had been bought, and it had been one of their greatest joys in life to sit down in the evening on their little sofa side by side, after one of these monster feasts, where sometimes over a hundred persons had eaten and drunk prodigally, and with their account book before them make out their long-winded accounts, and add up the columns of figures as long as their arms.

"And then Sören, Heaven's hound as we used to call him," continued Aggerbölle, carried away by his reminiscences. "Do you remember, Villing, when he killed a fat ox for his brandy carouse. . . . And what do you get now? A drop of lukewarm coffee and a sweet biscuit, . . . and for the rest pious comic songs, jocular speeches, friendly words, and sweaty hands to shake! That's an example to set the rising generation. Instead of working as the old people used to do, and amusing oneself like them, they sit there singing themselves fat, and turning up their eyes enough to make you sick. And these are the new 'Progressives!' This is the marrow of the land! Down with the rabble! Down with the rascals, I say!"

The recollection of the two hours slow torture he had been forced to endure at the Parsonage embittered him beyond measure. Villing "hushed" him in alarm, and he became somewhat doubtful about his last brave words. He suddenly pulled himself up, and for a few minutes there was silence, as if the shadow of the weaver were passing through the room.

"How are they all at home, Aggerbölle?" asked Mrs. Villing again, after a pause, so as to lead the conversation into a new channel.

The vet. made a deprecating movement with his hand, and turned away his head with the painful contortion which his face always wore at mention of his wife.

"Don't let's talk about it, Mrs. Villing! it distracts me, . . . my only consolation is, that all I suffer—on account of bad times—and let me add, my own weaknesses—I suffer for the sake of my poor wife and my innocent little children. If it hadn't been for them, I should have risen and spit my contempt in the faces of the scoundrels, you may depend upon that, Mrs. Villing. But I have promised myself once for all that, for the sake of my poor wife and children, I will drain the bitter cup to the dregs. No, indeed! You make a mistake, my good Mrs. Villing! I'm not such a brutal tormentor, that for the sake of my pride I would let my little Sophie suffer more than she already does!"

"But, my dear Mr. Aggerbölle, I never said—" objected Mrs. Villing, gently.

"No, no, my good lady! you don't know my Sophie, . . . that's the fact! You haven't loved her as I have for twenty years of bitter sorrows and anxieties. Then one learns to thank God for a good and faithful wife, . . . and that my Sophie has been! A pattern wife and mother . . . noble, self-sacrificing, an angel of patience and so lovely as she still is upon her bed of pain. . . ."

The brandy was having its usual effect upon him. He put up his *pince-nez* to hide the tears which were starting up. His voice was husky, his words and gestures showed the fiery passion he still bore to his wife, though they had a somewhat uncomfortable effect upon those who knew the little pining remnant of humanity which bore the name of Mrs. Aggerbölle.

"My poor wife is always ill now," he continued, abandoning all efforts to hide his emotion. "You know she suffers from these fearful visions, or hallucinations when she is alone. You may fancy that it is fearful for me to think of, for she is quite helpless. We live in such an out of the way place . . . it's dreadful! The other night when I went home from you . . . it was rather late I think . . . I saw a long way off that there was a light in the bedroom. I thought something must be wrong, and when I got in—Ah, I shall never forget the sight! I found my little wife sitting up in bed, as white as a sheet, her teeth chattering. I rushed up to her and clasped her in my arms, but at first she couldn't speak, she was shaking all over. 'My beloved Sophie,' I called—'what has happened?' At last she got strength to say that she had heard someone moving about the house, saw frightful faces at the windows, and that someone had shouted to her that they would murder her and her children. —All delirious fancies of course, but so terrible—so heartrending to witness!"

He no longer tried to control himself. The tears rolled down his shaggy beard, and he leaned forward, burying his face in his hands.

"My good Mr. Aggerbölle," said Mrs. Villing, while her husband patted him on the knees encouragingly and said: "Don't take on so my dear fellow! You'll see that the summer will set your wife up again. When the spring comes we forget all the troubles of the winter."

But he did not hear their words. He had fallen into a kind of stupor which was one of the forms of drunkenness in him. All at once he looked up. His face which was blue when he came in, had become fiery red, and reeked of the spirit.

"But do you know what I think?" he said in a strange voice, looking from one to the other and lifting up his hand. "There's some witchcraft in the air here . . . some devilry going about."

"But Mr. Aggerbölle, I say!" whimpered Mrs. Villing. "You said that the other day too; you make us feel quite uncanny."

"Forgive me, my dear Mrs. Villing, you do not understand me, I neither believe in ghosts nor spirits with grinning heads under their arms . . . that kind of folly I leave to the 'Dunderheads.' But I say there is some other sort of sorcery in the air here which steals one's life blood, Mrs. Villing. Something which draws heart, and blood, and marrow out of one's body if one has not been cradled under these skies. You may depend upon my words! I have always felt it! Why should my poor Sophie and I have got on so badly otherwise?"

He again hid his face in his hands, while his heavy sobs sounded like hollow groans of pain.

"But, dear Mr. Aggerbölle!" exclaimed both Villing and his wife with real sympathy, as they tried to reason with him.

"For heaven's sake don't give way so, my dear friend . . . mix yourself another glass and get these ideas out of your head. We must have one of our little games. We all want a little amusement."

As if waking from a dream, Aggerbölle lifted his head and ran his fingers through his hair with a gesture peculiar to him. With a gloomy look he first glanced up at Villing and then at the clock.

"I ought to be thinking of . . . I believe I promised my wife——" he murmured.

"Oh you can't go home in your present state, my dear fellow. You would be infecting your wife with your melancholy. We can't allow that. Remember that I won 5300 kr. from you the other day, you must have your revenge! . . . Little Sine, get out the cards and mix another half-glass for Mr. Aggerbölle."

The sight of the cards quickly overcame Aggerbölle's power of resistance.

These little card parties were not such a self-sacrifice on the part of the Villings as they would have had people to believe. Certainly they had been obliged to give up playing for money, as Aggerbölle's total bankruptcy crushed every hope of gain; but their old interest in the game was roused anew, after they hit on the happy device of keeping a kind of account, and making the stakes of dazzling value, and so tickling their fancy and satisfying their craving for figures and addition.

After Villing had made a trip into the shop to assure himself that the boy was really asleep, they took their seats round the table and dealt out the cards for a game.

"I announce," growled Aggerbölle immediately.

"I ask leave too," murmured Mrs. Villing.

"Oh, I go above you," chimed in Villing, and was about to take the two cards on the table.

But Aggerbölle laid his spongy hand over them and said:

"You take yourself out of the mess. . . . I'll play what I have."

"Stop the ship, skipper, we're rolling," laughed Villing. "You seem to have got the lucky place today."

Aggerbölle put on his *pince-nez* again, which he had started a couple of years before to add to his importance in the eyes of the "Dunderheads." He laughed with all his flaming face, and never heard the clock strike ten warning strokes.

When he had won his trick and made his opponent "Jan," he put both his big hands on his sides, and looked gleefully from one to the other, and said:

"I say, friends . . . we're very cozy here!"

BOOK TWO

CHAPTER I

After some days of mild spring weather, a strong northerly gale sprang up at sunset. Hansine was alone at home with the children, who had been put to bed early. Emanuel and the servants, as well as the usual evening guests, were gone to the great "Protest" meeting in the Skibberup meeting-house. The people had been streaming into it in the course of the day without intermission from all the country round. Ever since the morning conveyances had been arriving, many of them dropping people at the Parsonage, who wished to call upon Emanuel, or take part in the service at Veilby Church. Besides which the two members of Parliament, who had been sent to speak—peasants from the west coast—had been there on a long visit, and in the afternoon a party of pupils had come over from the Sandinge High School with greetings and messages from the old invalided director. All these people either had to have coffee or something to eat, so there had been a great deal to do all day—as much as at an inn on a market day.

Hansine had been looking forward to a quiet evening after the long and busy day. It was not often that she could secure quiet, nor did she by any means share Emanuel's delight in always having the house full of people. She often wished he would open the doors less wide for the many friends who by degrees had accustomed themselves to go in and out of the Parsonage as if it were their own home. . . . But now, when she was alone and the children in bed, and she had lighted the lamp and seated herself at the long table with some darning, she felt rather low-spirited and lonely in the big empty house, where she had never felt thoroughly at home. Although it had been her home for seven years she never could rid herself of a feeling that she was an unbidden guest in these lofty halls, which had been destined to house grand people, and to ring with music and conversation. It appeared to her sometimes that all the former inhabitants—but especially Provst Tönnesen and his proud daughter—still haunted the house and watched her with threatening glances from the dark corners. She often wondered how Emanuel could be so contented here, notwithstanding that everything was so different from the quiet secluded peasant life which at first they had both pictured to themselves. She many a time sent a sad thought—especially after a troubled day—to the little house overgrown with wild roses by the stream among the green hills, which they thought of buying when they were first engaged; and when her fancy painted how happily and peacefully they might have lived in the small cozy rooms, away from these crowds of people, with the open shore for neighbors, she felt more than ever imprisoned in the empty Parsonage.

Added to this, tonight there was the noise of the rising storm, which howled round the house and brought in its train all kinds of sounds from the out-houses. A shutter was banging about in the barn, and from the shaking of the front door she perceived that Niels had again forgotten to shut the outer gates. A cow was lowing in the byre—and all these trifles roused the housewifely anxiety, which the feeling of responsibility for the management of this great house so often caused her. She wondered if Abelone had remembered to milk the broken-winded cow before she went away, and if she had looked after the ashes properly which were thrown out in the afternoon.

Abelone had become so abstracted lately, and was always busy looking out of the window as soon as Niels appeared in the yard. . . . If only Niels was not being spoiled by all the fuss which was made of him since he began to write in the papers. He had already become very neglectful over his work she thought. . . . She was interrupted in her thoughts by a moaning sound from the bedroom, to which the door was ajar. It was Laddie wailing in his sleep. He had been to Skibberup in the morning with his father, so that he might run about on the shore with the fishermen's children during the service. But on their return he had disappeared, and had not been to be found all the afternoon. Only at dusk, after Emanuel had left, did she find him sitting at the top of the attic stairs, with his hands over his bad ear and his face swelled with crying. She had put him to bed at once, and dropped a little of old Strynö-grethe's flax-seed oil into his ear, after which he soon fell asleep. But he kept on moaning in his sleep, and this new outbreak of the boy's old suffering contributed to her depression this evening.

She had never reconciled herself to Emanuel's fancy for taking the children about with him wherever he went in all weathers—and still less did she understand his allowing them to romp about with the poor children, and exposing them to so much that was unpleasant. She remembered from her own childhood the many ugly things which were prevalent among the poor; and when she saw Laddie and Sigrid running about with them just as she herself had done in patched clothes and stockings in holes, she could not keep back a certain feeling of dissatisfaction with the difference between her, and Emanuel's actual life, and the pictures she had formed for herself on the benches of the High School, of the higher intellectual life, which by her marriage, she had expected to realize.

Time after time she had made up her mind to speak to Emanuel about the children's bringing-up, but her heart had always failed her. As soon as he entered the room with his cheerful, happy manner, quite absorbed in his great work she lost confidence in herself. In the face of the unshaken confidence and cheerful self-sacrifice with which he threw himself into his lofty vocation, she could never find words for her every day troubles.

. . . She raised her head. A series of little shrieks were making themselves heard in the bedroom, she quickly laid her work aside and rose. But when she reached Laddie's bed she was surprised to find him apparently sleeping quietly. She did not understand it, but she calmed herself by thinking that she could not have heard aright, and was just turning away when the boy threw himself on his back, ground his teeth, and again gave three frightened shrieks.

"But child! . . . whatever is the matter?" she cried, and raised him up to wake him.

The boy rubbed his eyes and looked about in surprise, and said at last:

"I'm quite well."

"What did you call out for then? . . . Did you have a bad dream? Have you any pain?"

He did not seem to hear her. His eyes had suddenly grown very big, and he stared straight before him with a mingled expression of fear and lively interest.

"Mother!" he whispered.

"Yes, what is it, my boy?"

"A fly has got into my head."

"Nonsense, child. It's something you're dreaming. Lie down again and go to sleep, you'll forget all about it then."

"No, it's really true. . . . I can feel it all the time. I expect it can't get out, mother."

His face worked, the mouth widened, and after a short struggle with his pride, he threw himself into her arms and began to cry. She stroked his hair and tried to comfort and soothe him, and with his usual good temper he soon dried his eyes and laid himself down under the clothes. With a little sigh he folded his hands under his cheek and in a few minutes fell asleep.

Hansine remained standing by the bed. The boy's words and strange behavior had inspired her with new fears. She did not know what to think of him. . . . And standing there looking at him with the light from the sitting-room shining on to his pillow, she made a new resolution that she would no longer put off having certainty as to his condition. This very evening she would talk to Emanuel about her fears, and she would not desist until the doctor was fetched to her child.

CHAPTER II

It was nearly ten o'clock, and Hansine was again sitting by the lamp darning the children's stockings, when Emanuel came home.

"God's peace be here!" he said on entering; an old greeting of the peasants' which he had adopted. He remained standing a moment in the darkness near the door, with an extinguished lantern in one hand, and an oak stick in the other. His light beard streamed wind-tossed over his dark, monkish cloak, the hood of which covered his head like a cowl.

"Has Niels come home?"

"No, I have not heard anyone."

"Nor Abelone?"

"No."

"Poor child! she will find it difficult to struggle against the wind. It's blowing half a hurricane, and so dark you can't see your hand before you. My lantern blew out down under the ridge, I could hardly find my way.—Well, 'All is rest, home is best.' "

He put the lantern down on a bench near the door and laid aside his cloak and stick.

"I've got plenty to tell you!" he continued excitedly, as he came nearer blowing on his frozen fingers. It was not before he came quite close to her and was about to lay his hands on her head and give her his usual kiss of greeting, that he noticed her perturbed and absent expression.

"What is the matter, dear? Has anything happened since I have been away?"

"Oh, it's Laddie again, Emanuel."

"Laddie! what is the matter with him? He can't be lost? I didn't see him all the afternoon."

"No, I discovered how that was. . . . I found him on the attic stairs after you left. His ear was bad again, and I had to put him to bed. I don't know what's the matter with him; I've never seen him so strange as he is this evening."

"What do you say? Let me see him!"

He was taking the lamp off the table, but she held his hand back.

"You won't want that. It might wake him, I have lighted the night lamp in there."

She rose and followed him into the bedroom, where the boy lay, asleep with both hands under his cheeks and his knees drawn up—in the dim light of a little flame swimming on a layer of oil in a glass of water, which stood behind his pillow. Not a line in his face showed a trace at this moment of anything but sound and healthy sleep.

"Why, he's sleeping like a god!" whispered Emanuel, stooping over the little iron bed to listen to his breathing. "There can't possibly be anything the matter with him. You've alarmed yourself for nothing, Hansine!"

"I can't make it out, he was talking quite wildly before and shrieking fearfully. It comes over him by fits and starts."

"Then it's the spring air you may be sure! It generally makes children's sleep uneasy. You'll see in the morning by God's help he'll be quite brisk again."

"I seriously think all the same that the doctor ought to see him."

"How pretty he looks!" continued Emanuel, who, like most great talkers, seldom heard other people's remarks. He had put his arm round Hansine's waist and was looking with a happy smile at the three little golden heads lying there buried in the white pillows. "Just like a little angel in our Father's bosom. Isn't it a beautiful sight! Can you understand Hansine how anyone with children can deny God? To my mind there is always a reflection of the light from beyond.—such a beautiful revelation of the heavenly peace on a sleeping child's face. . . . It reminds me of an answer our dear old High School director once made to a man who asked him what eternal happiness would be like. 'Like this,' he said, pointing to a child which had fallen asleep at its mother's breast. I thought it was so beautifully expressed.——Well!" he interrupted himself, letting Hansine go, "How are the other two little fairies? I suppose they're all right. You can hear Fattie snoring well enough. I've quite longed for the dear little creatures. I've hardly seen them today."

He moved about on tiptoe round the beds while he spoke, bending over the three little beings whom he often called his "three golden treasures." He took a caraway cake out of his pocket by each bedside, and put it half under the pillow, so that the children might see them as soon as they woke.

"I just looked in at the baker's a moment, I didn't want to come home empty handed. Now we'd better leave them. I have such a lot to tell you about tonight. Come along."

They went back into the sitting-room, and he began walking up and down the big room, the better to give her a detailed account of the events in the meeting-house. Hansine only listened with half an ear. She had not given up her intention, and was determined to lead the conversation back to Laddie at the first opportunity.

"But do you know what was the greatest success of the whole meeting?" exclaimed Emanuel, stopping in the middle of the room with his hands on his sides and bending forward. "Try to guess, Hansine."

"Oh, that's no use . . . you'd better tell me."

"Your Father!"

She looked up from her darning.

"Father?"

"Yes—no other than your dear, old, blind Father!"

"Father spoke?"

"Yes, indeed! . . . I wish I could give you any idea of the enthusiasm, nay downright jubilation, his appearance called forth. It was really most affecting."

"But can Father speak?" asked Hansine in growing astonishment.

"It was not so much the words. It was his whole appearance and his extreme agitation. You see the chairman had just spoken rather lengthily, and the resolution was about to be read, when your father who was sitting just under the platform, stood up because he couldn't hear. His movement was misunderstood in the hall, people thought he was going to speak, and they began shouting on all sides—'Up on to the platform! Up on to the platform!'—In short, before your father had time to object, he was led up into the Tribune by two men. He didn't make any great opposition . . . and you know his bashfulness, so you can imagine his attitude and the feeling of the meeting. I shall never forget that moment."

"But—but, what did he say?"

"Well, as I said before it was not so

much the words—as the sight of that old blind man with his snow-white hair, appearing there as a living witness of the days of slavery which he almost himself experienced. It was like a voice from the grave, when he lifted his shaking hand and shouted with his old man's voice: 'Are we to have the 'wooden horse'* again? Is that the idea? Are we peasants to be cattle again for the nobles?' —He didn't say much more, but you should have heard the thundering.

" 'No, no, that we never will!' rang through the Hall. I only wished that the enemies of Freedom might have been present, to hear the iron wills in that cry;—they would have seen then, how hopeless their opposition is. . . .

"Oh, what a fortunate man I am!" he burst out going along to Hansine and laying his hand on her head. "Never can I thank the Lord enough that he led me out of that Sodom, where life is a daily struggle with death and annihilation. How different it is here where everything is in its origin—all is spring, breaking day, and song of larks! And how beautiful to be permitted according to one's poor abilities, to help to build up the promised kingdoms of truth and justice! . . . When I think of myself in former days, I seem to be a new creature, and to have thrown off an old, vile slough. And next to God, I owe you thanks for all this happiness my dearest one! . . . Now you look down and blush, but it's true all the same, you are the Princess without whom I could never have won my half kingdom!"

CHAPTER III

It was only next morning that Hansine took courage to urge with sufficient persistency her desire that the doctor should be sent for. Emanuel was almost angry at first. He reproached her for her never ending solicitude, the weakness of her faith in the mercy of Providence, and her inclination to believe in the devices of man rather than laying everything trustfully in God's gracious hands.

He spoke so convincingly with such faith and in so sorrowful a tone that Hansine felt quite guilty, and began to cry.

But he was softened at once at the sight of her tears and kissed her. By this he made matters worse, and she turned away with despairing sobs.

He was quite surprised. He was not used to see her give way to her feelings. He had hardly ever seen her cry since that moment on the evening of their engagement, when she had involuntarily betrayed her love by her passionate and irrepressible weeping— The recollection of that happy hour now made his heart tender, and he bent over her, stroking her hair and cheek.

"But, my dear, my dear, had I known that my words would hurt you so, I would never have said what I did. I did not mean to hurt you. And you know—don't you, that if it really will give you any satisfaction to hear Doctor Hassing's opinion, that it would never occur to me to oppose you. I will tell Niels to put the horses to at once. Then the doctor will be here this morning."

When Hansine heard the carriage roll through the archway a quarter of an hour later, she set to work with Abelone to tidy the rooms for the doctor's reception. It was the first time that she expected a visit from a stranger, who might look upon her home with unfriendly eyes; and she knew that exception might be taken to various things. The floor of the big room was sprinkled with water and swept, and the benches dusted—there was no more to be done to it. But

* Wooden horse. A favorite instrument of torture in the days of serfdom. Equivalent to "Riding the Rail" in England.

in the bedroom clean linen was put on all the beds, and Sigrid and little Dagny were brought in from the yard to be smartened a little. She would have preferred to put their Sunday clothes on, but she thought Emanuel would not like it, so she contented herself with scrubbing their faces and putting on clean pinafores. Laddie, she was obliged to leave as he was. He had been fairly quiet in the latter part of the night, and now slept so soundly that she was loath to wake him.

She thought of Emanuel too, but she had seen him cross the yard in his usual working smock and big field boots. She knew it would be useless to try and get him to make any alteration in his dress out of regard for the doctor, so she had to console herself with the reflection that as it was Monday, both smock and boots were fairly clean.

There was a threefold reason for Emanuel's pronounced objection to seeing the doctor of the neighborhood in his house. In the first place he had a great aversion to the whole profession, because it appeared to him that modern Society made it of too much importance, and that it was the cause of much of the effeminacy and dissolute living which undermined the cultivated classes in the present day. He was convinced that the almost idolatrous confidence with which they threw themselves into the arms of doctors and chemists was a serious danger to their sound moral development. So many people were under the impression that they could patch up their mental and bodily excesses by the help of pills, potions, and electricity, and that therefore they could afford to disdain the only true permanent healing measures—self-control, frugality, and bodily exercise. Besides this, he had a special reason for shunning Dr. Hassing. He was the only person outside the circle of "Friends" with whom he came in contact, by meeting him occasionally among the sick and dying;—and the doctor's bearing and carefully tended person, his measured gait, and conventional phrases forced him unpleasantly into renewed contact with the social forms which he despised and had fled. He was reminded of persons he had known formerly—and he did not wish to disturb the calm of that sepulchral chamber in which he had long since laid all bitter memories of the past to rest.

Finally, it was the general opinion of the neighborhood that Dr. Hassing was a very mediocre practitioner, whose real interests lay in collecting and surrounding himself with works of art, rebuilding his villa, giving dinner-parties, and taking an annual trip in foreign countries—in short, in spending as pleasant a life as possible with the help of a considerable private fortune.

It was therefore no small sacrifice Emanuel made to Hansine in consenting to send for this man to see his dear Laddie, as to whose sound constitution he was so convinced that it almost seemed ungrateful to the Almighty to doubt it. So he did not go to the stables in his usual good spirits to feed the cattle and get the straw down from the loft. He also had the annoyance of discovering various pieces of damage wrought by the storm in the night.

It could not be denied that the formerly stately Parsonage began to have a somewhat dilapidated appearance. Emanuel had come here at a very unfavorable time for farms, with falling prices and an increased demand for improvements. Besides, he had been pursued by a series of misfortunes with his cattle, and had come to grief over experiments in feeding and new ways of manuring, which he had tried to introduce for the benefit of the community. Also his housekeeping was more costly than he really was aware of, and although he had his mother's heritage to fall back on, and though he never spared himself, and was in the stable by five in the morning, yet he could not manage the work with the assistance he had hitherto been able to afford.

The fact was that, true to his purpose, he obstinately declined to accept any stipend for his ministerial work beyond the free use of the Parsonage and the land. So as to share the life and means of the "friends," he maintained himself exclusively by the land, and immediately on his institution had required the peasants to pay their tithes and offerings into the Poor Relief Fund, which defrayed the expenses of the congregational charities. Above all, he was anxious to be looked upon, not as a priest, but as a peasant, who, like the churchwardens and fire inspectors, had had posts of honor and trust bestowed upon them by the congregation. He generally called himself their "Templeserver," and was highly pleased with the word, because, as he said—it put an end to "his reverence" so effectually.

CHAPTER IV

It was ten o'clock when Niels came back with the doctor, who sat at the back of the wagon in his own swing chair, wrapped in a big fur coat and brown gloves. When the doctor had alighted the two men shook hands in an equally stiff and reserved manner, and then went up the steps in silence. The doctor took off his fur coat in the entrance hall, and revealed a tight-fitting black coat and a large satin tie with a diamond pin. He was a man of about forty, with a fine figure, sharply cut features, and small whiskers. From the first moment he evidently took great pains not to betray any surprise at Emanuel's peculiar costume, and when he entered the "Hall" he also appeared not to notice anything unusual in it. In his care not to show the least misplaced curiosity, he even dropped the gold pince-nez from his prominent nose, and with an effort to be unconstrained, said:

"Well, we'd better go and look at the little chap."

"It is my wife who wishes to have your opinion about my son," answered Emanuel, hurt by the doctor's tone. "I don't think there is much the matter with him . . . probably an ordinary spring cold."

"Well, we shall see."

Hansine rose from the chair by the boy's bed when the doctor appeared at the door. He remained standing a moment on the threshold—and this time he did not succeed so well in hiding a certain surprise. It was clear that rumor or his own fancy had pictured something quite different as the much talked-of clergyman's wife of Veilby.

"Your son is ill," he said with sudden sympathy, after approaching and shaking hands with her. "I hope it is nothing much . . . a common cold your husband thinks."

He took a chair and sat down by the bed, where the boy was still asleep; nor did he wake when the doctor, after taking off a huge pair of cuffs, began to feel his head and his pulse with his long white hands. When the wadding over the bad ear was touched, he slowly opened his eyes, and then lay for a long time without moving, looking at the strange man. He only seemed to become fully conscious when his eyes fell upon his mother at the other side of the bed. He again looked at the mysterious stranger, examined his black coat, his diamond pin, and his large white teeth, while a dawning fear rose in his pale blue eyes.

Hansine raised him carefully into a sitting posture, and said brightly,

"Don't be frightened, my boy. It is the

doctor who wants to look at your ear. All that earache is so tiresome, and the doctor is a nice man who will make it better."

Then the boy seemed to understand it all. His mouth widened, and the tears came into his eyes. But when he discovered Emanuel at the foot of the bed, he quickly swallowed his tears. It was as if he understood that it would please his father if he showed himself as a brave and fearless lad to the stranger. The doctor in the meantime had begun to examine the bad ear. When the wadding was removed there was a flow of an evil-smelling discharge.

His face took a critical expression.

"How long has this been going on?" he asked.

"We have noticed it on and off for two years," answered Hansine.

The doctor looked up as if he could not believe his ears.

"For two years?"

"Yes."

He glanced up at Emanuel, who misunderstood it, and with a quiet nod confirmed his wife's words.

Hansine began telling him about the beginning of the illness, its periodic recurrence, and the disturbance of the previous night. The doctor listened attentively, but seemed to have his thoughts elsewhere. When she stopped he asked for a candle, and waved it backwards and forwards before the boy's eyes, then held both his hands for some time on the back of his head, and finally examined the part at the back of the ear with great care. The skin was slightly distended here on account of an incipient swelling.

Up to this point Emanuel had stood quietly with his hands behind him looking on. He had made up his mind that Hansine should have her way this time; and though he was sorry for the boy, who sat there with big tears in his eyes, struggling to preserve his equanimity, he had not disturbed the doctor in his examination.

But when the doctor took out his instrument case and produced various sharp-pointed instruments, he could no longer remain passive.

"Is that really necessary?" he asked in a tolerably aggressive tone.

The doctor looked up in astonishment.

"Yes," he answered shortly, and asked for warm water, a towel, and several other things which all pointed to an operation. Emanuel stood irresolute. Was he really to allow this person to do violence to his son? He hardly dared look at the boy, who at sight of the instruments had turned as white as a sheet, and begged for protection with his eyes. But he was almost more tortured by seeing the readiness with which Hansine helped the doctor, the cold-bloodedness with which she put her child into the hands of this charlatan.

When the doctor approached with the first instrument—a sharp silver needle—the last remnant of Laddie's courage forsook him, and he threw himself into his mother's arms. Emanuel then left the room; he would not be a witness to the ill-treatment for which Hansine must be responsible. He went into the sitting-room, and when he heard his son's first heart-rending scream there, he went on into his own room, and walked up and down to deaden the sound from the bedroom. He was most violently agitated. He could not understand Hansine. He felt as if he was put into the background in his own house, and shamefully betrayed by those in whom he trusted most implicitly.

In about a quarter of an hour he heard voices in the sitting-room, and on going in found the doctor with his hat in his hand giving final directions to Hansine. He took leave at once on his appearance.

"I think you are too sanguine about your son's illness," the doctor continued in the passage, whither Emanuel had followed him in silence. "I did not express myself so plainly in your wife's presence . . . but I consider it is my duty not to conceal from you that his condition is not without gravity. He is suffering from a long-standing, hardened, and, I fear, a somewhat malignant inflammation, which unfortunately has been allowed to spread all over the internal passages. How the case will run it is of course impossible for me to say at present; but after the turn the illness has latterly taken, we must be prepared for an imminent crisis. For the moment I have done what I could by piercing the drum, to secure a free passage for the discharge, and I have also ordered leaven to his feet and cold bandages to relieve the pressure on the head. . . . I cannot do more today. Everything now depends on keeping the child as quiet as possible, until we see what course the inflammation will take. Should there be the slightest sign of rigidity during sleep—not to mention actual convulsions—you must send for me at once. It is this calamity and its attendant fever which we must try to avert at any price."

CHAPTER V

The doctor's decided tone, and apparent absolute certainty as to the boy's condition, necessarily had a certain effect upon Emanuel. As soon as the doctor had driven off he went back to the bedroom. He found Laddie lying on his back with his head bound up, and apparently sunk in wonder.

When the child saw his father he smiled, and when Emanuel sat down cautiously by the bed and asked him how he was, he sat up without help and began to tell him quite brightly, and with some importance, all that the doctor had done to him.

"But what in the world is the meaning of all this?" exclaimed Emanuel turning to Hansine, who came in from the kitchen with Sigrid and little Dagny, who had been sent to Abelone during the doctor's visit. "The child is quite lively! What was all that rubbish about fever and convulsions and I don't know what."

"Did the doctor say anything about that?" asked Hansine, stopping suddenly in the middle of the room.

"Oh," he rambled on, "but that's a way doctors have, if only they can get people to believe them. Who's that coming now?" Heavy steps and the sound of a stick were heard in the big room. A moment later a stout elderly woman appeared at the door. "Grannie!" cried Emanuel and the children, at the same time stretching out their arms towards her.

"Ay, indeed it's me!" she said in her childlike voice, nodding and smiling to them all. "We heard tell of your sending for the Kyndlöse doctor at the Stous, an' I just had the chance of a lift to the mill, so it didn't take me long to get on me things. Seemed like I wanted to know what was the matter."

"Oh, I hope to God all the fuss is about nothing. Laddie has had a little of his old earache, and Hansine frightened herself about him and would have the doctor."

"Thank the Lord and praise him! Then it's nothing worse. Me and Daddy got a bit scared as ye may think. We're not much used to doctor's visits here."

She undid the big silver clasp of her heavy green linsey cloak, took the little shawl off her head, and smoothed her iron-gray hair with her fingers. It was as thick as ever in front under her gold-embroidered cap with the wide red ribbon tied at one side. She had become more portly than ever in the course of years, and both hands and feet were swelled up with dropsy to such an extent, that she could not move outside the house without a stick.

"Oh, so he's the one supposed to be bad, and who must needs hae the doctor fetched," she said, dropping heavily on to a chair by the little iron bed, when she looked at the boy for a time. His pleasure in seeing his grandmother, to say nothing of a little bundle tied up in a handkerchief which she had on her knee, brought the color to his cheeks and made him quite lively. "I'm sure *he* doesn't look very bad. You're a reg'lar little silly Hansine to let yourself be scared like that. You're just like the Copenhagen folks who tear away both to doctor and chemist as soon as they've got a bit of an ache. If the boy hadn't got all those trappings on his head, he'd be quite a Sunday bairn."

Hansine was sitting by the big bed nursing the baby.

"All the same the Doctor said he wasn't a bit well, and we ought to have sent for him long since." She tried to defend herself, although the boy's bright looks and the unconcern of the others had begun to make her waver.

"Oh, the doctor," laughed her mother, fondling Sigrid, who was leaning against her in an ingratiating way, staring at the little bundle with hungry eyes.

"If everything came about as folks preach we'd all have been in our black graves long since. Why, only the other days, Pér Persen's bit lassie was thought to have swallowed a needle. The doctor stuffed her wi' potatoes and doughy bread till the bairn was like to choke . . . and then they found the needle, as large as life, in grandmother's pincushion. . . . I'm blest if they didn't."

"That wasn't the doctor's fault," murmured Hansine.

"Well, well, maybe not. Then I mind about Sören Seiler—it was in old Dr. Vellöv's time, who was thought to have more learnin' than this here Hassing. Vellöv said Sören hadn't three days to live, and all the family were that busy dividing the property and writing out the inventory, hearthstoning the big room for the funeral—aye, and I believe the coffin was ordered too—and three days later Sören was about again in his usual way with his pipe in his mouth; and he's walking about to this day, though he must be nigh on ninety. What d'ye say to that story? No, it's to be wished these good doctor folks wouldn't carry it off so high, but let the Lord rule over life and death, then perhaps there wouldn't be so much misery."

"Yes; quite true; my very words," said Emanuel, who was walking up and down with his hands behind him.

"It's my mind that we'd far better stick to the good old home-made things rather than all this new doctoring, with their medicines and poison stuffs. For all me haste, I didn't forget to bring along some soothing syrup and some angel balsam. I didn't know what might be the matter. Then I just stepped in to Maren Nilen and brought a bit of her worm's-grease . . . it's a fine thing for festerings." . . . While she talked she undid her little bundle and took out various packets which smelled strongly of herbs. At last she produced three pink sugar pigs and gave one to each of the children. Laddie took his with the shy smile with which he always expressed his thanks, while Sigrid snatched at her's and dashed away with it to the other room.

"Well, and how is all at home, Else?" asked Emanuel, to change the subject. He had looked at Hansine and felt quite sorry for her, because she had evidently begun to repent of her obstinacy. "Dear old grandfather must be quite proud of the success of his speech the other night. It was a solemn moment for all of us."

"Oh, ay, he was as pleased as any bairn. He'd never expected to come out as a speaker. But he's thankful that the

Lord was willing to use him as his instrument, and put the right words into his mouth at the moment. Such graciousness is enough to please and comfort a man in his old age."

They were interrupted by Abelone, who came to the door and said dinner was ready. The grandmother got up to go. Emanuel tried to persuade her to stay and dine, but she had promised Kristen Hansen to meet him again by the mill when he came back, and it was high time for her to start.

"I must get home an' quiet Daddy, too. He's thinking all the time that there's something ever so bad the matter."

She clasped her cloak and put the little shawl over her head again. At the door she turned and nodded to Laddie, and said:

"Now mind you come an' see us o' Sunday, Laddie, an' you shall have a biestings cake, if the red cow calves."

Then she turned to Emanuel, and said: "Daddy has sold the brindled cow, but they're very bad prices this year."

CHAPTER VI

The upper end of the long table was covered with brown oilcloth, upon which stood two earthenware dishes of steaming cabbage soup, half a rye loaf, a saucer of coarse salt, and the usual jar of water with a wooden lid. Emanuel took his seat at the head of the table. Under the window on his left sat Niels and old Sören the cowherd; he was all joints and knuckles, with a head at the top which was not much more than a couple of huge jaws. The lower part of his face and the upper part of his neck down to the prominent Adam's apple was black with a thick growth of stubble. He had a red nose, and over his low yellow forehead his hair tumbled, looking as if ashes had been strewed over his head. But his ears were the most curious part—large, flat, wounded patches of skin, both in shape and color like bats'-wings.

Hansine and the two children were on the other side of the table with Abelone; and besides these there was a little old body with a green shade over her eyes, and two children from the street—who, according to the custom of the poor—had come in of their own accord at the dinner hour, and were evidently quite at home. Laddie remained in bed. He had settled himself to rest soon after his grandmother's departure, and had fallen asleep embracing his sugar pig.

With bent heads, all at the table folded their hands, while Emanuel in a loud voice said grace:

"We seat us here in Jesu's name,
To eat and drink unto the same.
To honor God, ourselves to save.
We thank him for the food he gave."

"Amen," they all said in chorus, and the old woman with the shade added to herself, "God grant we have our fill."

At first they ate in silence. The only sounds were the scraping of the horn spoons against the plates, and the supping of many mouths. Sören was particularly audible. He held a piece of warm pork in his left hand, and between each spoonful or so of soup he dipped it in the saucer of salt and gnawed a piece off it. Even Emanuel helped himself of the dishes with the ravenous appetite and the craving to fill the stomach which comes of constant hard, bodily labor and an innutritious diet. Niels, on the other hand, was too much taken up today with his literary efforts, to have any thoughts for the care of his body. He sat there with his back rounded and his arms on the table, slowly moving the spoon to and from his wide mouth, while his little black eyes stole from Emanuel to Abelone, and back again to Emanuel—as if expecting him to turn the conversation to his new article.

But Emanuel had quite other thoughts. He had decided to go to Skibberup in the afternoon to hear if anything new was known there from parliamentary circles. He had lately found it very difficult to stay quietly at home; every day brought new and disquieting rumors. First it was said that the King had already sent for the leader of the people's party; then, that the existing government had decided to brave the wish of the people by passing laws in the future by their own authority. And the 31st of March was approaching, the end of the financial year—a day which perhaps would mark a boundary between two ages.

"Have none of you any news from Copenhagen?" he asked when he had finished eating. "You, Sören? you generally know all about politics!"

"Eh, well a man picks up one thing an' another," answered Sören with his immense mouth full of food, lifting his eyebrows at the same time in an attempt to give himself a diplomatic air. He was uncle to a member of parliament, and this circumstance caused him to be looked upon as an oracle in political matters among his friends. "A' fancy they're makin' ready for a birth in parliament, an' mayhap us electors might be called in to a christenin' afore long!"

"You mean parliament will be dissolved . . . new elections, eh? Do you think the government will try that measure again? What good would that do?"

"Oh—no, but it wasn't a bit too soon that the workin' man got his say in the country."

"No, there you're right, Sören! They ought to have had it long ago, and then there wouldn't have been all the bitterness there has been.—Well shall we say 'Tak for mad,' " he broke off, seeing they had all finished eating. Even Sören had at last laid down his spoon, after first licking it and then wiping it with his thumb.

A short prayer was again said, and then everyone went his own way.

Emanuel as usual sought the oilcloth sofa in his own room, so as, before he went to Skibberup, to take "a peep into dreamland," in the High School phraseology.

Sören sauntered across the yard with the heavy steps of reflection, into the barn where summer and winter he took his mid-day nap on a bundle of straw, and where he regularly drove away the cat with his snores.

Niels went to his own room, a little white-washed space beside the stable, which he had arranged as much like a study as possible; a washhandstand by the window was made into a writing-table, there was a shelf of nicely bound books, and a long row of pipes carefully arranged according to their length along the wall. Above the bed was hung a framed photograph of Sandinge High School. It showed the ivy-covered gateway with a group of teachers and pupils. The old director was in the middle, with his round face, and long curls, and huge hat. Under the picture, in gold letters, were the words with which he always took leave of his pupils:

> "Be on your guard and keep up a good heart."

When Niels had filled his longest pipe, and put back the canister of tobacco into its place on the window sill, he sat down before the little table and stretched out his fat legs at ease. After sitting so for some time and filling the room with impenetrable clouds of smoke, he drew the "People's News" out of his breast pocket, spread it out with affectionate care on to the table, and began to read.

"SUNDAY HOLIDAYS IN THE COUNTRY.

"A CALL TO THE YOUNG.

"Today I am going to write about Sunday holidays in the country. How sad it is to see, as one often may in the country, the young men, ay, and maidens too, who ought to have better thoughts, wasting their hours of liberty on Sunday afternoons and week days too when the work is done, on all kinds of worldly and useless vanity, such as playing skittles in the public alleys for money or spirits, so that it often happens that the men get tipsy and go about shouting like animals, and indulging in much other ribaldry of the worst sort. Such sights must rouse the indignation of every spiritually-minded person; for one would think they must have something higher to think of and to strive after, especially in these times when the torch of freedom is lighted all over the country to gather everyone to battle for the freedom and rights of the people. Here in this district we do not, thanks to our good teachers and leaders, see anything of the sort, which is unworthy of a free people. But in other parishes such things are still prevalent, and therefore I send this appeal to the young, that we may all join on this point too, and fight for the victory of the spirit over the darkness of slavery, so that we may sing with the poet,

" 'Oh may all the blessed be led
To the city of beauty and light!' "

"Yours obediently
"N. NIELSEN DAMGAARD.
"Veilby Parsonage, 1st March 1885."

CHAPTER VII

When Emanuel came home at bedtime from Skibberup, Laddie was asleep, not having been awake all the afternoon.

"Do you see!" he said to Hansine. "He's wise enough to sleep it off. You'll have him out of bed again tomorrow!"

Hansine did not answer, but she by no means shared his sanguine expectations. This whole day of sleep seemed to her too unnatural, and it woke in her mind the alarming recollection of a child, the brother of her friend Ane, who died of a brain disease in her girlhood, and whom she had helped to nurse. She had tried to wake him several times in the course of the afternoon to take some food, but he had only half opened his eyes, for a time, and looked at her with a strange, dull glance, and utterly refused to eat, but he had once or twice drank greedily, and settled off to sleep again directly.

Towards midnight she and Emanuel were awakened by a strange noise which they could not explain. It sounded like chopping in the kitchen. Suddenly it dawned upon Hansine that it was Laddie's little bed which was in unceasing motion.

"Light the night-lamp," she said. "It is Laddie."

Emanuel struck a match, and by its light they saw the child's arms fighting the air. She was out of bed in an instant and by his side. She quickly took away the pillow from his head, and held his arms down to his body which trembled from head to foot.

Emanuel, who in the meantime had succeeded in lighting the lamp, could not imagine what was going on. At first he thought the child was playing, and when he saw Hansine take a hairpin from her hair and force the round end into his mouth, he cried—

"In Heaven's name, what are you doing, Hansine? What is the matter with the child?"

The oil flame blazed up at this moment, and by the brighter light he saw now that Laddie's face was quite dark, his teeth were clenched, and the lips covered with foam. Then the doctor's words in the morning came into his mind.

"It's surely not, . . . it's not convulsions, Hansine?"

She nodded.

"You must fetch the doctor," she added shortly, as Emanuel did not move. "And you must be quick. . . . Laddie is very ill."

"Yes—yes," he said, as if waking from his trance, quickly threw on some clothes, and groped through the dark of the big room to wake the servants. Seeing a light in the man's room he began to call from the top of the steps:

"Niels! . . . Niels!"

It sounded like a cry for help in the quiet night, and before he had crossed the yard the man appeared at the door in alarm. He was in his shirt sleeves with an open book in his hand, and smoking a long pipe which almost reached the ground.

"You must put the horses to at once, Niels, and fetch the doctor. Laddie is very ill."

"Fetch the doctor?" said Niels, looking at Emanuel's disturbed countenance. "But you can't find your way tonight, it's so dark. You can't—"

"It's got to be done. You must call Sören, and he must go with you with a lantern. . . . The horses know part of the way."

"Yes, but—" he was renewing his objections, but Emanuel cut him short at once.

"Do as I say, and don't waste time in objections!" said he, in such sudden and violent anger that the man was rendered speechless. "You hear that Laddie is very ill, and the doctor must be fetched without delay. Wake Sören at once and tell him to get up directly."

When he got back to the bedroom Hansine was still bending over the bed, holding Laddie's arms.

"Don't you think I should send for your mother, too? Wouldn't it be a comfort to you?"

"No, what's the good. But you must call Abelone, and tell her to light the fire and heat some water in the large new pot."

"Yes—yes."

He met Abelone in the kitchen, she had been wakened by the noise in the house. She was in a petticoat and had a candle in one hand; with the other she was holding her short bedgown together over the bosom.

"Laddie is never worse?" she asked, pale with alarm.

"Yes, you must light up at once and heat some water in the big kettle, but make haste."

"Is he very ill?"

"Yes, don't you hear. Be quick," said he, in an unusually peremptory tone. "It's wanted as quickly as possible."

He went back to the bedroom where Laddie at last was quiet, and seemed to be peacefully sleeping. Hansine, who had managed to throw on some clothes, sat bending over him at the head of the bed. With her chin resting in her hand and her elbow on her knee, she was looking at the child with the constrained, almost hard, expression her face always wore in moments of intense emotion.

Emanuel approached cautiously and sat down on the other side of the bed.

"Can you understand it, Hansine? Can you conceive how it has come about? When I left in the middle of the day he was well and lively . . . and now! Whatever do you think it can be?"

"I don't know," she said—and as if he had touched a thought she had not courage to pursue, she added directly, "Did you wake Niels?"

"Yes, he must be ready to go soon."

Just then the child's arms and shoulders began to work again, the little hands were clenched, the eyelids were raised over the unnaturally dilated pupils. . . . Signs that a new attack was coming on.

Emanuel could no longer endure the sight. He again groped through the outer room to the steps, and when he saw Niels and Sören still rummaging about in the coach-house with a lantern, he shouted in desperate impatience, "Good God, what are you about? How long will it be before you get off? . . . You must tell the doctor to come at once, Niels, the child is in frightful convulsions."

The boy got worse and worse in the succeeding hours. Even after repeated hot baths the fits increased in length and severity. His face was almost black, and in spite of all their care he had bitten his tongue in one of the fits, and a little blood was oozing out of the corners of his mouth.

Emanuel had to exert all his will power not to collapse in his wild despair at the frightful mystery which the child's fate was to him. He had not yet given up the hope that all might pass off as quickly as it had come on. He tried to console himself and Hansine with the thought that some children, with even slight indisposition, were very liable to convulsions; and he remained by her side to help in nursing. But as the hours went by without a sign of improvement, his courage gave way, and he now placed all his hopes on the doctor's aid. Long before there was any chance of his coming, he started up at every sound outside, thinking it was the carriage; at the end of the fourth hour he took up his hat and went out. He couldn't rest for the thought that an accident must have happened to Niels, or that the doctor had not been at home. Otherwise he couldn't imagine why they had not arrived long ago. He stood on the steps, holding his breath and listening . . . but not the slightest sound reached him. He went round the gable end and felt his way through the overgrown garden till he reached a little mound, from whence in the day the Kyndlöse road was overlooked. He stared out into the dark night with a beating heart, in the hope of catching a glimpse of a lantern. But heaven and earth were merged in one without a glimmer of light.

All at once it seemed as if this impenetrable darkness, this inexorable silence caused something within him to give way. Like a person who suddenly sees a yawning abyss at his feet, he pressed his hands to his forehead and groaned almost unconsciously:

"Oh, it is too terrible?" . . .

It was almost morning when the doctor came. The delay was caused by a mishap on the outward journey, Niels having driven into such a deep ditch that they had to wake up some people who lived near to help them out again.

As soon as the doctor saw the boy he gave him a dose of musk, which almost immediately relieved him. The rigid limbs relaxed, the eyes closed and he fell asleep.

For several minutes after they all sat silent round the little bed, watching how the usual expression came slowly back to his drawn face. It seemed as if none of them had courage to break the deep silence; or as if they were all under the influence of the curious light in the room like a sepulchral chamber. The little oil lamp on the green table was dying out and threw a wan light on their faces; the day was dawning outside, and the window frames were marked out against the blinds like two shadowy crosses in the pale morning light.

Emanuel, who for the last hour had been beside himself at the sight of the child's sufferings, sat holding Hansine's hand in both his, pressing it feverishly—as if in that way to gain strength to ask the doctor the question which for the last hour had been trembling on his lips. At last he summoned up courage, and asked shortly what the doctor thought of his son's state.

Dr. Hassing glanced furtively at him and Hansine—as if to judge how far he dared tell them the truth.

"Well, it can't be denied,"—he said, and it sounded as if he had to force out the words. "Your son is very severely attacked . . . and I cannot conceal from you that——"

"But the boy has an excellent constitution," Emanuel interrupted him, as if to ward off an unfavorable (hopeless) opinion: "With the exception of this earache he has never had anything the matter with him. Besides, both my wife and I are perfectly strong and healthy—so there is no possibility of hereditary taint."

A gleam of pity which he could never succeed in entirely hiding with regard to Emanuel came into the doctor's eyes behind his gold *pince-nez*. "Well," he said slowly, dropping his eyes before the glance which tried to force him to believe in the boy's strength. "Of course much may be hoped for with a good constitution."

As the doctor had foreseen, no particular change took place for the next few days in the boy's condition. He mostly lay in a heavy torpor produced by the musk, with half open eyes, without taking nourishment or being conscious of his surroundings. When the dressings on his ear were touched, a faint shadow of the little forced smile, with which he always used to assert that he "did not feel any pain now" would flit across his face, but otherwise it was entirely expressionless, and the light of life in his half closed eyes seemed already quenched.

Hansine nursed him day and night with her usual patience and self control. To look at her, no one could have said that she was cognizant of her child's fate; and yet, from the first convulsions, she had been aware that he had only a few more days to live.

Emanuel on the other hand hoped almost to the last. Even when the doctor, on his next visit informed him in cautious terms that he must be prepared for his son's death very shortly, he did not give up his faith in the boy's power of resistance, and the strength of his prayers. At every glimpse of returning life in the child's face, he saw a sign that heaven had heard his prayers. It seemed as if he could not believe that the Almighty would bereave him of this child, which ever since its birth—because it was the eldest—had been to him a special pledge of the blessing and grace of God.

It was not until the unmistakable signs of death appeared, that he gave way utterly to despair. He sat by the bed for hours, sobbing aloud, so that at last Hansine began to have fears for his reason . . . All work in the yard and stables was stopped as far as possible, because every sound from the outer world increased his pain. He wanted all the doors and gates shut, and not even the closest friends of the house were admitted when they came to ask after the boy, because he couldn't bear the sight of a strange face. At last in the evening of the following day, while the sun was sinking behind the hills in the west, and tinging the scudding clouds with red, the boy sank peacefully to rest. When Emanuel saw death approaching, and felt the cold of the grave creeping over the child's limbs, the dread of its annihilation roused him to a last desperate struggle to save it. He took it up in his arms wrapped in a blanket, and pressed it to him as if to shelter it from the embrace of death. Hansine implored him to be calm and to lay the child down again, but he did not hear her. With the tears streaming unceasingly down his face, he walked up and down the floor, with the child in his bosom, now lulling it, then praying and singing, as if by his pain and despair, he would extort God's mercy . . . until all at once he felt the little body relax in his arms, and the head sink on the breast with a long sigh, which announced that the last hope was over, and the boy was dead.

Then his spirit bowed humbly before the will of the Almighty. His tears stopped; quietly he laid the little body on the bed, closed the eyes, and laying his hand on the thoughtful forehead, said:

"The Lord gave, and the Lord hath taken away; blessed be the name of the Lord."

CHAPTER VIII

The funeral was to take place that day week, from the home, with the usual tolling of bells for an hour, and a big lunch to all the followers preceding it. In his deep depression, Emanuel would much have preferred that it should take place as quietly as possible. But he had always spoken too eagerly in favor of keeping up the old peasant customs, to be able to break them now; and some dissatisfaction had already been aroused, by his unwillingness to see any of his friends who came to offer their sympathy during the last few days of Laddie's life.

A great bustle therefore prevailed at the Parsonage for a few days, in cleaning the whole house and cooking as for a wedding or christening. Emanuel was in a way grateful to Hansine because during these days she ordered everything so calmly; and so self-sacrificingly took everything upon her shoulders. But at the same time he could not help wondering how in her sorrow, she could turn her thoughts to all these everyday matters, and he was almost wounded, because she did not shed a tear, when Laddie was laid out and wrapped in the winding sheet.

In his overwrought condition he could not free himself from the painful thought that he was alone in his great sorrow; and although he saw the injustice of it, and fought against it, he spent most of his time on the sofa in his own room, or in the garden, so as to give way to his grief in solitude.

He liked to be in the garden best . . . and the big, secluded, almost overgrown park which surrounded the Parsonage, like a small primeval forest. He wandered up and down for hours, in the most remote alleys, where the smell of cooking from the kitchen, and the gossip of the cleaners could not reach him.

The hand of spring had already touched the earth, the grass was showing signs of green, and the little blackthorn bushes were shooting out a yellowish fringe of leaves, and the air was scented with violets and half-wild primulas. Larks were singing in the blue sky, and starlings and tomtits were twittering in the tree tops, and a warm breeze brought a message of new life from the earth. But Emanuel felt nothing of all this; for him the garden paths only rang with Laddie's voice, it was the child's face he saw among the trees, and every day his sobs broke out anew at the sight of a little upturned heap under a thorn bush, where shortly before Laddie's illness he had buried a crow. He could still plainly see the traces of his little wooden shoes, and the marks of his fingers where he had carefully patted down the earth and planted a cross made of a split withy. The cross still stood there, untouched since he had left it; a little way off was a whip of his own manufacture, which he had forgotten, with five rusty nails in a heap.

. . . On the day of the funeral all the flags waved half-mast high in the village, and by mid-day the roads and paths were black with vehicles and pedestrians. The streets of Veilby were strewn with fir branches, and even the little children had come in their best clothes, and were running about excitedly with various sweetmeats in their hands. Inside the Parsonage, the doors between the rooms were thrown open, and even then there was hardly room for the crowd. The yard and the meadow were full of conveyances and neighing horses.

Laddie's coffin, which was placed on two black stools in Emanuel's room, was soon entirely covered with wreaths of artificial flowers, and crosses of beads on gold and silver pasteboard; some had printed inscriptions, and a few, poetry. There was a constant crowd round it, chiefly of women, who with folded hands, admired the unusual display and read the inscriptions in whispers: "sleep sweetly," "an angel thou wast like," and so on.

The lunch was set out on long tables in the great room, and Emanuel and Hansine stood at the entrance to receive the sympathizing greeting of their friends. Grandmother Else, Abelone, and a few laborers' wives attended to the waiting, and Else's voice was heard saying aloud through the subdued buzz of conversation:

"Take your seats if you please, friends! make yourselves at home!"

There was an unusual sense of oppression over the company. Rarely at any funeral were so many perturbed faces seen, or so much anxious whispering heard. It was not only grief for the death of the boy which caused this dejection, it was due to constant disturbing rumors from Copenhagen parliamentary circles. It was known that yesterday must have decided the struggle, but no communication had yet reached them. There was, however, reason to fear the worst. The increasingly threatening language in the House, of the friends of the government, and the rebuffs administered by the ministry in the face of every attempt at reconciliation, foreboded a real intention to thwart the people and to substitute Might for Right.

The chairman of the Parish Council was standing with his hands behind him on the veranda, to which the door had been opened for the occasion; he was surrounded by people who wanted to hear his opinion on the situation. His nose was remarkably pale, and his otherwise boisterous voice was unusually subdued. He regularly answered the anxious inquiries with an attempt to preserve a reassuring calmness.

"Let us wait a little, friends! And whatever happens . . . let us be calm! Don't let us be excited or carried away to excesses, that's the chief thing! If we only hold firmly to our demands, our enemies will be obliged to give in sometime—be sure of that."

The weaver was asked for on every side. It was known that he had gone to the country town in the morning, and it had been calculated that he might be back before dinner-time. But nobody had seen him yet, and the bells had begun to toll, and the people had to mount their vehicles without seeing him.

It was a clear, sunny day, with a blue sky, the fields were turning green, and the larks were singing loudly. Amid all this rejoicing, the long dark funeral train, which moved slowly at a foot's pace southwards along the winding road, had a doubly sad effect. It was Emanuel's wish that the boy should be laid to rest by old Anders Jörgen in his grandfather's burial-place at Skibberup, in the churchyard on the Ness. He had long had a particular affection for his solitary spot with its wide view over the Fiord, and its deep, solemn silence, broken only by the wild screams of the gulls on the beach.

After an hour's drive the train reached the churchyard. A band of young girls led the way strewing sprigs of fir and moss, and the procession followed singing a hymn. At this moment a rumor ran like wildfire through the people that Hansen, the weaver, had arrived. Whispered questions and answers went from mouth to mouth, and even before the coffin was lowered into the ground they all knew that "the impossible" had happened, a violation of the constitution was accomplished, the parliament sent home, and the government was making laws by its arbitrary power and calling in the taxes.

Very scant attention was paid to the little speech, in which Emanuel—struggling with his tears—took leave of his son, and thanked him for the six years they had passed together "in happy fellowship"; and hardly were the three shovels of earth thrown on to the coffin and the silent prayer ended before the party dispersed with loud exclamations of indignation.

One of the few who happily did not notice the disturbance was Emanuel, who remained standing by the grave with Hansine, Else, and the blind grandfather, while some men of their most intimate acquaintance according to custom proceeded to fill it in with shovel and spade. He did not move until the men had accomplished their task, and finally laid all the shovels crosswise over the mound during a moment's silent prayer.

In the meantime people had crowded outside the gates. In the general confusion they all sought the Chairman of the Parish Council, who was nowhere to be found. It was discovered at last that, immediately after the end of the ceremony, he had mounted his conveyance and driven home. The weaver had disappeared too—according to some—accompanied by Maren Smeds. Of all the "Select Committee" only the fat little Veilby peasant, with the childish red cheeks, was to be found. This man had been elected to the political committee chiefly as an acknowledgment of his services in the milk trade, and he was so bewildered on suddenly finding himself surrounded by a group of young men clamoring for information that he almost began to cry.

It was quite correct that the weaver had left with Maren Smeds—the little, ugly, poorly-dressed woman, who at one time used regularly to address the meeting, and who always met the strongest opposition on account of her attacks, full of hatred, on the speakers. This woman, whose life had been an incessant swaying from one extreme standpoint to another, had at length found a haven as a "Saint." She and three or four other persons held daily prayer meetings in her hovel among the desolate fields, where, in loud, piercing voices, which could be heard a long way off, they read portions of the Bible, sang hymns, and poured out curses upon the rest of the ungodly congregation. It therefore caused some astonishment that the weaver should latterly have taken her under his protection. Some even asserted that he sometimes took part in the prayer meetings; in any case, they were often seen walking together along the high field path leading to her cottage.

They were walking there now—Maren in front continually gesticulating with her claw-like hand and talking incessantly. The weaver followed her silently. He had, as a matter of fact, gone with her to avoid other company, and when they had reached a point where they could not be seen from the church, he took leave of her in Jesu's name, and went over the fields towards Skibberup. He stopped a moment on the top of a hill where there was a view of the long dale with the church road. He watched the groups of dejected looking men and women in their black clothes, with a triumphant smile, as they slowly wended their way homewards.

BOOK THREE

CHAPTER I

One afternoon in the middle of July Emanuel and Hansine were walking along the road from Skibberup church where they had been to lay fresh wreaths on Laddie's grave. They were walking silently on different sides of the steep road—Emanuel in his long light gray coat, Hansine in a church hood and a black shawl, which she held together in front with her brown, somewhat bony hands. There was a burning sun and not a cloud in the sky; a thick layer of white dust was raised by their footsteps like clouds of flour.

When they reached the top of the hill Emanuel stopped under a solitary mountain ash which threw a slight shade over the road. He remained standing for a long time with his hat and stick resting on his back, without stirring; buried in contemplation of the fruitful landscape. On all sides he saw ripe or ripening fields. The whole district was changed to an endless sea of corn, which rocked the sunshine on its yellow waves.

"Isn't it a beautiful sight?" he said at last in a subdued voice. "It seems as though one could feel the richness of the soil in the air! . . . and listen to the larks over Niels Jensen's rye there! . . . Isn't it curious I always feel in a solemn mood when I see the harvest approaching. It is so strange to see the fruit of a whole long year of labor and struggle ripening, so to speak, all at once before our eyes. And it is stranger still to think of the wonderful and indomitable power of nature which is here revealed to us. Whether the winter has been bitter or mild, . . . the summer wet or dry . . . year by year the corn ripens at the same time, nay, even on the same date. And each kind of grain has its own ripening day! Isn't it almost a miracle?" . . . He was silent a moment and then continued: "There is really a deep lesson contained in it for us!" And after another silence he went on—

"I think I will take this subject for my sermon on Sunday. Much can be said on it—and perhaps especially at this time —which will be good for all of us."

He continued his walk, stopping now and then before the different fields with bursts of admiration. He put on his white straw hat again, and turned the wide brim down to shade his eyes, which had been rather weak lately. His somewhat tired look showed that he had not got over the heavy trials of the last few months.

Hansine followed him patiently on the other side of the road, notwithstanding his frequent stoppages; she listened to him attentively, with an inquiring expression when he spoke. She was silent herself . . . until Emanuel suddenly fell into rather melancholy reflections on comparing his own meager crops with the fruitfulness he saw around him.

"Oh, but it's not so bad as all that," she said in a cheering tone, which sounded quite strange in her mouth; nor did it produce quite a natural effect. "The rye is pretty good; it's only the six rayed which is a little stunted."

"But look at the clover! We only had five loads this year, against twelve last, and fourteen the year before. It's a sad falling off."

"But then you've had so many other things in hand these years, Emanuel . . . politics, and that sort of thing. I suppose that will be changed now, and you'll see, when you have more time to look after the land you'll get as good crops as any one. It seems to me we're settling down here now, . . . and no harm either. I daresay you think so too, Emanuel!"

As so often happened, he did not hear the end of what she said, and continued his own train of thought.

"I must try a different succession of crops next year. Do you remember a new system of manuring I spoke to you about once. I wonder if I should try it seriously. . . . We can't go on as we have been," he said with sudden impatience. "We must pull ourselves together. I have been very lazy myself lately; but I feel that's over. I'm longing to begin afresh." They had been walking for some time between two walls of rye above a man's height, over which yellow and many-colored butterflies were gamboling in the sunshine like flying pansies. Then the view again opened out over the dale northwards, where Skibberup, with its many little white-washed houses and orchards, and its new, imposing Meeting-house, was reflected on the bosom of the widely-stretching pond.

At the foot of the hill, where the road branched, one way leading to the village and the other to the western boundaries, Emanuel stopped again.

"By-the-bye . . . didn't you say you were going to see your parents?"

"Yes, aren't you coming? I think they're expecting us."

"No, I haven't time today. I have so much to think about. I want to make my sermon as powerful as possible, so that it may be rightly understood, . . . and I'm still quite unprepared. But remember me to them, and say that I'll look in on them in the course of the week.——I say!" he shouted after her when she had gone a little way, "if you can remember it tell your father that I've not forgotten the rye seed I had of him in the spring. He shall have it back as soon as I get the first load in."

CHAPTER II

Hansine continued her walk towards Skibberup without turning at his words.

To avoid going through the village she took a grass path which ran behind the meadows and thickly-planted gardens. She knew of old that at this hour all the women of the place would be sitting in their doorways with their infants or their knitting, gossiping to each other across the street—and she had an ever-growing distaste to meeting her former companions.

She only found her father at home.

The old man was sitting in the half dark room in an arm-chair by the bed half-asleep; he was in his shirt-sleeves and knitted drawers, and had a fur cap pressed down on his rough mane, and he was surrounded by a swarm of flies, which flew buzzing about the room at her entrance.

"Is that you, Hansine?" he said, raising his white eyebrows over the blind eyes. "What? Are you alone? Where's Emanuel?"

"He hadn't time today. I was to remember him to you. He'll look in in the course of the week, he said."

"Oh, it's that way. Well, well, mother'll be comin' directly. She's just slipped in to Sören's to fetch the paper. I believe there's a speech of Barré's in it. Has Emanuel said ought about it?"

"No, I don't think he's seen the paper today."

"He gives it them hot does Barré—by what I've heard tell. But that's as it should be. It's not too much for them—the scoundrels. For what else are they? Thieves and rascals! But what was it I said . . . do you mind, Hansine? . . . Are we to have the wooden horse again, said I? Are we peasants to be beasts of burden for the nobles?"

He got up with some difficulty and

trudged about with his stick in a great pair of slippers. His little, bent, and shrunken figure trembled with anger, and he stammered over the words he couldn't get out of his toothless mouth. With one hand on his back he moved up and down at the darkest end of the room, talking incessantly, repeating long portions of speeches by different members which he had learned by heart and kept in his retentive memory. Hansine took off her things and sat by the window.

The sight of her father had lately made her more and more uncomfortable; she thought him quite changed since he had been unable to go about the farm on account of his blindness, and especially since he had come out as a speaker at the great "Protest" meeting.

Without listening to him, she sat looking out of the window into the shady little garden, where the egg-shaped spots of sunshine crawled over the grass and the paths, and where the hens scratched about under the gooseberry bushes—just as they used to do when she sat at the same window in her girlhood mapping out her future in golden dreams. She sat now thinking of that time, and of the first year of her marriage, when Emanuel and she lived alone, with and for each other, and life was every day a revelation of rich and unknown happiness. She lived over again in memory the peaceful evenings of the first winter when they sat together round the lamp while Emanuel read his books aloud, or told her about his childhood. She thought of the quiet sunset hours of the first summer on the Parsonage hill, of the Sunday visits to her parents, of all this life—so like a fairy tale now—which she had never given up hoping might yet return. Sometimes, especially since Laddie's death, she had also fancied she saw in Emanuel a longing for the peace and happiness of the old days. But she saw every day now more plainly that his thoughts went their own way. She did not know whither they were leading; but in the sense of her powerlessness with regard to the impatient depression which grew upon him, she had no rest for the thought that he was hiding something from her . . . brooding over an incipient want, which he had not the courage to confess to her, a dawning longing for the life and the people whom, mainly for her sake, he had left.

The kitchen door was opened, and Else put her big head in.

"Oh, is it you, Hansine? Well, we'd been expecting you. . . . But where's Emanuel?"

"He hadn't time today. He will come in one day this week. He asked to be remembered."

Else's face quickly took a severe expression, and disappeared from the doorway. After a few minutes she said from the kitchen, where she was rummaging about with the dishes:

"It's strange how busy Emanuel's got lately. He ne'er seems to hae time to come an' see us old folks. It looks queer, I'm thinkin'."

Hansine did not answer. She knew there had been a little misunderstanding latterly between Emanuel and her mother, because Emanuel did not like her taking Laddie's death as a matter of course, in the same way as she had always insisted on the harmlessness of his illness. Certainly he himself looked upon what had happened as an inevitable stroke of the unfathomable will of God; but at the same time he thought that she ought to have been surprised, as it was she who specially supported him in his hopeful view of the boy's state.

"But the paper, mother . . . the paper!" called out Anders Jörgen, who had groped his way back to the armchair, and was waiting for the coming treat.

"Ay, I'm coming, daddy. I've on'y got

to set up the milk for the calves. . . . Hae ye heard anything of Ole?"

"No, deed hae I not. I expect he's gone to the mill. Hae ye remembered to feed the pigs?"

"Ay, sure enough," said Else, coming to the door tying her apron round her extensive waist.

"Now, let's hear!" exclaimed the old man gaily, when he heard the paper rustling under Else's arm. "He gives it them hot, I warrant. Ay, Barré's a good un'! He says like me—do you mind?—Is it the wooden horse?—"

"That's well enough, daddy, but be quiet now," Else interrupted him, sinking heavily into a chair by the stove, with her usual exclamation, "Aa Herre Zósses ja."

With the show of dignity which had come over her since Hansine had been a clergyman's wife, which was again increased when Anders Jörgen had come forward as a speaker, and had had his name in the papers, she carefully spread out the paper on her lap, put Anders Jörgen's old brass spectacles on her nose, and in a drawling voice began to read an article of six columns, "Our Leader's speech at Vemmelöv."

CHAPTER III

Emanuel had left the high road and taken a solitary field path, so as to be undisturbed in working out his sermon for Sunday. He had lately often gone to church somewhat unprepared, and had himself suffered from the want of power and inspiration in his discourses.

He did not succeed today either in concentrating himself on his work. His thoughts wandered constantly, without his being aware of it. Every moment he caught himself deep in contemplation quite remote from the Sunday's gospel. First it was some trifling thing, such as a gay butterfly, which enticed him to stop and follow its airy flutterings, or revel in its color . . . now against the blue sky . . . now against the golden corn. Then the self-conscious way in which the red roof of the new Meeting-house stuck up among the trees caught his eye, and plunged him into his usual brooding over the curious, almost indifferent calmness with which his friends, and those of his party all over the country, were submitting to their political humiliation, and looking on at their most sacred laws being trampled under foot.

He could not understand them on this point. Although he had been bowed to the ground by the loss of his dear boy just at the time of the *coup d'état,* he had immediately felt it to be his duty to urge them by every Christian and legal means in their power to oppose the law-breakers. But then the "Select Committee" had come to him one day and begged him not to get up an agitation. They had—so they said—"by written communications with other circles," come to the conclusion that for the present it would be right to bend to those in power, as they had no means of raising active resistance. Even Nielsen the carpenter, from whom he had rather expected a too unbridled outburst of wounded pride, consented—although with gloomy looks—to the injunctions of the others, and explained that, as matters now stood, it would be better to let their opponents have a little more rope.

He also had a visit from Hansen the weaver, late one evening, in which, with his usual mysterious manner and much beating about the bush, he announced a "change of tactics." On the same occasion he dropped some hints about the Chairman of the Parish Council having hardly shown himself worthy of his position. And, finally, brought out some enigmatical allusions as to his private life, which he said would not bear looking into, and was unfortunate for a man who was the political leader of a large circle of the spiritually awakened—allusions which Emanuel did not understand, nor did he care to enter into them more closely. He made up his mind to have nothing more to do with the politics of the people, in which he had never been particularly interested, and of the worthlessness of which he now had abundant proof. The cause to whose furtherance he had consecrated his life would grow and ripen independently of all law-giving and law-breaking—just like the seed of the earth, which offered to mankind its swelling grains, in spite of the winter's cold or the drought of summer.

One thing these months had taught him. He knew now there was still much dormant power to be roused in the people, much self-confidence and self-esteem before there could be serious hope of the dawn of the new times he had thought so near. Possibly he might one day see it. But he would not be disheartened nor weary. There was joy even in the conviction that he was preparing the way for the victorious march of truth and justice on earth. There was joy and recompense in the announcement even of the coming of the kingdom of peace.

He had reached the broad bay which shot in between the bare hills of Skibberup and the flat, idyllic wooded hills of the neighboring parish of Kyndlöse. He remained standing on the sand, which glittered in the sun, lost in indefinite dreams of the future. His eye followed his old friends the silvery gulls, as they wheeled silently round some point in the air as if they were guarding some important secret. He gazed out over the wide shining surface of the water towards the distant blue mountainous clouds, which now and then rose above the horizon, and then slowly sank again. It was like an aerial kingdom of beauty rising enticingly from the deep and again fading away. Like magic forms beckoning and disappearing, . . . or, as in a dream, hearing distant voices call and softly die away. "Why sorrow?" they seemed to say. "Why weary oneself with the burdens of others? Cast away your heavy pilgrim's staff and come out here, where happiness dwells high above the clouds, and where sorrow hides itself in dark valleys where none may see it. Come out here where life is a festive rest round sparkling wells, and dancing in green meadows." . . . He woke from his dreams with a start, and left the beach. The day was beginning to decline, and it was time to go home.

He quickened his pace, and hurried to the high road. He would try to reach the Parsonage before sunset, so as to help Sören with feeding the cattle.

CHAPTER IV

He had not gone far when he was surprised by the sight of a lively party of five or six persons of both sexes seated round a cloth spread in a meadow a little way off the road.

A lady, or rather a very young girl in a white dress and blue waistband, had just got up and was making a speech. She held a wine-glass in her uplifted hand, and in the other a man's gray hat, which she lifted on and off her head with a solemn bow, amid the laughter and applause of the rest of the company—two ladies and a couple of men. On the grass behind the ladies was an upturned red silk parasol, and by the side of it a spiral walking-stick was stuck into the ground with a lady's pale blue hat on it. At a little distance, a smart shooting carriage and two little roan Russian ponies were standing under the shade of a pollard willow, guarded by a coachman in plush breeches and drab gaiters.

A sort of shyness came over Emanuel on suddenly coming upon these town-dressed people in his own domains. He turned his head away, and appeared not to notice them.

"Allow me, therefore, most noble friends,"—he heard the young girl say—"to empty . . . to drink a health to our beloved and amiable host."

She stopped suddenly; the laughter also ceased, and a dead silence fell upon them.

Emanuel, who perceived that he was seen, crossed his hands behind his back and went by without either slackening or quickening his pace in the slightest degree.

All at once he seemed to hear some one call out his name.

He did not look back. He was certain he had made a mistake. He had nothing to do with those people.

But shortly afterwards he heard the voice again, and this time quite plainly. At the same time it sounded curiously familiar.

"Mr. Hansted! . . . Pastor Hansted!"

He turned sharply, half defiantly, and saw a man coming towards him, waving his hand gaily. He had the sun in his eyes, and could not at once see who it was. A tall, somewhat stout man with whiskers, measured gait and stately carriage. It was not till the stranger was quite close to him and offering his hand with slightly embarrassed cordiality that he recognized Dr. Hassing.

"How do you do, Pastor Hansted? How are you? It's a long time since I have had the pleasure of seeing you."

Emanuel was at first so astonished at the meeting, and particularly by the doctor's extraordinary cordiality, that he quite forgot to answer.

"I come to you as a messenger," said Hassing, showing his large white teeth when he smiled. "We have a little family party there, and the ladies would like to have the pleasure of speaking to you. . . . Will you not do us the honor of drinking a glass of wine with us? You will find an old acquaintance."

Emanuel's inclination was to give a short refusal. He was not at all tempted by the prospect of meeting an old friend in this company. But as he had no reasonable excuse to offer, and did not wish to hurt the Doctor who had shown so much attention to Hansine and himself during Laddie's illness, there was nothing for it but to accept the invitation.

The meeting of the two men was carefully watched by the party round the cloth, and when they saw them both approaching, the ladies took up their parasols, while the remaining man—a youth in a melon colored summer suit—rose, and pulling down his long cuffs retired behind the young lady, leaning on his spiral stick as if in readiness to come to the rescue if required.

"If you make me laugh, Alfred, I shall beat you," she whispered to him when the doctor and Emanuel were within a few steps.

"Yes, but good heavens! . . . he's a regular antediluvian animal," he whispered behind the hand, with which he was twirling his small fair moustache.

"Just look . . . a Voice from a theological College!"

"Be quiet, I say."

"Hush!"

At this moment the two men reached the circle. One of the ladies—a little brunette, dressed in brown silk, with soft outlines, and sweet, gentle, womanly features—came forward and shook hands with Emanuel.

"My wife," said the doctor.

"I am very glad to make your acquaintance," she said, in such a gentle voice that it was almost like a strange accent. "We have been neighbors for some years now, and I have always been astonished that we have never met. One generally comes across people in the country I think."

Emanuel lifted his hat an inch from his head without a change in the grave, somewhat amazed expression, beneath which he sought to hide a feeling of uncertainty into which he was thrown by the unaccustomed ceremoniousness and the polite phrases.

Dr. Hassing continued his introductions in a lively voice.

"Allow me to introduce you, Pastor Hansted,—first to the youngest member of our little party, my wife's amiable cousin, Miss Gerda Zoff, whom you interrupted a few minutes ago in a remarkably successful speech. It is a pity you did not come a few minutes sooner, you missed a masterpiece of oratory.—And this same cousin's cousin, my own hopeful nephew, Mr. Alfred Hassing. If you subscribe to any sporting paper you must certainly often have met his world renowned name in the cycling columns."

Emanuel looked at the young pair somewhat disdainfully, their greetings certainly betrayed more curiosity than deference. "Good heavens," he thought, when he saw the baggy melon colored clothes, the pointed shoes, and monster studs—"so these are fashions for the Heroes of the day!"

"And here at last," continued the doctor, as he turned towards a tall, slim, very fashionably dressed lady, who had kept behind Emanuel during the other introductions, as if purposely keeping out of sight till the last.—"Well, here you need no introduction."

Emanuel faced her, and was turned to stone. The doctor was right, any introduction was here superfluous. As the slender lady stood there smiling in the red light thrown by her parasol—dressed in white with large mauve stars, a wide brimmed white lace hat perched upon her chestnut hair—dignified, and mistress of herself from the firm glance of her beautiful blue-gray eyes, to the frill at the border of her gown, which was so subdued, and at the same time so daring in its cut and the arrangement of its coloring, as to enhance the slimness of her figure, and the creamy pallor of her complexion . . . she was so exactly like herself in the former days, that Emanuel at once recognized Miss Ragnhild Tönnesen.

"Of course you can't imagine how I have suddenly appeared here," she said, giving him her slender, smoothly gloved hand, with her old air of comradeship. "You might almost be ready to look upon me as a spy, otherwise. . . . I must tell you at once how it comes about. I had the pleasure of making Dr. and Mrs. Hassing's acquaintance in the spring, and as they were kind enough to invite me here, I could not resist the temptation. I have only been here two days. I can assure you there has not been the least indiscretion on my part so far. . . . Are you satisfied now?"

Her easy, joking tone, and the perfect conviction of making an impression on him which was apparent in her whole bearing, at once offended Emanuel, and strengthened him in that feeling of self-esteem which the young people's inspection had called forth.

He kept his astonishment under, and answered with fairly successful dissimulation:

"I do not understand how I could suspect you of any kind of espionage, Miss Tönnesen. It is so natural that you should wish to revisit your former home, that it hardly seems to require any explanation."

His speech was harder and colder than he had either meant or calculated; and when he noticed the constraint which it produced on the whole company, he was preparing to add a few softer words.

But he just happened to see the young cyclist nudge his cousin, and whisper a remark to her which made her convulsively bite her pocket-handkerchief.

The blood rushed to his cheeks. Irrepressible anger such as he had not felt since his youth burst out within him, making his heart beat fast.

"Shan't we sit down again?" said the doctor, in his untiring efforts to bring about a more easy tone. "You will drink a glass of wine with us, Mr. Hansted? . . . Oh, Johan!" he called to the coachman; "bring another glass and——"

"Thank you, I do not drink wine," interrupted Emanuel curtly.

"Indeed!"

This was followed by a moment's painful silence, and no one knew where to look. The doctor stood with a blank countenance, pulling his whiskers, while he furtively looked at Miss Tönnesen with a comically puzzled glance, as much as to say, "We have made fools of ourselves. But what did I say?"

Emanuel stood motionless, looking straight before him, without noticing the perplexity of the others. His anger had quickly turned against himself. What business had he here? he thought. What did he want among these people with whom he had not a single thought or feeling in common, nay, whose very language had become so strange to him that it almost sounded like a foreign tongue.

It was Miss Ragnhild with her old readiness who got them out of their difficulty.

Stepping forward she said: "I think Pastor Hansted spoke a word in season, . . . we have all had enough wine. I propose that we make use of this lovely evening to take a little walk. We can send the carriage on, and persuade Pastor Hansted to walk part of the way back with us. You will come, won't you? Our roads are the same, at first in any case—if I am not mistaken."

The proposal was instantly accepted by the Hassings; the doctor again sent Miss Ragnhild a furtive glance—this time a grateful one.

Miss Tönnesen's words also came as a relief to Emanuel. He saw that in this way he could most quickly and easily get away from the party. If he accompanied them to the place where the Kyndlöse road crossed his boundaries the demands of politeness would be satisfied, and he could still get home early enough to feed the cattle and partake of the evening porridge.

The coachman was called up and had his orders, and then they started.

The cyclist immediately drew his aunt's arm within his, and strode off with her in front of the others, so as to ease his mind.

"Who on earth is this sheep? . . . Is it he you called 'an original and interesting man'? Why, he's a complete idiot!"

"You always use such strong expressions, my dear Alfred," answered Mrs. Hassing, gently reproaching him. "He is perhaps not very talented, and may be rather peculiar . . . I don't know anything about that. But in any case, I must acknowledge the way he has sacrificed himself to his opinions. . . . You must admit that, Alfred."

"I believe, upon my honor, that you already have a *tendresse* for him, Aunt. Isn't it so? You might even invite him to supper."

"We shall be obliged to ask him if he goes far with us. But it is not to say that he will accept the invitation. I shan't object to his coming. There are many subjects on which I should like Pastor Hansted's opinion."

"Ah, you are thoroughly bitten then! Yes, Aunt, you have a soft and indulgent heart! But you quite forget Uncle Joachim!"

"Uncle Joachim!" and her face became somewhat doubtful. "You are right—I really didn't think of him."

CHAPTER V

It was not long before Miss Ragnhild and Emanuel found themselves walking alone a good way behind the others. The doctor, who at first walked with them, talking to Emanuel about the harvest and the fine weather, had been called away by the lively young girl to admire her discoveries of flowers.

As long as the doctor was near, Miss Ragnhild was silent and looked pensively at the ground. Even after he had gone she remained silent a while, a smile now and then flitting over her face.

Suddenly she lifted her head, and said with a little laugh:

"You certainly are a curious person, Mr. Hansted! For seven years I have been looking forward to the day when I should take you by surprise out here, and then you receive me as if we had only parted three days ago. I may tell you that you put me in an awkward position just now; I had of course prepared the others for a grand scene of recognition! . . . Well, I admit it was my own stupidity," she continued, as Emanuel remained silent. "I ought to have remembered that in many ways you were unlike other people. And with regard to unreliability, you have not changed in the least."

Emanuel did not notice the little effort she had to make, to speak in the same easy tone which they formerly used to each other. He was too much taken up with the awkwardness he was feeling at walking alone with her here after all these years, and listening again to the defiant, and yet ingratiating voice with its peculiar metallic ring. Without allowing himself to be affected in the slightest degree by her words, he said:

"It seems that we have had somewhat the same impression of each other, Miss Tönnesen. Both before, when I first saw you, and now on hearing you speak, I see that you are exactly the same as you were seven or eight years ago."

"I daresay," she answered with a shrug of the shoulders: "What, after all, should have changed me? I am Miss Tönnesen now, as I was then; and the intervening romance of my life might be written on the back of a visiting card. Such is life to us, unmarried women. . . . But with you it is another matter. I am not such a stranger to your experiences as you might think. A year ago I had the pleasure of making the acquaintance of your sister, General-consulinde Torm, and your brother, the Kammerjunker. Your sister and I have since then become good friends. She is charming, is she not? I am quite in love with her refined womanly nature. As you may imagine, we have talked of you from time to time. . . . She often regrets that she so seldom hears from you."

Emanuel became attentive. It suddenly occurred to him, that perhaps—in spite of her ridicule—the young lady might have come as a spy. And—was it possible that his family had a finger in it?

"So before I came here, I knew what a big—an influential man you had become; what a revolution you have brought about in the district since father left, and how all your parishioners worship you . . . in short, that you and they have in every respect realized your wishes, nay, even with good 'measure running over,' as one says. They have even given you the name of 'Apostle,' I have been told."

A little start went through Emanuel. After a moment's silence, he said:

"But I thought you had your wishes satisfied too, Miss Ragnhild. You were so pleased to get away from this neighborhood which you hated, to go to town, to the center of Danish culture, to society, fashion and the theaters; you have our world-famed Tivoli next door, so I don't understand——"

"Well, yes," she interrupted him, with

a little impatient toss of the head. "As I said, it is a different matter for me. Besides, I have not complained, so I do not know to what you are alluding. As things go, I have a very good time. I can tell you that I have become a philosopher in my old age. . . . A stoic, I think it is called. That is to say, I have gradually accustomed myself to be that rock of offense which I and my kind have once for all become to our dear contemporaries . . . yes, I almost feel a little proud of belonging to those who foretell the imminent downfall of the great Babylon."

Emanuel wanted to say something. But his thoughts had lost the habit of moving nimbly, and before he had put a sentence together, Miss Ragnhild spoke again.

"Don't let us discuss me. It is a frightfully uninteresting subject, I assure you. But tell me something about yourself. I hardly knew you just now, you have altered so much. You are as brown as an Indian. And that great beard, like a wild man of the woods! . . . So it's really true that for eight long years you have been happy in this desert, where I was ready to pine away with—well, with many things. So different can human nature be! And you have never felt the least craving for any of the now much abused goods of civilization . . . such as sociability, . . . art, or good music? Not even my little Lark Étude of Schubert's? you used to be very fond of it at one time, I remember, and I have often played it to you!"

She looked at him over the ivory handle of her parasol while speaking, and again in glance and smile showed all her charm.

Emanuel preserved his gravity immovably, and answered in his former measured tone:

"I don't see how I can miss the very thing which I am in possession of; if you will take the trouble to open your ears, Miss Tönnesen, you will hear the larks singing over your head at this very moment—far more beautifully than any virtuoso in the world can imitate them in any Étude; I have a perfect orchestra all the summer, playing outside my windows. Starlings in the treetops, blackbirds in the bushes, the little tits——"

"Yes, and the crows! Pray don't forget them!—and the cocks! Good heavens, the cocks!" she exclaimed, putting her fingers to her ears in comical despair. "Just now there is such a wretch that comes every morning while I am in my sweetest sleep and stands outside my widow, shrieking, and screaming, and crowing. . . . Oh, it's like lying on a red-hot gridiron!"

This time Emanuel could not prevent his risible muscles relaxing a little.

He stopped a moment, and said, shaking his head, and looking at her for the first time:

"Truly! you have not changed, Miss Tönnesen. You have kept up your hatred for our splendid heralds of day."

"Yes, I admit, in these ways, I am as great a heretic as ever. As far as I am concerned, you are welcome to keep the singing birds, the green woods, and the so-called fresh sea-breeze with its disgusting smell of sea-weed—the flower-strewn fields—and whatever you like, if only I am allowed to remain within four walls, where I can gather round me cosily, all the things which suit my taste and my temperament. . . . You think I am past hope, now, don't you?"

Emanuel was about to answer, but again she was first.

"I could annoy you still more if I would. And why shouldn't I? . . . In my opinion, a great deal of all this about the beauties of nature, which artists have got us to believe in, is frightful hypocrisy on the part of most people. For my part, I never go beyond the streets of Copenhagen and see the bare fields, the sameness of the roads, and the absurd extent of desolate sky, without thinking of the cold mangling-room where I used to have my bath as a child. However much the sun shines, however green the fields, it all seems so barren, so desolate, and so sad that it makes me shiver. I quite admit that towns may be horrid too, dusty and dirty and smoke-blackened. But there you are not an absolute slave to sun or moon. There you have some idea of what a human being is . . . and the meaning of being lord and master of creation, which, after all, it is one's intention of becoming some day—at any rate that is my ideal of freedom!"

She worked herself up at last into such genuine passion that it, as well as her words, produced a most unpleasant impression upon Emanuel. By her words she had roused anew the memory of moments of weakness in his own life, when the sight of his corn laid by the hail, flooded fields, or trees overturned by a storm had led him into a similar misjudgment of the stern order of nature. He thought especially of that dark night in Laddie's illness when he stood listening and watching for the doctor on the mound in his garden. In his despair and perplexity much the same thoughts had surged through his own brain, and he therefore now felt it a double duty to meet her now with the full strength of his conviction.

They had reached the top of a hill whence there was one of those extended views in which the district was so rich. They had long passed the parish boundaries, and from the place where they stood they could see the whole of Veilby and the semi-island parish of Skibberup with its softly rounded but bare hills, its two church towers and three wind-mills, and the swampy bog land which connected it with the outer world. On the other side in the west, was to be seen the flatter but more varied and smiling landscape of Kyndlöse, Vesterby, with one or two small woods, a brimming stream among green meadows, and a number of little, scattered, white cottages, besides the large village of Kyndlöse with its fiery red mission house, and a curious round church, the gilt weathercock of which glittered in the setting sun like a newly lighted star. Far away to the north and north-west, finally appeared, like a bank of dark clouds, a hazy belt of forest behind which the sun had just gone down, lighting up the horizon with flaming colors.

"And you have the courage to speak like that here!" said Emanuel, as with a wide sweep of the hand he pointed to the landscape in its gorgeous sunset coloring. The mists of evening had already begun to rise over the water meadows, and to spread themselves like gigantic spiders' webs over the blood-red, many branched stream. "You really can't find anything to satisfy you in such a scene as this. It can't rouse any thoughts or feelings in you other than an uncomfortable recollection of your childhood?"

Miss Ragnhild looked at the landscape for a moment with twitching eyes. Then she said with a bright little smile, which she generally put on when she was about to say something specially audacious:

"I certainly can't understand why that should be so wondrously beautiful that one should be forced, from the cradle to the grave, to fall into a state of delight every time one sees it. It doesn't appeal to me in the least. The combination of colors even offends my eye. This blue sky, that shrieking red horizon, all this orange-colored corn, and the meadows down there like spinach . . . blue, red, green, and yellow! Those are just the colors which are used for the so-called Hottentot pocket-handkerchiefs. . . . You know, those flaring stuffs which the English send out to the wilds of Africa and which put our black fellow creatures into such a blessed state of mind. Don't you think, Pastor Hansted—it is my real opinion—that a phenomenon of nature like this sunset has no other meaning than that of being a higher form of diversion for semi-human beings, both black and white, and perhaps also for the animals? Such a fiery heaven, I have no doubt, answers to that sort of creature's ideas of splendor; it probably also rouses their softer feelings. . . . The nightingales begin to sing and the frogs to croak. . . ."

"I have no doubt you are right, Miss Tönnesen," Emanuel interrupted her with an ironical bow, and continued his walk; he saw it was no use trying to take her seriously. "It's only a pity that the Almighty did not have an opportunity of consulting you, when He created this bungle of a world which is only suitable for Kabyles and Hottentots. But it just occurs to me—when I met you just now, you had condescended to sit down in quite a common grass field—nay, as far as I remember, both you and the others were in quite lively spirits. It appears therefore that a sojourn in the midst of nature can all the same have an enlivening effect on you."

"Well, what can I say? There will always remain so much of the animal in us, I suppose, that at times we may wish for a meadow to sun ourselves in, or a wood to run about in. But what does that show? I also know that lovers delight in wandering about by moonlight. Now I, who am not in love, think a moonlight night one of the most disagreeable things I know; it always reminds me of a death chamber."

She stopped suddenly, burst into a little laugh, and said, "It is really too stupid. Here we are carrying on the same sort of nonsensical dispute as we used to eight or nine years ago . . . and with exactly the same result. Do you remember how we used to talk ourselves red in the face, and then turn our backs on each other in anger, and wouldn't look at each other for days. Shall we make peace now? Now we've each got what we wanted—you your country, I my town—so we have nothing more to quarrel about."

"Exactly my opinion," said Emanuel dryly.

"Then, at last, we are agreed on one point! But I have talked too much. . . . You know it's a way old maids have. Now, it's your turn to be entertaining, Pastor Hansted. Now tell me kindly about yourself. I know—from your sister, and, for that matter, I have heard the same here—what a happy family life you lead, that you have a couple of sweet little children, and that your wife continues to be famed for her good looks . . . in short, that you are a regular child of fortune."

Emanuel did not intend to enter into any discussion with her on this subject. But the love of argument had been awakened in him, and he could not help saying:

"I can hear by your voice that you are surprised."

"As you say it yourself, I will not deny it."

"I can quite understand it. With your conception of family happiness, and your view that marriage is a kind of erotic game or amusement . . . views which I also at one time held, but of which I happily discovered the fallacy in time——"

"Excuse me, Pastor Hansted—but where did you acquire the habit of attributing a meaning to people which suits you, but which they have never expressed. You did it before, and again now. For what, in fact, do you know of my opinions on matrimony?"

"I should be very much interested in hearing them. They are no doubt highly original."

She went on for a minute smiling to herself.

"Would it really interest you? Well, then, I won't make myself precious. But I will begin by saying that you won't hear anything new. . . . You know that I am conservative in all my views, and perhaps on this point more so than on any other. My opinion as to what is requisite for matrimonial happiness is simply the same as that to which our grandparents gave the somewhat inflated expression in the words, 'The harmony of souls.' In our day I suppose we should call it something like 'nerve sympathy.' "

"Nerve sympathy! Truly a delightful modern expression! If only one knew what it meant. Can't you give a little explanation?"

"Oh, yes," she laughed. "But I told you I had become a philosopher, so if I should not be very clear, you must excuse me, it is because of the depth of my thoughts. Well, then——"

She stopped, rested her cheek on her ivory-handled parasol, and looked straight before her with a thoughtful smile.

"In this way, then," she said, and continued her walk. "By nerve sympathy between two persons, I mean that everything these two persons see, hear, experience, read, etc., has a similar effect upon them both. The sight of such a landscape, for example, or the enjoyment of a piece of music, must put them into the same frame of mind; it must not enliven one and depress the other.—Am I expressing myself plainly?—All the manifold affairs of life, from the most trifling —such as the breaking of a plate—up to the most fateful—sad or happy—must affect the feelings of both, must move their nerves with the same degree of emotion. To continue—the requirement for bringing about between two persons the state which used to be called 'The harmony of souls' is, therefore, that their nerves have the same kind of receptivity, and are just as easily moved by some impressions and just as little by others— Don't you admire my logic?—But the kind and the degree of the receptivity," she continued, as Emanuel did not speak, "is the result of our education, of our intercourse, of our occupations, reading, etc., . . . and not alone of our own, but of our parents, our grandparents, down to our most remote forefathers, is it not? You can now see——"

"Splendid!" Emanuel interrupted her, suddenly raising his head with a broad smile. "I understand now, that what is required for one person to be thoroughly happy with another, is that this other person must resemble him in every way. That is to say, must have the same education, the same friends; and to complete everything, the same father, mother, and ancestors—in other words, it must be himself! Yes, there you are right, Miss Tönnesen. Self-love—egoism—is without doubt, according to modern conservative views, the only lasting and trustworthy love. There I agree with you!"

Miss Ragnhild's brows contracted somewhat moodily, and she made no answer.

"Now, allow me to moralize a little," continued Emanuel, with increasing liveliness. "I daresay, even from your point of view, you will admit that the highest object of man—and at the same time his joy and happiness—consists in developing himself, and in feeling the growth of his powers and the widening of his views . . . in short, in making the most of his possibilities. Am I not right?"

"Well, yes!"

"But from whose friendship—not to use such a bygone inflated word as love —from whose intimacy may one expect to reap the richest harvest for the development of one's spiritual 'Ego,' and therefore expect the greatest joy and happiness? Would it be from that person who sees, feels, thinks, and acts exactly as one does oneself? Would it not rather be from the person who would open up new views one never before had dreamed of, who would give one new thoughts and feelings, who, from a different education, would be able to enrich one's knowledge, widen one's limitations on every side, and, as it were, make one's world twice as large? I believe so—nay, I know it. I speak from dearly bought experience."

"But you are turning the matter upside down," said Miss Ragnhild, who had not listened to what he was saying.

At this moment they were interrupted by the doctor and his wife, who had been standing on the road waiting for them to come up.

"Now, we really can't allow you to run away from us, Pastor Hansted," said the doctor with the vague smile, which showed his large white teeth. "It is only a few steps to our door, and you couldn't get home now in time for supper."

Emanuel looked about him in astonishment. Without being aware of it, he had come nearly the whole way to Kyndlöse; its gilded weathercock was shining just in front of him almost like a full moon.

"You must not refuse us," chimed in Mrs. Hassing, with all the cordiality she could put into her gentle voice. "If you think your wife will be anxious about you, we will send a messenger on horseback to her."

Emanuel hesitated a moment before accepting their invitation. He would much have preferred to decline. For seven years now he had shut himself up within his own circle of the "Friends" where he alone felt quite at home; and he did not wish to have any lasting acquaintance with the Hassing family. But on the other hand he was afraid they would look upon a refusal as the result of fright or shyness. He was sure Miss Ragnhild would look upon it in that light, and report it to his sister and the rest of the family. Besides which, he could not hide from himself that he was partly actuated by curiosity and a slight craving for diversion. He rather wanted to see Dr. Hassing's so much talked of house with all its artistic decorations. Moreover, the conversation with Miss Ragnhild was just beginning to interest him when it was interrupted, and he was not averse to have an opportunity of continuing the discussion.

CHAPTER VI

An hour later, Emanuel sat at a delicately setout supper table in Dr. Hassing's well-lighted dining-room.

He had not entirely got over the feeling of constraint and discomfort which had involuntarily come over him on entering this house with its distinguished style of decoration, which in so many ways reminded him of his father's home —on again stepping on carpeted floors, among carved furniture and large mirrors, which reflected the whole figure in every direction—on being surrounded by paintings and statues of nude men and women—and on again sinking among the cushions of a velvet arm-chair. At first he was so disturbed by the sight of all the luxury that he regretted having allowed himself to be persuaded. But he was specially upset on being received in the hall by a smart parlor-maid, with short puffed sleeves, and a stiffly starched frilled cap, who came forward at once with many curtseys and conventional smiles to take away his hat and stick. She next proceeded to brush his coat, constantly addressing him as "your Reverence." He had the strongest inclination all the time to take the brush from her and to say plainly:

"I say, my child, don't let us make fools of ourselves, I am in the habit of cleaning my own shoes—so surely I can brush the dust off my own breeches."

To one of his habits a similar spirit of opposition rose within him at the sight of the luxurious supper table, with its many tempting delicacies, its Venetian decanters, and costly china. He felt the responsibility he had taken upon himself in the eyes of the Cause and the Friends in accepting hospitality here in the enemies' camp. He answered all Mrs. Hassing's interesting questions about his parishioners politely and even fully, but he kept on his guard all the time, and never for a moment relaxed the serious, almost gloomy expression, which was his silent protest against all that he saw around him.

Dr. Hassing's dining-room was decorated in a somewhat peculiar style, half Pompeian, half modern. Slender, long necked vases and jars were placed on small console tables against the two long terra cotta colored walls, while the walls at the ends of the room were covered with dark green cloth, and on this was hung a costly collection of old faïence and Majolica dishes, and antique hand weapons. At the upper end of the table, Miss Ragnhild and the doctor were carrying on a lively dispute about modern music; the two young people at the lower end were mostly putting their heads together and talking in an undertone. Judging from their glances to each other, first tender and then reproachful, it seemed not unlikely that they were on the highroad to a closer relationship than that of cousins. Immediately opposite to Emanuel and Mrs. Hassing sat a silent little lady in black, and by her side an elderly man of most peculiar appearance. He was about seventy years of age, tall, and stoutly built with an absolutely bald head which was so shiny that all the lights in the room were reflected in it. His purple face was divided in the middle by a broad mouth, which every moment opened up a view of a large thick tongue which prevented him from talking plainly. His eyes were small, with a slight squint, and his nose was a perfect parrot's beak; the skin of his neck hung loosely from his chin, in a purple pouch, like that of a pelican. To complete this face he had a tiny white imperial, and two little half-moon shaped whiskers, which according to an old court fashion stretched from below the ear to the middle of the cheek. A stiff black satin stock was in keeping with these aristocratic whiskers, an oval diamond pin stuck in it, with a little chain and a brooch fastened into the middle of his shirt front, and a large variegated silk handkerchief, with which he constantly, though without apparent reason, wiped the back of his neck. He was otherwise dressed in a plain grey coat, and neither his linen nor his hands betrayed any strong sense of cleanliness.

This man was the "Uncle Joachim" so anxiously spoken of by Mrs. Hassing and her nephew, a former landed proprietor with the title of Jægermester, who had recently, owing to a too gentlemanly weakness for blood-horses, expensive carriages, many servants, fine wines, illicit affairs of the heart, been obliged to sell his property, and now lived chiefly on the bounty of his family. Together with his sister—the little lady in black—he was for the present "on a visit" to the Hassings, which had already extended over several months.

In accordance with his other qualities, Uncle Joachim had always prided himself on belonging to "the few" who still swore allegiance to the most extreme reactionary views on every subject. He always called himself—at the same time striking his broad chest—"a representative of the ideas previous to the year of misfortune, '48"; and his feelings were not softened towards the ever-encroaching democracy by finding that it was a rich peasant who bought his property at the sale. Dr. Hassing's home, which otherwise was hushed to all politics, had latterly resounded from morning till night with ragings against the peasants, the parliament, the high schools, and even the government. Although he was loyal to the King and government, he considered that they paid too much attention to the "agitators"; his plan would have been to transport them all in warships to Christiansö, there to break stones till they had amended their ways. He held that nothing short of this would be of the slightest avail.

This being so, there was really some cause for anxiety in the meeting of this man with Emanuel, and it was not long before their expectations were realized. As soon as the Jægermester heard Emanuel's name, his whole head became purple, and without shaking hands or answering the somewhat cool greetings of the latter he rushed into the dining-room where Mrs. Hassing was superintending the arrangements.

"What is the meaning of this?" he shouted with his indistinct speech, the loudness of which he never could estimate on account of his deafness. "Isn't this that mad rhapsodist and agitator from Veilby? Do you visit people of that sort? You ask me to meet a fellow like that? What is the meaning of it, Ludovica?"

"Now Uncle!" answered Mrs. Hassing with decision quite foreign to her, and which therefore made a deep impression upon Uncle Joachim, "you know that neither Hassing nor I meddle with politics. But Pastor Hansted is an exceedingly cultivated and interesting man, from whose conversation one may gather both pleasure and information, without being bound to admire his views. I therefore beg, Uncle, that you will not in any way offend him, but bear in mind that tonight he is our guest."

The effect of this warning was apparent at the beginning of the meal, when he sat as stiff as a post, refusing all the dishes with a haughty and offended air. But when he saw that his silent protests were quite unnoticed—or perhaps in the long run they demanded too much self-denial—he suddenly changed his tactics, and helped himself greedily to every dish, clattered his knife and fork, and interrupted the others every moment with loud requests for bread, butter, "a little more *foie gras,* Ludovica," to show thereby that he cared nothing for the rhapsodist.

The conversation after a time became quite lively; Emanuel's slow, thoughtful remarks were oftener heard among the lighter conversation of the others.

His conversation with Mrs. Hassing had little by little drifted into the burning question of the day—the higher education of the people, especially of the peasant class. Emanuel freely expressed his views, and intentionally brought forward the importance he attached to the High Schools in this direction. Mrs. Hassing was all attention. She belonged to that impressionable class who are at once roused to enthusiasm when they see others enthusiastic. When others spoke an expression of deep thoughtfulness always came into her regular, pretty, but not specially intelligent face, with its softly rounded cheeks and Madonna smile—as if by their words they were making plain to her something on which she had long been pondering in vain. She sat like this now—one elbow resting lightly on the edge of the table, her cheek on her hand—and when now and then in her singing voice she raised "objections," it was in reality less to oppose him than to give him a further opportunity of explaining his views.

But the others began to listen too. Emanuel's unshaken earnestness and strong self-confidence, combined with his rough clothes and big beard to give an impression of manliness and power . . . nay, even his somewhat didactic manner of speaking, which he had acquired by constantly appearing as a teacher to the peasants, made him more and more interesting in their eyes. Besides, the subjects of his conversation were so new to them, his expressions were so fresh and surprising, that he involuntarily compelled their respect.

Even the young people stopped their whispering to listen to him, and the cyclist glanced at his aunt once or twice as much as to say:

"You were right, Aunt! . . . There's stuff in the man!"

Miss Ragnhild, on the other hand, was visibly out of spirits. She leaned against the back of her chair, nervously crumbling her bread with her long tapered finger as more and more attention was directed towards Emanuel.

Emanuel was himself somewhat excited by the attention his conversation roused. Besides—forgetting his previous refusal out of doors—he had drunk two or three glasses of wine in the course of the meal. His tone became easier, and after a time he put his sentences together with a clearness and emphasis which surprised himself.

But at the same time, a spirit of opposition rose in him, a feeling that it was his duty to tell these people the truth, which had been smoldering within him ever since he came. Why not point bravely to the burning spot? he asked himself. Had he the right to sit here in the midst of all this frivolity and refinement, without raising his voice against it? Was it not his duty to do what he could to wake these people from the security of their self-complacency, from their haughty ignorance of all which made the hearts of the people beat with joy and expectation?

A little uneasiness now arose round the table. Passing suddenly from his tolerably defiant praise of the High Schools and the spirit which had spread from them among the country people, he entered upon the great strife of the moment, between the government and the people.

They all looked nervously at Uncle Joachim. His head had again become purple and swollen like a balloon filling; and no sooner did Emanuel pause, than he leaned over the table towards him.

"Excuse me, sir!" he burst out in his thick, lisping voice, putting his hand behind his ear—in the manner of deaf people—a highly unaristocratic fist, with tufts of long hair on every joint,—"I hear that you are an ardent admirer of this so-called Emancipation of the People and this . . . this, universal suffrage."

"Undoubtedly," answered Emanuel, a little impatient at being interrupted in this quarter.

"You will perhaps allow me to bring to your notice, sir, an example which will cause you to alter your views. I need only give you one example to show you clearly how disastrous, nay, how destructive . . . this universal suffrage is, to the future, and the well-being of a country."

Mrs. Hassing looked at her husband, to get him to stop Uncle Joachim. But the doctor, who behind his correct and dignified exterior hid a fair amount of youthful waggishness, appeared not to see it. He thought that it might be rather amusing to see a battle between these two men, both burning for the fray.

"I take the liberty therefore—quite shortly—to put before you the following fact," continued the Jægermester. "I once had . . . some time ago, hm! . . . a cowherd . . . a cowherd, do you understand? Perhaps a very sober and worthy person, but quite ignorant . . . with hardly the most elementary knowledge. With regard to legal matters, he knew just about as much of our constitutional laws, as about the Turkish or the Chinese! Now, I ask you," he continued with rising self-complacency, as from the general silence he discovered that he was making a point. "Is it really your opinion, that such a person ought to have as much influence on the guidance of the State, as a man like . . . well, like our honored host, Dr. Hassing? I ask you."

He threw himself back in his chair, crossed his arms, and in this position sure of victory, awaited Emanuel's reply.

Emanuel would have preferred to answer the Jægermester's question with the indulgence which he deemed this person required. But he perceived the expectancy with which the others awaited his answer; and after a moment's consideration, during which he took a draught from his glass, he said:

"I consider that the cowherd, notwithstanding his ignorance, not only ought to have had equal rights with Dr. Hassing—but if justice had been done—perhaps rather the double."

The answer came with such conviction, and sounded so paradoxical, that they all burst out into protests.

"You surely do not mean that," said even Mrs. Hassing, while Uncle Joachim, with his hand behind his ear—leaned over towards his sister and said, in a voice which he probably took to be a whisper: "What does he say? What is it he says?"

"It seems to me quite simple and obvious," continued Emanuel, again made more talkative by the opposition. "I do not understand why a man's birth should have any influence on his relation to the State. That a man is born in poverty, may be a misfortune to him, so there would be the more reason to raise him than the reverse. As far as his ignorance goes, or rather, want of book knowledge—well, that only means that the State was not willing to spend more on his education. . . . But that is no reason for treating him like a step-child; on the contrary . . . It is always the poor and weak who suffer most in bad times, therefore it is no more than fair to give them by preference the casting vote. If justice is to play any part, it is neither those who know most or those who spend most, who ought to have the greatest influence on the government of the country . . . but those who risk most. Such is in any case my political science!"

"But then you are almost . . . you are really a socialist," said Mrs. Hassing, who was sitting with her hand under her chin, looking up thoughtfully at the corner of the ceiling.

"Whether I am a socialist or not, I can't precisely say. If the views I have expressed are socialistic . . . well, then I am a socialist. I am not alarmed by the designation!"

"What does he say? . . . Does he say Socialist?" stammered the Jægermester again leaning towards his sister, whose sole occupation seemed to be that of a living ear-trumpet.

"But you must really admit, Pastor Hansted,"—the Doctor now took up the conversation—"that the People, in general,—in most cases at any rate,—are not in a condition to form a judgment as to what is best for them. For that presupposes knowledge, experience, etc.,—in which, for instance, a country laborer must be entirely wanting. Of course there are always exceptions to be found; that I shall never deny; but, speaking generally, I am sure that our peasant class must be regarded as a great, inexperienced—and perhaps for the time—unmanageable child, who would inevitably precipitate itself into all kinds of disasters were it left to its own judgment. Don't you think I am right?"

"I do not know how the want of confidence in the peasant has arisen," answered Emanuel. "We do not get it from history. On the contrary, it teaches us how unjust that estimate is.

"You can't point to a single event where by meeting the wishes of the lower classes, and following their advice, the slightest harm has come to the country. But, on the other hand, example after example may be quoted where our country has been plunged into one disaster after another in the face of the warnings of the people. But this is not all! I dare to maintain that all that our country possesses in the way of talent, clear understanding, the spirit of enterprise, industry, and endurance may be entirely traced to the peasants. It can be historically proved, in ancient times as well as now, that there is hardly a single great personality, or a single great intellect who has risen above his contemporaries, but you may find the peasant blood in his lineage, by going back only a generation or two. But we shall hardly find a single prominent person who has had his root in the higher classes for several generations. It is the industry of our peasants, their frugality and tenacious endurance which all our capable men have inherited; . . . it was so in former times, and it is so still. Year by year, young, fresh, active life has been sent from the country to the towns . . . and every year these in return send out a collection of sickly wretches crippled in body or mind, to be set up again by country life and country air. It is just the same with our good, patient, Danish soil, which year by year sends its nutritious grain 'among the red roofs' . . . and gets it back as manure!"

He spoke with rising passion. Perhaps his transports were a trifle calculated; but it was very becoming, as he sat there with his brown hair and light beard, flushed by his speech, the wine, and the earnestness of his convictions. Something of a real prophetic expression had come into his face, and the strong light had converted his eyes into blue shining stars.

A moment's silence arose after his speech. It was broken by the Doctor, who turned to Miss Ragnhild, and said:

"Well, what do you say now, Miss Tönnesen? Let us hear your opinion on the subject."

She raised herself slowly from her languid position, and said:

"I hold with Pastor Hansted."

"What? . . . you too!" they all burst out; while Uncle Joachim, after having her words repeated by his sister, put his hands above his head and exclaimed: "God bless my soul!"

"Yes, I acknowledge it," she said quietly. "I am also of opinion that in a country like ours, with its endlessly long, dark winter and other hard conditions of life . . . that in this dear land of our birth, which perhaps, like the whole of the North ought never to have been civilized, but should have remained like a sort of big Greenland to which one could go in summer time for hunting and fishing, . . . Now what was I going to say?"

She looked round with a constrained smile.

"Yes, now I remember; it was only this . . . that, in a country such as Mr. Hansted indicated, it is, as a matter of course, strong shoulders and broad foreheads which are of the greatest importance. And as Mr. Hansted also pointed out, it is just what history teaches us, that here in Denmark everything soon perishes, is frozen to death or blown away, which does not measure forty inches round the chest, or twenty from ear to ear. I entirely agree with Mr. Hansted that it is only by favor of the peasants that we poor wretches live. I have always had a lively perception of that."

There was again a moment's constrained silence after words. They were not sure how much was to be taken seriously, or how much ironically.

However, the doctor, seeing that the air was somewhat stormy, thought it well to break up before it got beyond a joke.

"Shall we adjourn to the next room?" he said.

They rose and bade each other "Velbekomme." Miss Ragnhild and Emanuel also shook hands with each other.

"My sincere compliments, Pastor Hansted!" she said. "I must acknowledge that . . . you have really become a ready controversialist!"

CHAPTER VII

The large drawing-room was lighted by seven or eight lamps standing about on tables, all with dark shades over them. In this way there was a pleasant subdued light in the room, thoroughly conducive to peaceful rest in the velvet-covered armchairs, with which the room was liberally supplied.

There was a door between two windows, leading into a glass-covered verandah, which formed a perfect little winter garden, full of palms and tall-stemmed plants; a red lantern hanging from the roof shed a soft light, like a rising moon, among the flowering shrubs and shining leaves. This again opened on to the garden, on a much lower level. From the room there was a peep of lawns with a stone vase, rose bushes, a honeysuckle arbor, and a couple of tall poplars, all bathed in the pale, almost solemn, light of a summer night.

"Now, I daresay you will be kind enough to give us a little music, Miss Tönnesen," said the doctor. "I daresay we all feel that we shall be the better for a little soothing."

"With pleasure," answered Miss Ragnhild. ". . . if I could only remember anything!" she added, as she stood by the piano, bending her fingers about after the manner of pianists to make them supple.

Emanuel placed himself in an armchair near the verandah. He was not very well pleased at the idea of the music. He was still too much taken up with the conversation at the table, and would rather have continued the discussion. In the meantime the others had settled themselves comfortably in the easy chairs. Only Uncle Joachim had remained behind in the dining-room, where he could be heard easing his mind to his sister . . . but when Miss Ragnhild struck the first chords, Mrs. Hassing went along, opened the door, and with a "hush!" silenced him.

Miss Ragnhild began by a few powerful runs up and down the piano, as if to clear the air. Then she sat a moment, with her hands on her lap, in silence, and the music already seemed to echo from afar.

Little Miss Gerda had hidden herself in the darkest corner of the room.

A striking change had come over the young girl in the course of the evening; she had become wonderfully quiet and almost solemn. During the meal she had taken less and less interest in her cousin, and paid him but scant attention; but, on the other hand, she watched Emanuel closely, and listened eagerly when he spoke.

Now she sat gazing at him with her big wondering eyes. She bent forward, resting her elbow on her knees. Her face was lighted up by a red glow from the lamp which stood near, the rest of her figure was in shadow. There was a family likeness to Mrs. Hassing in every feature; she had the same oval, madonna face, the soft lines of the mouth and chin betrayed the same tendency to sentimentality, but the nose was more powerful, the curves of the cheek firmer, the fire of dormant passion smoldered in her large velvety brown eyes, above which the dark eyebrows were penciled like a pair of wings preparing for flight.

At the end of the first piece, while Miss Ragnhild and the doctor were exchanging a few remarks about the composer, she stole along to Mrs. Hassing, who was sitting at the other end of the room.

"Auntie," she whispered, as she bent right over her, "is it really true that he is married to a peasant girl?"

"Yes, my child!"

"To a real peasant girl?"

"Yes, my child," repeated Mrs. Hassing, patting her cheek.

She remained standing a moment with her hand on the back of her aunt's chair, looking at the ground. When Miss Ragnhild began another piece, she stole back to her seat to gaze at Emanuel again.

Her cousin, who was sitting a little way off, tried to attract her attention, but she appeared not to notice him. When he tried to reach her with a long feather brush, which he found in his neighborhood, she darted such a lightning glance at him that he nearly fell off his chair, he was so taken aback.

At first Emanuel did not pay much attention to the music. The first piece was a modern composition, difficult to take in, which sounded to him like a cats' concert. He leaned back in his chair and gave himself up to his thoughts. His glance wandered over the room, with its pictures and white statuettes on pedestals in the corners . . . and at the same time a heavy drowsiness crept over him. It was long past his usual bedtime, and the dimness of the room, the many new impressions of the day, the reaction after his extreme exertion, and perhaps also the effect of the wine at supper, soon made him so heavy and weary that he had to make a strong effort to keep awake.

But after a time he began to listen. Well-known tones reached his ears . . . solemn, rushing harmonies which seemed to come from another world. At first he could not give a name to them, nor did he understand the state of emotion into which he was thrown by them—a mingling of sadness and rejoicing, which made his heart beat. Then he recognized Chopin's funeral march, a favorite of his sister's, which in his youth he had often heard her play in the mornings at home, . . . and then it seemed as if a change came over his surroundings. It was no longer Dr. Hassing's drawing-room in which he was sitting, but his own old home; it was his own sister Betty sitting on the stool at the piano between the candles. . . . Yes, even the scent of heliotrope wafted in from the verandah seemed to belong to his childhood and his father's house. The impression at last became so vivid that he could not rid himself of it; it was just as if the music stole away his thoughts and his will. He felt himself enchained by a fascination over which he could not get the mastery.

As soon as the music came to an end he rose. He must go home.

He took leave of the company in rather a headlong fashion, thanked his host and hostess, and a few minutes later was out on the road.

Even here he could not at once free himself from the enchantment, although as he walked he drove his oaken stick so hard against the ground, that its iron ferrule struck sparks against the stones. The quiet landscape in the pale solemn light of the summer night, the softly-dappled sky, and the dark cypress-like poplars by the roadside, at first heightened the effect of Miss Ragnhild's music, as if it were bringing it to life. Its tones continued to pursue him along the winding road, and he was not quite himself till he had passed the parish boundaries and saw the homelike hills darkly massed against the horizon.

In the meantime he was the subject of a lively discussion in the doctor's drawing-room. Uncle Joachim had come on the scene, and had been allowed to give vent to his feelings—of which he took advantage to the fullest extent. To make up, Mrs. Hassing sang Emanuel's praises, and even the doctor was obliged to admit "that he really was a very remarkable man, by no means without intelligence."

Directly after Emanuel left, Miss Gerda said good-night and went to bed.

Miss Ragnhild was rather silent; but then she had no cause to be particularly satisfied with her evening. What she had said to Emanuel was quite true—that for seven years she had been longing for the day when she could surprise him out here . . . and the prospect of so doing had contributed considerably in inducing her to overcome her dread of country life, and to accept Mrs. Hassing's invitation.

Nor was it merely curiosity which had brought her. Since she took leave of the then curate, seven years ago, she had carried about with her a certain feeling of shame, from which she was anxious to free herself. Soon after their parting it had become clear to her that the interest she had felt in him had not been based on such mere friendship as she had imagined, but that by the daily intercourse with him, a cool, northern breath of love had passed over her spirit, and she had often since felt degraded by the remembrance of it. There was something intolerably humiliating to her in the thought that she could have given even the smallest particle of her heart to a man who had married a peasant girl; she could not get rest for her soul before she had again raised herself by feeling her superiority to him . . . and alas! in this respect her meeting with Emanuel had by no means given her the hoped-for gratification.

CHAPTER VIII

There was no surprise at the Parsonage when Emanuel did not come back; and on his return Hansine did not even ask him where he had been. She was used to his being persuaded by the Friends to stay, wherever he dropped in, and by his entirely forgetting time and place. Next morning he told her where he had been and whom he had met . . . and after that he would have liked to bury the whole story in oblivion. He woke up feeling that he had a bad conscience, and the more he recalled the occurrences of the evening, so much the more annoyed he was with himself for what he called his stupid presumptuousness.

"One can see how poisoned the air must be among such people," he thought. "Even after eight years one can't put one's nose among them without losing the mastery over oneself and falling into evil ways."

He took warning by what had happened to keep a better watch over himself for the future; and in many ways his visit to Dr. Hassing's was not without its effect upon him. It roused him from the apathy from which he had so long suffered, ... gave him fresh spiritual vigor to rise out of the state of inertia into which he had fallen since Laddie's death. He once again felt thoroughly happy and contented in his home, and every morning went out singing to the stables, and was never tired of giving Hansine comical descriptions of the doctor's house and family, especially of Uncle Joachim. He told her about the decoration of the rooms, and gave an accurate description of the supper-table and the various dishes. Though Hansine never asked questions about his visit, and observed him closely while he was talking, as if she did not quite believe in his mirth, he always came back to the conversation at the supper-table, and the remarks of the different persons.

On Sunday he preached—almost without preparation—with all his old power and fervor. The day's text was from the gospel of St. Mark: the feeding of the multitude in the wilderness with five loaves and a few small fishes. According to his custom, he first brought the whole picture before his hearers, poetically painting the solemn silence of the desert, its illimitable blue sky, and its jagged rocks, on which the burning rays of the sun glowed from morning till night.

Then he went on in a changed voice—

"Then this about the five loaves, and the small fishes, which so many doubters can't swallow. 'No,' they say, 'to satisfy four thousand people with so little food, and to have five basketsful over, is the talk of a madman. You may get the peasants to believe it, but try it on with us! . . .' Yes, that's what those poor people say who don't know or won't acknowledge any other kind of hunger than that which they feel gnawing at their stomachs. But we who know the meaning of spiritual hunger and thirst—oh! we understand it all so well. We have all experienced those moments of weak despondency, we fancy that all around us is a stony desert, and we can't catch a glimpse of a cooling spring and think that not all the treasures of heaven and earth could satisfy the hunger of our souls. . . . Then one fine day some little thing happens, or we hear some refreshing words containing the blessing of our Lord, and lo! everything springs out into bud before our eyes, and our heart . . . oh, it fills almost to bursting with hope and joy, enough for us to take of them in both hands and give to others! Yes, my friends, we all know such moments of weakness, do we not? But the only thing is to endure, and to hold fast by one's faith and hope. In my opinion we are going through just such a period of apathy in Denmark at present. We hear despondent voices everywhere saying, 'What is the use of it all? We are struggling for truth and justice here on earth, but we only see lies and arbitrariness flourishing around us. We have let ourselves be enticed into a pathless desert, which we can never pass through nor make fruitful. Let us give up the task, let us return to the yoke of the Egyptians and their fleshpots.' And the tempter, who is always at the heels of doubt, like a shadow, answers in his soft, coaxing, serpent's whisper: 'Yea, only bow down to me, and I will give you all the treasure of earth! . . .' No, no," he exclaimed in a louder voice, his cheeks suddenly flaming. "We won't give in! We trust in that God who sent manna to the Israelites, and satisfied the five thousand in the wilderness with his blessing. Besides, we are God's chosen people, whom He has favored, and called to be His instruments, and we will thank and praise His name for ever. No, away with all weakness, away with all doubt."

After the service the people assembled as usual, outside the church door, to shake hands with him, and thank him for his words. But some went away in anger, because they thought that his last words were aimed at the weaver and the other leaders of the change of political tactics . . . and lately, more and more of them felt their honor wounded by the least opposition on this point.

Emanuel himself had not noticed anything of their discontent, and for a long time had not felt so happy and lighthearted as now.

In the afternoon, he proposed at home

in the Parsonage, that they should all—including Abelone, Niels, and Sören—go for a drive in the lovely weather, and take their afternoon meal out of doors. The big spring wagon was got out and washed, a basket was filled with food, and Hansine and the children dressed in their best clothes. This last was by Emanuel's special desire, "so that for once in a way we may show that we have nice clothes"; and when he saw Hansine in a black silk apron, and the little beaded cap which had been part of her wedding costume, he put his hands round her waist and said: "I will bet anyone there's not a prettier parson's wife in the whole kingdom of Denmark." At four o'clock he crossed the yard himself to harness the horses. But he had hardly taken the halters off when Sigrid rushed in, in all her finery—with her eyes starting out of her head, and so breathless in her excitement, that she could hardly speak.

"Father!" she cried. "Two fine, fine ladies have come. . . . Oh, you should see them! They have just gone into the sitting-room!"

Emanuel very nearly swore. He knew at once that it must be Miss Ragnhild, and one of the other ladies from the doctor's house.

"Is mother in the sitting-room?" he asked.

"Yes, she is. Oh, father, you should see . . . you should see!"

"Don't stand there making a fool of yourself," he interrupted her angrily, and the child, who had been clapping her hands and jumping about in delight became crimson, and stole away ashamed.

Emanuel gave himself plenty of time to finish what he was doing with the horses . . . but his heart beat uneasily. His thoughts, however, were not so much on the two ladies as on Hansine. What would she think of this visit? And how would she receive the visitors?

Now Abelone came pelting over the yard in her wooden shoes, and stuck her head and shoulders in over the half door of the stable.

"Is Emanuel here? . . . You must come in directly; two ladies have come——"

"Good gracious! how often am I to hear that?" he stopped her impatiently. "I know very well, Sigrid told me."

She looked at him in astonishment; she was not used to his speaking to her like that.

"How should I know that? Beside Hansine told me to come over and tell you."

She turned away offended, and clattered quickly back over the yard.

CHAPTER IX

In the meantime Miss Ragnhild was sitting in the great room on one of the rush chairs by the table, doing her best to keep up a conversation with Hansine who had taken her usual place in the armchair near the stove. With her usual want of amiability towards strangers, she was taking very little pains to hide her astonishment at the visit. Old Sören was crouching on the bench under the window behind the table, in his not very becoming holiday clothes—an old, blue frieze coat with white seams, and a bright yellow neckerchief—staring at Miss Ragnhild and her young companion, Miss Gerda, as hard as he could.

Miss Ragnhild wore a kind of bead cape over a walking dress of green checked silk, and a black toque with tall up-standing bows. Miss Gerda had on the same white dress and pale blue hat which she had worn on the day of Emanuel's visit to Dr. Hassing.

She sat on the edge of her chair, and her position, her burning cheeks, and the glance with which she looked round the large empty room, or scrutinized Hansine and her peasant costume, all betrayed strong excitement. But when the door opened and Emanuel came in, her face fell. She had heard from Dr. Hassing of the fantastic smock in which he dressed at home, and on his now appearing in the long gray cloth coat and closely buttoned waistcoat which she had seen him in before, she was deeply disappointed.

"Well, here you see me again, Pastor Hansted," exclaimed Miss Ragnhild rising. "We have certainly dropped in very unceremoniously, but your wife was kind enough to say that you are used to that here, so I hope we are not disturbing you. . . . You remember my little friend, Mr. Hansted," she added, turning towards Miss Gerda, who had also risen at his entrance.

Emanuel greeted them in silence, and with a wave of the hand invited them to be seated again, taking his place on the bench at the upper end of the table.

"You have had a long way to walk," he said after a moment's silence.

"Oh, not so far as you think," laughed Miss Ragnhild. "It would have been beyond my powers to walk all the way from Kyndlöse, but we haven't done that. Dr. Hassing had to visit a patient near here, and we could not resist the temptation of paying you"—she bowed slightly towards Hansine and Emanuel—"and my old home a little visit. We drove with the doctor to the 'Ridge'—as far as I remember—and we are to meet him there again. It is at least half an hour from here, and I am quite proud of having walked so far in the heat of the sun."

"Yes, it really is warm today."

She began talking about the neighborhood and the novelties she had seen on the way. It seemed to her that everything was so changed since she used to live here; the village had especially astonished her. "It looks so much more comfortable," she said; and Emanuel explained that the gardens which had been burned had grown up again, and the trees had gained in size.

Hansine took no part in the conversation, and Emanuel made no effort to draw her into it. On the contrary he avoided looking at her and mostly sat with his face turned towards the windows and the garden. He did not himself understand what it was in this visit which depressed him so much; or why he felt Hansine's glance wander backwards and forwards all the time from him to the two ladies. He hadn't concealed anything from her; he had told her every day what had passed on that evening. And what indeed had there been to make a secret of?

"There are a good many changes, too, here in the Parsonage," said he, noticing that Miss Ragnhild was looking about her with interest. "I don't suppose the changes will be to your taste . . . but every one has his own."

"There you are doing me an injustice, Mr. Hansted! I like this room, for instance, very much. It is uncommon, but it appeals to me. There is an air of restful individuality about it. . . . I was just admiring it. You certainly understand the art of making much out of little."

Although Emanuel well understood that her words were only the phrases of polite speech, he was yet grateful for them on Hansine's account. But, all the same, he at once turned the conversation to other subjects.

In the meantime Miss Gerda's illusions were being rapidly dispelled. There was none of the prophetic glamour about Emanuel today which had taken such a hold upon her at the Hassings' supper-table. The big unfurnished room made her almost uncomfortable, it reminded her of an empty barn; then the presence of Sören the cowherd made her feel quite creepy, and she also felt ill at ease under

Hansine's glance, which was peculiarly searching.

After a time she was enlivened by watching little Sigrid, who was standing by Hansine in a pink cotton frock, with a black ribbon round her golden brown and well-oiled hair, hiding her face in her mother's lap. Every time she discovered that Miss Gerda was looking at her, she hid her face again; but the next moment a large dark blue eye peeped out from behind her sunburned arm, and as soon as she thought she was unobserved she stood on tiptoe and whispered something to her mother.

Hansine nodded absently, and stroked her hair caressingly—with a motherly tenderness which she seldom displayed towards her children.

The conversation by the table threatened every moment to come to a standstill, although Miss Ragnhild exerted herself to the utmost. Emanuel found it impossible to collect his thoughts. Hansine's silence made him more nervous every moment. He felt that she was reproaching him for something, what, he did not know. Besides which he felt the awkwardness of Sören's presence. Sören had always had bad habits, which they generally overlooked on account of his many good qualities; but it seemed to Emanuel that he had never displayed them so unpleasantly as he did today.

"Shall we go into the garden?" he said, rising. And with a slightly constrained smile, he added, "We can't show you such a model park as your father's used to be, Miss Tönnesen, . . . but at any rate it will be a little cooler out there!"

"Oh, that will be delightful!"

They all rose, Hansine first, as Emanuel asked her if she would not go with them. Only Sören remained behind, his eyes fixed first on one lady, then on the other, till the last fold of their dresses had disappeared.

At the same moment Abelone stuck her head in at the kitchen door, where she had been on the look-out.

"Are they gone?"

Sören nodded silently, and winked meaningly towards the garden, afterwhich Abelone came right in and went to the window.

"Well, there they go! . . . A can't see what Emanuel wants wi' two such baggages. They don't look no better than a pair o' hussies."

Her indignation did not sound very sincere. But Abelone had been altogether "rather queer in her head" lately, and Sören looked at her with a deeply sympathic glance. It was, in fact, an open secret that she was suffering from an unrequited attachment to Niels the stableman, who, for some unknown cause, had lately become insensible to her mature charms.

CHAPTER X

The first impression of Veilby Parsonage garden would not have pleased every one. Emanuel was right in saying that not much remained of the lordly Park which Archdeacon Tönnesen had left behind him. The hedges, which in his time were so carefully clipped, now sent straggling branches out on every side, grass had spread over the paths, dandelion and sandwort flourished on the lawns; the shrubberies had become impenetrable thickets, in which various song-birds had their nests; the ground under the big trees were strewn with branches and moldering building boxes for the starlings. The Chinese wooden bridge, which had been the pride of the "millionaire priest," was now little more than a collection of rotten planks. The only things which had braved the effects of time, and withstood its destructive hand, were three or four large stone vases like churchyard urns.

Miss Ragnhild and Emanuel, who happened to be walking a little in advance of the others, turned down the thickly overgrown hazel alley leading to the wide, open chestnut avenue which formed the boundary between the garden and the fields.

It was the same place where they used once to take their daily walks and hold their lively debates. Emanuel experienced a sudden irresistible emotion as he found himself walking alone with her again in these desolate empty paths, and by again hearing the mysterious murmur of a lady's rustling garments, and also by the faint odor of violets which used always to be perceptible in her presence in the old days. He walked—just as he used to then—with a slight stoop, and his arms behind him, looking at the ground; whereas Miss Ragnhild looked about freely, while holding up her dress with her left hand, just so much, that from behind, the frills of a starched skirt and the heels of her patent leather shoes were revealed.

She was all smiles and natural amiability, and not in the least as she had been the other day. The insight which her short visit had given her into the family life at the Parsonage had entirely reinstated her in her own self-esteem, and she began to feel something of her former sisterly sympathy and her old desire to win his confidence, so as to be able to distract and cheer him a little.

Meanwhile the others had stopped by the sunny lawn in the nearest part of the garden. Hansine tried to begin a conversation with Miss Gerda, but after they had exchanged a few words without being in the least intelligible to each other, the young girl, at her wit's end, began to play with little Sigrid.

The two ran about in the sun playing Tiggy Touchwood, while Hansine sat on a bench in the shade, from whence she closely watched the young girl, scrutinized her costume, her happy smile, her airy movements, and her pretty white teeth.

After a time she was roused from her meditations by the sound of voices approaching. Miss Ragnhild and Emanuel were coming back through the closed hazel alley which ran just behind her.

"——We generally see each other once a fortnight," she heard Miss Ragnhild say. "As a rule we play duets together. But of course we gossip too . . . sometimes about you, as I daresay I have told you. I have always seen that your sister is tenderly attached to you. She often tells me how much she misses you, and longs to see you again."

"Indeed! does Betty talk about me?"

"Yes, it's natural enough; she hasn't seen you for years now. You really ought to go to town sometime to see her. She needs cheering, poor thing. She is so desolate since—as I daresay you know—she had the sorrow of losing her only child. It was a heavy blow to her, she is still young, and needs somebody or something to fill up her life. . . . It can't be denied, you know, that the Consul-general has his weaknesses; besides, he is almost an old man and rather decrepit——"

The voices here became inaudible to Hansine. She again betook herself to looking at the two young creatures, who were sitting in the long grass. A moment later Sigrid rushed towards her, eyes and cheeks blazing with excitement.

"Mother," she shouted. "Do you know what she says? She says she has a big doll that can go to sleep like a real person, and a doll's house with real tables and chairs and a kitchen. And do you know what she says? It's got a pond to it with ducks and a boat. Do you believe it's true, mother?"

"Are you coming, Sigrid?" called Miss Gerda from the lawn.

Without waiting for her mother's answer, the child ran back to the girl, and in her wildness, threw herself right on to her knee.

Now the voices again approached in the hazel alley. It was Emanuel's words this time which Hansine first caught.

"——Granted that in itself there's not much harm in that way of living, you will admit that alone with regard to one's less fortunate fellowmen, one ought to withhold people from giving themselves up to such a display of luxury, as for example—my brother-in-law's. The sight of such lavishness makes the yoke of poverty doubly heavy to those who have to struggle and strive all the year round to get dry bread; it breeds bitterness, envy, and bad feeling——"

"No, no, I don't believe a word of what you say. A scene which I once saw just occurs to me; it was in a great labor yard where a number of by no means well-to-do people were working in the heat of the sun, loading carts with gravel, heavy blocks of stone, and so on. Just as I passed, two charmingly dressed young girls, probably the owner's daughters, came through the yard, laughing and talking . . . undoubtedly a pair of 'useless' creatures, like little Miss Gerda here. I saw how all the work-begrimed laborers raised their heads and gazed at them; but I can assure you, I didn't see the least trace of envy in a single face. On the contrary, it was evident that the sight of the two pretty, happy creatures, gay as birds, cheered them in the middle of their toil; they looked after them with the kindly glance with which we all greet a swallow as it skims gaily past us on the road. People like that know quite well that they are made of very different stuff from the young daughters of their master; and if they are not absolutely worked up to it, they would no more think of complaining of it, than any sensible people would entertain bitter thoughts of the swallows, because the Almighty has made them with a pair of nimble wings, and has given us two heavy legs as a means of progression. Am I not right?"

Emanuel began an eager answer, but they had got too far off for Hansine to hear his words.

Shortly afterwards they appeared at the upper end of the lawn, and when they saw her they came towards her over the grass.

"Ah, there you are, Mrs. Hansted," said Miss Ragnhild. "Your husband and I have been quarreling fearfully. Pastor Hansted and I never agree on any point."

She sat down by Hansine on the bench, and without giving her time to answer, began hurriedly talking about the garden, its shade and its primitive character. She soon rose, saying:

"Well, it's time for us to get off, Dr. Hassing won't wait for us.—Gerda," she called, "we must say good-bye."

She began to take leave. When she gave her hand to Emanuel, he said:

"No, I will go a little way with you. I will show you a path which will save you half the distance."

"Oh, that will be capital!"

A minute later they were gone, and Hansine turned to go in.

She stopped by the garden fence, and looked over the fields, where the strangers were disappearing along the path through the high corn.

"Mother!" said Sigrid, who was holding her hand. . . . "Mother!" repeated the child, pulling her skirt. "Do you know what she said? She said that I should come and see her in Cop'nhagen, and she would give me the big doll, she said."

Hansine did not hear her. She followed Emanuel with her eyes, he was walking between the two ladies, talking with youthful eagerness and lively gestures, stopping every moment to point out something in the landscape.

BOOK FOUR

CHAPTER I

The rye harvest began in rain, and it looked as if it would end in rain. Every morning the sun rose in a clear sky, falsely heralding a fine day. But no sooner had the peasants driven out their wagons into the fields and bound up their first load, then up came heavy lowering clouds above the horizon, and throughout the day fierce showers of hail fell, while the thunder rolled unceasingly in the distance, first in one quarter, then in the other.

One of these days in the afternoon, Niels the Parsonage stableman was lying on his back on his bed, with his clothes unbuttoned, and one hand under his head. He had passed a couple of hours in this position, and, as usual, had filled his little chamber with impenetrable clouds of tobacco smoke; and although it was long past the mid-day hour of rest, he did not think of rising. He was quite lost in his favorite occupation—building castles in the air. He saw before him a large room, the walls lined from ceiling to floor with well bound books . . . a room with two high windows and a thick carpet covering the floor, just like the study of the learned priest at Kyndlöse, whither he had once gone to get his certificate of baptism. There was a large square table in the middle of the room with a green cloth, loaded with folios; in one corner of the room there was a large globe, the size of a cartwheel. The curtains were drawn, a lamp was burning on the table, at one end of which he saw himself in a dressing gown and embroidered slippers sitting in a large arm-chair, reading a very old Greek book. It was the middle of the night, and all was silent around him; only an owl now and then hooted as it flew over the house. On the shelves he saw his own works handsomely bound. Some were religious books bound in black with gold lettering, some were learned works, and others were great social dramas and novels chastising the community, such as the Norwegians write——

He was torn from his dreams by hearing the clattering of wooden shoes in the yard and then a lengthy creaking and groaning sound. It was Abelone at the pump.

He lay still, smiling to himself . . . he reposed calmly, feeling with satisfaction that he had happily got out of the temptation which Abelone at one time was to him. He had not found it easy to give her up, though she was poor. But he saw plainly that if he gave in to his weakness, he would probably never rise above his ignominious position of "Niels the stableman." He must be free and independent, or, at any rate, make quite a different match if he was to reach the goal he had set himself to win—to make the name of Niels Damgaard famous throughout the land. He had difficulties enough to contend with as it was. If, for instance, his name had been Frithiof, or Arne, or Björnstjerne, it would have been much easier to impress it on people's memories.

He sometimes grew quite cold when he reflected how nearly he had thrown himself away on Abelone. But now at last he had gained a complete victory over himself. He had become blind to her ingratiating glances, and contented himself with lying here in the hours of rest listening to her clattering steps in the yard. He pictured vividly to himself her powerful figure, red cheeks, and heaving bosom; and shutting his eyes, he almost felt her kisses and the delight of her embraces.

He started up hastily, buttoning his clothes. He again heard steps in the yard, but this time a strong heavy tread . . . Emanuel's.

He stole along to the window to peep out behind the white curtain, and saw his master coming hurriedly round the gable end with rapid steps. His ears began to burn; in the very middle of the yard lay the harness, betraying that he had not gone out to the fields yet . . . and lately Emanuel had become so unreasonable, and had such singular ideas, there was no knowing him. Happily he neither looked to the right nor to the left, but went straight up the steps into the house.

Niels smiled a smile of relief, then stretched himself with a tremendous yawn and went into the stable.

CHAPTER II

When Emanuel, in his stocking feet, went into the living room and saw Hansine sitting in her arm-chair with a bowl on her lap shelling peas, the excited expression immediately left his face.

"Oh, there you are, my dear!" he said, and nodded to her with a smile, and then went into the bedroom.

He soon came out again in his gray coat and leather boots, engaged in tying on the red neckerchief, which he invariably wore instead of a collar.

"Are you going out?" asked Hansine.

"Yes, I am obliged to go. I have to go to the Fen cottages. There's some botheration with the people again; they won't take work. And now just at harvest time, it really won't do."

He was just going out of the door when Hansine said:

"Oh, by-the-bye, don't let me forget to tell you that young Rasmus Jörgen was in here this morning while you were in the fields. I was to tell you that he must have back that load of barley straw he lent you sometime last winter. He could not do without it any longer he said."

Emanuel stood with his hand on the lock, getting redder and redder.

"A load of barley straw, do you say?"

"Yes; you seem to have promised it to him in the spring," continued Hansine. "But he must have it now, or he will be obliged to buy."

"But barley straw at this time of year . . . Where in the world should I get it from? I suppose you said that to him too?"

"No; I only said I would give you the message."

"But I don't understand it at all," burst out Emanuel, letting go the door and walking backwards and forwards. "It's not like young Rasmus Jörgen a bit. You must have offended him somehow, Hansine, and made him say it in anger. . . . It is very curious that you never can learn to be pleasant to people. It has become quite a morbid eccentricity. You offend one after another of our friends, and it always falls to me to make it up again. I'm really getting tired of it. God knows, how——"

He stopped suddenly on discovering Sigrid, who was sitting on a stool by one of the windows, busily sewing colored stitches on to a bit of rag.

"Well, it's no use talking about it," he concluded in a low voice, and left the room—banging the door behind him.

In a few minutes he came back, went up to Hansine, and put his hand on her head.

"Forgive me!" he said. "I did not mean what I said, I spoke hastily. Don't be angry with me. Will you promise me that? . . . I have had so many worries today," he continued, again beginning to pace up and down the long room. "Just fancy, when I got down to the low lots just after dinner, there was the barley still not set up in shocks, though I particularly told Niels this morning, it was to be done immediately. Now, of course, it's soaking wet at the top after the rain this morning—everything is swimming in water down there; it really is too bad, isn't it? We can't go on like this with Niels and his idleness; I must speak to him seriously some time when I have an opportunity! I believe it's all this newspaper scribbling which has turned his head. And I hear he has begun to attend Maren Smed's prayer-meetings. Maren seems to have got a great following lately; I am always hearing of first one and then of another who has been there. The weaver's at the bottom of it all, I believe. I don't know what kind of a conspiracy he is hatching, but I am sure he is the originator of the malicious reports against the chairman of the Parish Council, which I told you about the other day. I remember now that once in the spring he hinted at something of a dishonorable character between him and big Sidse. A stop must soon be put to these disorders in the congregation. Otherwise we shall be swamped in squabbles! . . . Well, I must be off."

He nodded again both to Hansine and Sigrid, and left the room.

Not a muscle had moved in Hansine's gloomy face, in which the lines had perceptibly deepened during the last few weeks. She was getting accustomed both to Emanuel's sudden outbursts of anger, and to his rapid repentance for the same . . . she also thought she perfectly understood the cause of his irritable frame of mind.

For a long time after Emanuel left there was dead silence in the room. Little Dagny was sleeping in her flower-painted wooden cradle by Hansine's side, and Sigrid sat by the window absorbed in her work. She was in fact under punishment for having again come in from her play by the village pond, with her clothes soiled; when Hansine scolded her, she answered with a naughty word, which she declared she had learned from the wheelwright's boys. It was Emanuel himself who had ordered that she was to be kept in all the afternoon; and he also said, that no doubt it would be better in future to keep a more watchful eye on her playfellows.

Suddenly the child dropped her work on her lap, put her head on one side, and began gazing fixedly at the ceiling. After a time she rose and went along to her mother.

"Mother," she said softly. "Do you remember her, the fine lady who came that day, . . . the one that played with me in the garden?"

"Yes, child, I do. You have talked about her so often."

"Yes, but do you remember, mother, that she said I was to go in to Copenhagen, and I should have the big doll, she said. I might stay with her always . . . and I could have the doll's house too, she said."

"I don't think she did. There you're saying something that isn't quite true, Sigrid," said Hansine, looking at her reprovingly.

The child reddened and looked down.

"For that matter . . . it might do you good to go away for a bit," continued Hansine. "Then you would not learn so many bad things, and you would have to take care of your clothes."

These words of her mother's again brought her imprisonment to her mind; Sigrid blushed redder than ever, and crept back to her stool shamefacedly.

Again there was complete silence in the room. Only the buzzing flies were heard against the window panes, and the sound of Abelone's scrubbing-brush in the kitchen.

"Mother," said Sigrid, again in a low voice. "If I never make my frock in a

mess again, or say any more naughty words, may I go to Copenhagen?"

Hansine could not help smiling a little.

"Are you so anxious to go to the lady in Copenhagen, Sigrid?"

"Yes, indeed, I am; she was so pretty. Wasn't she, mother?"

"Yes. But how do you think you can go to such places? You saw how fine the ladies were, and they're all like that in Copenhagen . . . the children too, I can tell you. You would have to be as nice as they are first, or they wouldn't have anything to do with you."

"Can't I grow into a fine lady too, mother?" asked Sigrid, with wide open eyes.

Hansine did not answer at once.

"Oh, yes, I daresay you could," said she, becoming thoughtful again.

CHAPTER III

Meanwhile, Emanuel was well on his way to the Fen cottages.

In the need for solitude which had been growing upon him latterly, he left the highroad and walked along the narrow paths which formed the boundaries between the fields; he was even careful to keep out of the way of the little scattered groups of harvesters. Nor was it cheering at present to meet the people. The old enmity between the villagers of Skibberup and those of Veilby, which the common bond of politics had for a time kept under, now burst forth with renewed force after the collapse of the league; and on several occasions Emanuel had tried in vain to mediate between them. The quarrelsome Skibberup people had begun the wrangle by insisting that the Veilby people had taken upon themselves to exercise too much influence in all the affairs of the congregation; and it was also mainly from them that the offensive attacks on the chairman of the Parish Council proceeded, and the attempts to drive him from his position.

Moreover, there was another reason why Emanuel avoided the highways. He did not wish to run the risk of meeting Miss Ragnhild again. He felt that he had perhaps already involved himself somewhat deeply with her, and the society to which she belonged; and he fancied that she was still in the neighborhood. At any rate it was not many days since he had heard that she had been seen driving about with the doctor on his rounds.

After a good half hour's walk he reached the so-called Foxhills, a collection of wart-like mounds where the ground fell away towards the Fen district. He stopped here a moment and looked towards the idyllic little copse and the scattered cottages of the Kyndlöse-Vesterby parishes, whose walls looked doubly clean and white today against the dark rainy sky. He could also just catch a glimpse of the large village of Kyndlöse with its old round church and many high poplars, notwithstanding the mist . . . also the serpentine road along which he had wandered on that evening with Miss Ragnhild—the steep hill on the top of which he had stopped to point out the landscape in its glowing sunset colors . . . nay, at last he even fancied he could plainly see Dr. Hassing's villa close to the church, in the distinguished seclusion of its extensive garden. He suddenly withdrew his eyes and began walking down towards the swamp.

Just beneath him, on both sides of a little half dried up stream lay the Fen cottages—a collection of miserable earthen hovels, which, in their dilapidation, leaned one against the other, as if pondering on their fate. The ground round about the cottages was a hopeless rubbish heap of old straw, potsherds, and withered potato haulm, among which some ragged, bareheaded children were running about playing.

Emanuel always fell into melancholy reflections at the sight of all this misery. In spite of all that he and the congregation had done to help the distress here, there was still not a house without rags instead of window panes, or without great holes in the roof. And, what was worse, after seven years of self-sacrifice and exertions, not a single one of the unhappy inhabitants of the mud cabins had shown the slightest trace of appreciation of him as a man. . . . On the contrary, there were constant and increasing complaints of their nightly depredations among the potato mounds and bleaching grounds, and very often neither high pay nor soft words would induce them to take work with the peasants. He rushed down towards one of the nearest houses—a hut, the walls of which bulged out like a baker's oven, with tiny little windows and a moss-covered roof. A tall, bent, old man was standing at the gable end with an ax, chopping up faggots.

As he approached, a little fat cur—a fat spotted dumpling on four short legs—darted out between his feet, and, as if beside itself with rage, it danced round him showing its teeth and barking in a hoarse, almost inaudible voice, so that Emanuel who never could find it in his heart to strike an animal, could not advance.

Although the old man saw him very well and could not fail to notice the dog, he neither called it in nor allowed himself to be disturbed at his work.

"Is this your dog, Ole Sören?" Emanuel at last called out, in rather an angry voice.

"No," growled the old man without looking up. "I am a dog myself!"

At this moment a woman far advanced in pregnancy appeared at the door of the hut. But no sooner did her eye fall on Emanuel than she darted in again. Then a great bustle began inside; eager whispers mingled with the clatter of crockery. Startled faces also appeared at the other doors, and unkempt heads peeped round the gables.

Emanuel at last got rid of the raging dog and followed the woman into the house.

He detected a strong smell of spirits together with the odor of coffee and humanity as soon as he entered the little outer room, where he had to walk doubled up so as not to knock his head against the roof and its cobwebs. He knocked at a half-open door and walked into a very nearly dark cellar-like room with two broad straw beds, a flap table, a locker, and two bright red chairs.

It was the home of Beery Svend and Brandy Pér.

Although the first was married and had several children, and the other was a bachelor, these two inseparable friends had lived here together for many years in the same room and at the same table . . . nay, it was commonly believed that the good fellowship between them went much further, and had set its mark plainly upon more than one of the offspring of the married couple.

Beery Svend's little ill-favored person with the fat limbs and the huge lump over one eye rose with difficulty from the locker when Emanuel entered. He smilingly greeted the visitor with his head on one side and the upper part of his right arm stiffly pressed to his breast. The woman slunk out behind Emanuel's back as if ashamed of her condition.

"This is a pleasant surprise," he said, as he stretched out his dirty hand. "We never expected that the Pastor—Emanuel, I should say—would be givin' us a visitation today. But it comes just right; we all need a word of comfort in these times when the Lord has visited us with weaknesses of every kind——"

He was cut short here by Emanuel who had taken his seat on one of the red chairs and crossed his legs.

"I say, just let us have a serious talk, Svend! What is this I hear about you and Pér? You don't want to take work, they say! . . . what is the meaning of these tricks? Can't you soon show us that you are decent fellows, so that we shan't always need to be having rows with you. I'm sure we've only done good to you . . . it wouldn't be too much if for once you showed us some return. Don't you think so yourself?"

Beery Svend, who had again taken his seat on the locker, put on a sorrowful face and looked at the ground.

"As sure as I sit here a sinner before God . . . there's no one what would sooner toil and slave than me," said he, while with his left hand he carefully rubbed his right arm, which he continued to hold stiffly against his body, as if he had it in an invisible sling. "But what's a poor cripple to do when the rheumatiz gets hold on him. You may believe it's a pitiful thing for a poor chap with a wife and children to look after——"

"Oh, come, it's not as bad as that, Svend," Emanuel broke in, looking at him sternly. "You were well enough to be at the fight the other day at Veilby public-house. . . . Yes, I've heard all about it. Pér was there too. Where is he now?"

Beery Svend, who was visibly upset by Emanuel's unusually severe tone, let his eyes fall on one of the two wide straw beds which stood side by side against the wall.

There lay Brandy Pér asleep on his back under a dirty coverlet. Nothing was to be seen of him but his thick matted hair and a pale flat face, on which a little shining purple nose was stuck like an over-ripe plum.

"What is the meaning of that?" asked Emanuel, who was feeling a little uncomfortable in the gloom and bad air of the room. "Is Pér ill too?"

"Yes, he's very bad with headache . . . and the ague too. It comes on him all of a sudden. He may be sittin' there as well as can be when his teeth begin to chatter, an' he shivers an' shakes all over his body . . . it's a sight to see."—But Emanuel was no longer to be taken in. He had lately become watchful, even suspicious, and he soon saw that it was no fever patient before him, but a man lying there dead drunk under the covering, trying in vain to get the mastery over sleep and to raise his eyelids.

Suddenly he became so enraged at all this degradation, all these lies and deceptions, all the dirt and the smells, that he couldn't help easing his mind.

He got up and banged his chair against the floor.

"Now, look here, I'll just tell you two something! . . . You had better take care. Even our patience has its limits, and if you go on misusing our kindness and forbearance as you have been doing lately, everything must be at an end between us. Then the Poorhouse will have to look after you . . . we will have nothing more to do with you. Do you hear that?"

The fawning look disappeared suddenly from Svend's face; it was the first time that Emanuel had spoken to him in such an authoritative way. The great red lump on his forehead drooped lower over his eye, and his thick lips spread out into a malicious smile.

"Oh, it won't be as bad as that," he said, while—as if from habit—he went on rubbing his arm. "You know well enough what you can use us pore folks for."

"What's that you say?" asked Emanuel, with a start.

"What do I mean? Oh, I'm not such a fool either but I know what happens to folks in the Poorhouse. They lose their vote, I've heerd tell, . . . and I daresay it's true enough."

"That is so . . . but what do you mean by it?"

"I on'y mean that I daresay ye all like to get hold on our votes, . . . or else ye wouldn't be trying to please us in the way ye do, I fancy. Ye know well enough that at the elections a poor man's vote is worth as much as my lord's! . . . Oh, yes, ye know that well enough."

Emanuel stood speechless.

So this was the idea these people had of the charity of the congregation. On such miserable objects had they wasted their works of mercy, for such wretches had he given up his means, so that many a time he was almost in want himself!

He was pale with anger. He was quite unable to speak—the words were choked in his throat.

Then he suddenly took up his hat and rushed out of the room. Away, away! something shrieked within him. He could no longer endure these miserable human creatures; he must escape from all this swinishness, from all this filth which was suffocating him.

CHAPTER IV

He had not gone far, however, before he began to slacken his pace; and when he came to the end of the path leading out of the Fens on to the higher ground, he stopped, took his hat off, and pressed his hand to his burning and beating forehead.

"Judge not, that ye be not judged," he murmured to himself. "Why beholdest thou the mote that is in thy brother's eye, but considerest not the beam that is in thine own eye?"

He ought not to have forgotten these words of his Lord, he said to himself;—he continued his walk slowly, carrying his hat in his hand. Should he not go back? He had not acted as it became one who would humbly follow in his Master's footsteps. Was it not time to take in hand that demon, pride, which latterly had been pursuing him and throwing dust in his eyes, so that he could only see darkness and despair around him?

He had become so nervous in the last few weeks that he absolutely started when a man suddenly appeared on the path a little way in front, and his uneasiness was not allayed when in the short-necked and unnaturally long-limbed figure he recognized Hansen the weaver.

Emanuel put his hat on again and hastened his steps a little. He had always felt some little distrust of the weaver, whose peculiar and reserved demeanor was so different from his own open and straightforward nature. He had a feeling that this man was spying out his doings, and he could not make out what his hidden object was.

They greeted each other with a silent shake of the hand, and each kept his own side of the path.

"Well, how is all with you? Nothing new has happened, I suppose?" asked Emanuel, absently.

"Oh, something or other is always happening," answered the weaver; he stood there with his large red hands on his chest, the tips of his fingers stuck between his waistcoat and his black American cloth cuffs, and gazed at the fields. "But unfortunately that something is not always good."

Emanuel knew by his voice that he had evil tidings to impart.

"Indeed," he said.

"I can go part of the way back with you, if you like," continued the weaver. "I am not busy today.

"Very well—let us get on then!"

They walked for a time in silence.

"I hadn't expected to meet you so far from home, Emanuel. I've just seen the Kyndlöse doctor's carriage on the way to

Veilby . . . and, as far as I know, there's no illness there?"

Emanuel did not answer. It was by no means the first time he had had to endure much spiteful wit from his friends on account of his visit to Dr. Hassing. Moreover, the weaver's words filled him with new disquiet. Was it possible that the doctor and his party were paying him a return visit?

The weaver began to talk about the bad harvest prospects, about the rye, which was already getting black at the top on the low-lying ground, and about the heavy losses the peasants would suffer all over the country if the Almighty were not merciful enough to send the east wind.

Emanuel did not listen; he knew the weaver's roundabout ways, and knew that he must arm himself with patience.

His thoughts in the meantime went their own way. He was reminded of what he had been thinking about, an hour before, when he had been despondently looking down on the squalid Fen cottages from the Foxhills, . . . now here, by his side, was a person who actually had raised himself up from the swamp of debasement. The weaver was born in the Fen cottages; his father had been a swineherd on the Tryggerlöse estate in Vesterby parish, and as a child he had herded the sheep on the desolate heaths. He had always been very chary of words when any reference was made to his childhood, but there was a general idea that he had once as a boy been present when his father was flogged by his master, and it was thought that this experience had tinged his later development. Emanuel felt a pang at this moment when he reflected that it had been a deed of violence, and not one of love to which this poor child owed his spiritual elevation. His thoughts were arrested when the weaver suddenly stopped, and said:

"I suppose you know, Emanuel, that he has confessed his heavy sin? May God look upon him in his loving-kindness!"

"What do you say? Who has confessed?"

"The chairman of the Parish Council of course. Who else were you thinking of?"

"What has he confessed? . . . I don't understand a word!"

"He has at last humbled himself before the Lord, and brought himself to confess that he has been living in sin. People have long suspected it; but one could hardly think it possible that a man standing as the political leader of a Christian congregation could so forget the Holy Scripture about fornicators and the unclean. . . . So yesterday there seem to have been one or two who went to him, and in all Christian brotherliness warned him that it couldn't go on any longer . . . he must clear himself from the frightful imputations which were brought against him. He couldn't deny that by degrees several things had come up which were not in his favor, and when at last he perceived that big Sidse had not kept so quiet a tongue as he had given her credit for, he was obliged to own up."

"It can't be true!" exclaimed Emanuel in a low voice, resting on his stick as if the earth were giving away under him.

"You may well say that," answered the weaver, again looking at the fields. "It's an occurrence which may well give us all something to think about."

They walked on for a time in silence.

Then the weaver began saying that the best way would be to call a meeting of the church-wardens, so as to have the matter thoroughly sifted. Everybody must agree, he said, that a man who had sinned so deeply could not continue to occupy the highest posts of confidence in the circle of the Friends, and now there must be no delay in wiping out the stain on the congregation.

Emanuel, who thought he could detect a malicious satisfaction in the weaver's tone at the thought of the chairman's downfall, could not help saying:

"It is curious to hear you so eager in this case, Jens Hansen, when all the time you are the cause of Hans Jensen having been pushed into the foremost places in the congregation. I remember, at the time, many of us had our doubts about it . . . his previous life had not been blameless; but you always insisted that we were not to bother ourselves about that. He was just the very man, you said; and we allowed ourselves to be quieted. If any mistake has been made, you are the one to bear the blame for it."

The weaver's crooked mouth drew itself up towards his ear.

"Nay, I don't deny that I backed up Hans Jensen . . . and I still maintain, that for the kind of politics he had to take the lead in, he was just the right man. Any driver is good enough to drive into the ditch, as they say! . . . But now it's another matter. What we have to do is to get out of the ditch, in my opinion."

At this moment Emanuel started violently. During the conversation they had reached the high road, and there, hardly a gunshot length away, was a carriage advancing towards them with a pair of roans and a coachman in livery.

He immediately recognized Dr. Hassing's turnout. He even thought he could see Miss Ragnhild's fair head behind the coachman.

He struggled with all his might to hide his agitation from the weaver, and talked at random about "this meeting which we must have . . . there you're quite in the right, a meeting of the church council under these circumstances is, of course, necessary."

When the carriage came nearer it was apparent that he had made a mistake. There was no one beside the doctor on the wide seat; he was wrapped in a mackintosh, smoking a cigar.

When the doctor saw Emanuel, he called to the coachman and stopped the carriage.

"How d'ye do, how d'ye do, Pastor Hansted!" said he, putting out his gloved hand. "How are you? It's a long time since I've had the pleasure of seeing you . . . you are head over ears in your rye harvest, I suppose. For your sake I hope you can swim . . . for it's somewhat moist under foot just now."

"Yes, it is . . . rather a trying harvest," answered Emanuel without looking up. "You are on your rounds, I suppose, doctor."

"Yes, you've got a broken leg in your neighborhood. A farm hand got a cow tether round his foot . . . well, it was only a couple of ankle bones, as they say out here, no very serious business! But now don't let me forget the most important thing. I have no end of messages to you from Miss Tönnesen who left us about a week ago. She asked me particularly to remember her very kindly to you when I saw you."

"Is Miss Tönnesen gone?" exclaimed Emanuel, involuntarily looking up.

"Yes, she had promised us to make a longer stay, but I believe she was pining for the town air. You know she is no lover of being 'out at grass,' as she said. She stayed long enough to receive the formal announcement of an engagement in our house, between my nephew and my wife's little niece . . . I daresay you remember seeing them the other day. They are rather young, both of them. But, good heavens! we get old soon enough, don't we?"

"Yes, indeed—that's just—just the point," said Emanuel, without knowing himself exactly what he meant.

The doctor nodded to the coachman and the carriage rolled on.

The weaver had been keeping a close

watch upon the two men with his red eyes, from the side of the road; and when the doctor had driven off he walked for a time by Emanuel's side in silence, clearing his throat and smiling.

"He's a smartish man that Hassing—to judge from appearance anyhow," he said at last.

"Oh, yes!"

"That makes it all the harder to understand how he can hold such fearful political opinions. It's very queer."

"I don't think Dr. Hassing troubles himself about politics."

"No, that's just what I meant. Folks say, you know, that he only lives for the pleasures of this world. I've heard tell of his goings on at home, his good living, and his diversions . . . of the most spicy kind. And the talk that goes on is said to be of the most godless sort——"

He stopped when his ever watchful eye perceived that Emanuel was no longer listening to him. After a moment's silence he stopped and said good-bye in Jesus' name.

He went back the way he had come and gradually quickened his steps. The afternoon was already far advanced, and he still had a good deal to get through. His business now was to work up the feeling of the people before the church council was held.

Beyond this he had no anxieties. After having in this meeting with Emanuel arrived at a certainty on what he had long suspected, he did not doubt that the long abasement of the People's cause, here in this congregation, was at last drawing to a close.

CHAPTER V

Emanuel went slowly homewards.

The sky had become overcast. Without his noticing it, a fine rain had begun to fall. When he reached home, and from the entrance heard Hansine's and the children's voices in the sitting room, he stopped and stood a moment irresolute. Then he turned softly and went into his half empty room on the other side of the passage. Here he sat down heavily on the dusty sofa and buried his face in his hands—astonished and terrified at himself!

He had been so certain that the struggle he had been having with himself for the last few weeks would be fought out on the day he heard that Miss Ragnhild had left the neighborhood, . . . not that he thought she personally had any power over him, but the knowledge of her presence had kept him in a constant state of painful disquietude. He never knew when or where she would appear and draw him into the narcotic-laden atmosphere by which he had already once or twice been stupefied.

And now when at last he knew that she was gone, he was seized by a feeling of emptiness, overwhelmed by a sensation of desolation which he could not master.

He remained sitting in the same position with his face in his hands while the dusk crept in closer and closer around him. He was so absorbed in himself and in the heavy restless beating of his heart that he never heard the door open and Hansine come in.

"Are you there?" she said, after standing a moment motionless, looking at his bent figure.

He started up with almost a cry of dismay.

"What is it? . . . Is it you?"

She stood for a moment without answering.

"Sören said you had come home," she then said. "We have been looking for you everywhere. Why don't you come in to the evening porridge?"

Emanuel's eyes sought to pierce the

gloom of the room, so as to scrutinize her face. For the first time he heard her usually firm voice falter a moment.

"I am coming directly," he said in a muffled voice.

She remained standing a while with her hand on the lock, as if expecting him to say something more to her. Then she opened the door lingeringly and went slowly out.

Half-way out she said, without turning towards him:

"Have you seen the doctor? He seems to have been in the village this afternoon."

"The doctor? . . . Yes, I have. How did you know?"

"Oh, it was only an idea," she said, and closed the door quietly after her.

Emanuel did not move; he had turned pale.

After a time he rose, and walked up and down the room uneasily, and then stopped by the window, gazing out into the dark garden.

He saw that Hansine guessed all, and his heart bled when he thought what she must have been suffering in silence latterly. But now all must . . . should be over! He felt that it would be the final decisive struggle with the unhappy heritage of his blood; the last proof of his emancipation. And he would surely conquer.

CHAPTER VI

Next morning one of the Skibberup people came back from a visit to Sandinge, with the alarming intelligence that the old High School director, who had long been ailing, had suddenly become very ill and could not live. A few hours later an express came announcing his death. With this man disappeared one of the earliest champions of the enlightenment of the peasants; he was in fact the actual founder of the "People's" movement in this part of the country. For a period of thirty years the "Awakened" had looked up to him with veneration, and though latterly he had not altogether approved of the way in which the younger members gave themselves up to politics, instead of turning all their thoughts to what in his eyes was the only necessity of life, namely "spiritual advancement," yet there had never been the slightest break in the good understanding between himself and the Friends. On the contrary, the older he grew, and the more his large beard and long curls were touched with silver, so much the more inviolable was the reverence they all felt for him. To the young it was like hearing an old Saga when he used to tell them about the dark days at the beginning of the movement, when its champions were looked upon as corrupters of youth who deserved the stake. It sounded to them like a saintly martyrdom when he talked to them in his half-jokingly way of those early times when, after the manner of the Apostles, he wandered on foot from town to town, and had to give his lectures in outhouses and servants' rooms, pursued like a felon by the clergy and schoolmasters, despised and annoyed by the peasants themselves, who many a time had set their dogs on him to drive him out of the town.

So it was not merely the ordinary pain of losing a friend, which the news of his death called forth in every part of the district; it was that deep solemn grief which seizes people under a common misfortune. They all felt they had lost their chieftain; and to do honor to his memory—partly also under the influence of certain anxieties, because of internal dissensions, which now, when the central and conciliating bond was wanting, would be certain to break out with renewed strength—a sudden truce was proclaimed between the opposition camps within the congregation. The weaver resigned his secret agitation, the meeting of the church-wardens was postponed, and a veil of oblivion was, for the time, even thrown over the misdeeds of the chairman of the Parish Council. The old director was the only topic of conversation; his photographs were taken down from the walls over the drawers, the more closely to examine the beloved features and the two black spots which purported to represent his youthful, dancing brown eyes. His old stories were repeated, his old letters re-read—little hasty scraps full of exclamations of delight, and warm assurances of friendship; and in the evening people sat outside their doors singing the songs he loved.

The message of death made a deep impression in Veilby Parsonage too. Although Hansine had long had a presentiment that her acquaintance with Sandinge High School would be dearly bought, and although just lately she had plainly seen the vanity of the expectations which the enthusiastic faith and conversation of the deceased had raised in her mind in her girlhood, yet she had never nourished any feeling of bitterness towards him. In those moments when her future looked darkest, she had on the contrary always thought of her old teacher, as of one with whom in her hour of need she could find refuge and comfort. Now when he was gone, she remembered with gratitude all the good she had learned of him; and she particularly fixed her mind on the exhortations to live in truth and self-sacrifice, on which he so constantly dwelt in his speeches to the young. Under the impression caused by his death, and in Emanuel's continued silence, which was full evidence to her whither his yearning was leading him, a resolution was ripening within her, which had occupied her thoughts day and night, since the visit of Miss Ragnhild and Miss Gerda. She told herself it was fruitless any longer to give herself up to a hope which had already often enough disappointed her, and that therefore it would be better both for her and for Emanuel, but especially for the sake of the children's future, that a decisive change should take place in their whole life. One day she would talk plainly to him about their relations to each other; and quietly and cautiously tell him what had been more and more borne in upon her, as the only expedient towards a new and happier life for all of them.

BOOK FIVE

CHAPTER I

One day between the death and the burial of the High School director, when Emanuel went into the stable later than usual, he found Niels still in bed; he gave vent to his long repressed impatience and admonished him severely.

An angry altercation ensued, in the midst of which Emanuel ordered him to take his things and leave the Parsonage. Niels took him at his word immediately, and Emanuel noticed the next day when he wished to engage a new man, that the occurrence had roused a strong feeling against him among a certain section of the people. Niels had always been a pet of the congregation, and many said plainly that Emanuel had sent him away from jealousy, because of the sensation caused by his newspaper articles. Niels was the hero of the day, especially in Maren Smed's ever-growing "Brotherhood-Community."

Although, otherwise, everything was apparently going on as usual at the Parsonage, all the adversity Emanuel had been experiencing, and the increasing severity of his mental struggles had made him almost unrecognizable. His eyes twitched and blinked, he could no longer bear the sunlight, his face was ashen-gray and so thin that there were hollows in his cheeks above his beard. He had not yet exchanged any words with Hansine except on every-day matters. Something had latterly come over her which he could not understand. He saw that she was both seeking his confidence and drawing back from his advances; and he had found no opportunity of bringing out the explanatory and soothing words which he had made up his mind to say to her.

On the day of the funeral he was in a state of restless agitation from the earliest morning. The prospect of having to pass the whole day in the company of several hundred strangers, and of affronted, badly-disposed friends, but, above all, the thought that he would probably be expected to speak—to speak a word of comfort in the hour of depression—had all made him so nervous that he had not closed an eye all night.

It therefore came upon him as a relief that, just as he and Hansine were about to start for Sandinge, a messenger came in hot haste to say that Mrs. Aggerbölle was dying, and he must go at once to administer the sacrament.

"Then you must cross by yourself," he said to Hansine. "I will come over later. You will find plenty of people to go with. Tell Jörgen at the ferry to leave me a boat, and I'll row myself over."

It was a dull gloomy day which involuntarily made one melancholy. The sun as usual had risen in a clear blue sky; but already heavy rain clouds were lowering over the half-mown fields, with their long rows of wet sheaves. Flags were flying half-mast high all over the village, and on the outlying farms and solitary houses; and out on the gray fiord there was a whole fleet of fishing boats, which were being rowed with two or four oars towards the opposite shore, all of them filled with black-clad people bearing wreaths.

In the course of a quarter of an hour Emanuel—in his robes—reached Aggerbölle's dilapitated little house in the desolate and solitary outlying plantation; he walked over the broken-down garden fence, over a row of decaying cabbages and potato stems, and went into the passage. Here he was met by a little humpbacked woman who came crying towards him and called out, "she is just dead!"

He took off his hat and went softly through a half-empty room, with a patched carpet, into the bedroom. Aggerbölle was on his knees by the bed, with his arms round his wife's withered little corpse, sobbing and calling her name aloud. By the window sat or stood four fair-haired, uncommonly pretty, but very pale children.

They stared silently and immovably with their large melancholy eyes, as if they all, down to the smallest, a boy of six, who sat on a footstool with his hands under his cheek, were well aware of their fate.

Emanuel stopped a moment first at the foot of the bed and bowed his head in a silent prayer. Then he went along and gently put his hand on Aggerbölle's shoulder.

"Bernhard!" he said.

But Aggerbölle took no notice. He continued to call his dead wife, and to kiss her hands and press them to his breast amid his sobs.

Emanuel sat down to wait till he had

become calmer and more able to listen to his consolations.

He rested his elbow on the handle of his umbrella, put his hand under his chin, and glanced round the room. He looked towards the beds, the children, and the adjoining room, the door of which stood open—and his heart contracted with pain at the deep, hopeless want which was everywhere displayed.

He knew that Aggerbölle and his wife had moved out there from the noise and temptations of the capital to live their lives in rural peace and happiness. He had often been told how, as young, happy, rosy-cheeked people, they had wandered down by the sea on moonlight nights, arm in arm, cheek against cheek, full of courage and faith in life, and with a determined and honest intention of building up their future on the rocky ground of perseverance. And year by year the ground seemed to slip away from beneath them; hope after hope had sunk in ruins, and of the abode of their happiness nothing now remained but this skeleton of a home, into which death, the final annihilator, had made his solemn entry.

He started. Aggerbölle had at last raised his head, and sat up on the edge of his wife's bed. With his hands on his lap, he was a picture of the most complete helplessness.

"Yes, now it has come, Emanuel!" he said, in a broken voice, while the tears coursed down his swollen cheeks. "The Lord has taken my Sophie from me. Now I am quite alone in the world with our innocent little children! . . . God give thee joy in heaven, my little Sophie! You have been a good and faithful wife. And how happy we once were . . . but in the day of trouble you stood by me, and I thank you for it—I thank you——"

He was again overwhelmed by his tears, and buried his face in his hands.

Emanuel rose, and again went to him and touched his shoulder.

"Bernhard!" he began.

But Aggerbölle would not let him speak.

With his face hidden in his hands, he continued to praise his wife, telling him about the happiness of their early married life, her beauty, and her enjoyment of life, her self-sacrifice and patience.

All at once he raised his head and said wildly:

"But I have always said so, . . . there is some sorcery in this country air, Emanuel . . . something which steals away the strength from those whose cradles have been rocked among the chimney pots. I have felt it myself, . . . and my little Sophie felt it . . . it drains away soul, blood, and marrow from us, Emanuel. And we can make no stand against it . . . we are damned, damned!"

Emanuel turned pale. Aggerbölle had almost shrieked out the last words; and now he threw himself upon the corpse again, taking up in his hands the small head, in a nightcap many sizes too large, and kissing the forehead and the sunken eyes passionately. He was so swallowed up in his sorrow that Emanuel saw it was useless to talk to him, and decided to go.

He only said, "Good-bye, Bernhard, you will soon see me again."

Then he shook hands with each of the children, stroked their pretty fair hair, and took the smallest one up in his arms and kissed him. "God bless you!" he said, and softly left the room.

In the next room he was met by the little deformed woman, who began eagerly to tell him about Mrs. Aggerbölle's last hours of suffering.

"Yes, now her struggles are over . . . and it's a good thing; for it was a sorry sight to see her at the last. It's been a weary night, Emanuel. I was there myself when the Lord set her free. She was lying quite stiff, as if she was gone; then she gave a great sigh, and was dead.

Emanuel did not listen to her story, and tried to get rid of her. But the woman pursued him, first into the passage, then into the garden, full of her news. She did not leave him till he was in the road, then visibly relieved, she went back to the house.

Emanuel walked slowly towards the shore. He held his big blue cotton umbrella behind his back with both hands, and looked at the ground, while his eyes were filled with tears.

Why make oneself blind when one had been made to see? he thought. What was the use of going on lying to oneself . . . and to others? The scales had fallen from his eyes and he was terrified by what he saw! Yes, Bernhard was right. There must be magic in the air here; and he had been under the enchantment himself. He began to understand everything. He felt like one waking from a long heavy sleep, . . . like a captive mountaineer, who, after eight long years in the earthmounds of the gnomes, is suddenly brought to himself by hearing the bells of his native town.

CHAPTER II

When he reached Sandinge a few hours after mid-day, the actual funeral ceremonies were just over. The old High School director had been laid to rest in the village churchyard, in the presence of a couple of thousand persons, among whom were at least fifty priests, all in vestments. Speeches—eleven in all—had been made both in the large hall of the school, which was decorated with fir branches and pennons, and where the body had lain, and in the church and by the grave. Now the people were all partaking of the food they had brought with them in baskets. As the school buildings could not nearly hold all the people, they had, in spite of a continuous fine rain, scattered themselves about the garden and the adjoining fields, where they sought shelter under the trees and their umbrellas.

Many had been soaked on the way to the churchyard, and their boots were covered with mud from the clayey roads. The women had fastened their black skirts up round their waists, or drawn them right up over their heads. But neither the weather, nor the state of the roads had succeeded in robbing the mournful ceremony of its solemn character, or in depressing the spirits of the participators. In various directions was heard the singing of those who had finished their meal, or of the young girls who were wandering about the garden in long rows, too much overcome to eat.

In this multitude there were representatives of the great People's party of the most varied shades. Here were to be seen all kinds of figures, from a couple of Copenhagen liberal leaders—a lawyer with gold-rimmed spectacles, and a sugar merchant with *pince-nez,* who, together with their wives and a couple of young daughters, had driven from the station in a landau—down to soaking wet laborers, who had walked miles and given up a day's harvest wages to follow their faithful friend to his last resting-place. There were schoolmasters, theological students, and High School directors, both of the old type with large beards and quiet beatified smiles, and of the newly-arisen modern type, with the manners and dress of men of the world. Here and there was a young priest, walking arm in arm with his fiancée, under one umbrella, humming the hymns which were being sung around them, looking tenderly at each other now and then—he in a widebrimmed soft plush hat and with his trousers turned up, she with her skirt pinned up and long flat galoshes. There were peasant Members, who even here couldn't help putting their heads together and whispering to each other as they did in the "House." There were delegates from other parts of the country who had brought wreaths and greetings from distant friends; nay, there was even a great Norwegian writer, who at the moment was on a lecturing tour in Denmark—a giant with a huge bushy head of hair, an eagle's face, with spectacles and a white tie—who to the universal joy had appeared, and was attracting great attention by his appearance and loud voice. Wherever he showed himself, a solemn attentive crowd gathered round him, and he was particularly followed about by Niels and some other young men in rather an obtrusive manner; each strove to be the chosen one, upon whose shoulder he laid his hand when he spoke.

"Ah, this is brave!" he was heard to say in his broad sing-song dialect. "You're very fruitful here—I see that today. You are the old soil for the spiritual life of the north, mind that! We are young colonists up in our parts. And we have so much rock—such rocky ground?"

In such a large gathering, with so many well-known men, Emanuel's arrival of course attracted no attention; nor was his absence from the funeral ceremony noticed by any, save the members of his own congregation, among whom it had given rise to some caviling.

He had not, however, stood long among the crowd under the long wooden veranda—or "gallery," as it was called—looking for Hansine, before a loosely-jointed person with dark blue *pince-nez* in addition to a pair of spectacles, darted towards him and clapped both his hands on to his shoulders—

"At last I meet you, Hansted! How are you! how are you! You know me again, don't you? We have been looking for you everywhere . . . you must come with me to see Lena Gylling. She has been asking after you all the time; she is so anxious to make your acquaintance."

Emanuel had hardly time to recognize one of his old university comrades before his arm was taken and he was hurried off up the steps into the crowded lecture hall, which was scented with the fir branches, and filled with the buzz of voices. He was introduced to an elderly, refined, and handsome lady, wearing a peculiar velvet cap trimmed with lace, who was sitting in a corner of the room, surrounded by a number of very talkative persons who were all strangers to Emanuel. It was the well-known Mrs. Gylling, a wealthy widow, who held a kind of popular court in the capital, and whose house was the center of the democratic party. She greeted him with a mixture of youthful bashfulness and motherly warmth, and keeping his hand in hers, said:

"So at last I see you! I have been most impatient to make your acquaintance, as you may imagine. Why do you shut yourself up in your Eden and never let us get some pleasure out of you? You really ought to come and see us in town. We want young blood there too, I can assure you. I had the pleasure of speaking to your wife a little while ago, and I got a half-promise from her that she would prevail on you to come and speak to our community. Now I hope she has power enough over you to make you come; . . . and remember me to her. She was so charming, both to look at and to talk to."

Emanuel hardly listened to her; he was only anxious to get away. But first one and then another of the bystanders came up to shake hands with him, or pat him on the shoulder with exclamations of delight.

"Is this Emanuel Hansted! How delightful! You're just like what we thought you'd be!"

He did not know what to answer, and was quite uncomfortable at the advances of all these strangers. By good luck the Norwegian author came back at this moment from making the round of the garden, and at once drew all the attention to himself.

Emanuel seized the opportunity to slip away again to look for Hansine.

CHAPTER III

He found her at last sitting in the shelter of a briar rose on the outer side of the garden wall, with a strange peasant woman of a large and powerful build, and wearing a head-covering which was different from the stiff hood-shaped ones generally worn in this neighborhood; hers was tied at the back in a large loose knot.

Even from a distance Emanuel was surprised to see the stranger holding Hansine's hand in her lap; and when he got nearer, to see that they were both extremely agitated, and that the unknown had red eyes, as if she had been crying.

When he reached them she rose and stretched out her hand with a broad "How are you,"—her face at the same time turning fiery red, and all the freckles on her nose and under her pale eyes looking quite white.

Only now did Emanuel recognize the friend of Hansine's youth, the red-haired Ane, who had undergone the remarkable fate of being married to a "Skalling."

The Skallings were fisher-folk who inhabited a tongue of land right out by the open sea, from whence—just as in the time of the old inhabitants of Skibberup—they paddled about in near and distant fiords and sold the produce of their fishing round the shore. They were absolutely untouched by the new intellectual movements among the people, and were shunned by the rest of the coast population on account of their lawlessness and wild ways.

Seven or eight years ago—shortly after Hansine's marriage—Ane had met a handsome, young black-haired Skalling in the town, and to her great horror had fallen violently in love with him. She struggled for a long time against her inclinations, which from shame she had not even imparted to Hansine. But at last she could no longer withstand the young fisherman's daring advances, and one fine day, in a wild easterly storm, he sailed down in his boat and carried her back with him the same evening, soon after fetching away her old adoptive parents to a home in his seaweed thatched hut. The event had caused a painful sensation at the time in Skibberup and Veilby; no one had thought that Ane would let herself be hoodwinked like that by a pair of bright eyes, and she was sincerely pitied for the life she would have to lead among these wild people. For some time after the parting she and Hansine exchanged letters, which on Ane's side grew shorter and shorter, until they at last ceased. Hansine understood very well that it was because she was ashamed to acknowledge that she was happy; and the thought of the doings of the friend of her childhood out there by the fresh open sea, had often, in the course of these years, made her feel her own lot doubly heavy, and the restless life in Veilby Parsonage doubly depressing.

Emanuel was a little disturbed by again seeing Ane in close companionship with his wife. He had become quite unused to the slightest display of intimacy on Hansine's part towards any one except himself; and he saw at once that the two had taken up the threads of their old friendship, and had opened their hearts to one another.

He had just unrobed, and now sat down on the stump of a tree beside them. He asked Ane, with a certain amount of compassion in his voice, how she was getting on in Skallingland. She answered, very well, and told him that she had five fine children and three sheep, and that she and her Matthias had built themselves a new house last summer; and that it was Matthias' own idea to bring her over to the old director's funeral, as he had some herring nets near, which he could examine at the same time.

She spoke quietly, with some shyness and without ever looking up at Emanuel; but she kept tight hold of Hansine's hand all the time. Although she tried to conceal it, her tone plainly showed how the meeting with her old High School friends had disappointed her anticipations; and that she was only anxious to get back to her life on the shore,—her sheep, her children, and her Matthias.

Emanuel only listened carelessly; he soon fell back into his own thoughts. He sat with his cheek resting on his hand—a habit he had lately acquired—looking down at the ground.

"By the way, Hansine," he said, suddenly looking up. "Mrs. Gylling, from Copenhagen, tells me you have been talking to her. How do you like her?"

"Oh, pretty well!"

After a moment's silence, he continued:

"What did you find to say to each other?"

"Well, that's not easy to say, so many people spoke to me; but it seemed to be all about nothing."

"No one can accuse you of being enthusiastic, at any rate!" he said, with a forced smile.

"No; I don't suppose I am."

Again Emanuel was silent for a time.

The somewhat cool interest which Hansine took in the People's cause and its champions was nothing new to him; it had often surprised and grieved him. Nor did he yet understand her in the least on this point. He could not imagine what it was that had disappointed her; and at this moment he felt keenly how far they had latterly drifted apart, and what a long time it was since they had had any confidential conversation with each other.

He promised himself that from that day he would leave nothing undiscussed between them. Now when all other ties were breaking, now when they found themselves standing alone, they must come together again in full mutual understanding; and in his life with her and the children his soul should find satisfaction and peace. . . .

In the meantime the weather had cleared up. The clouds had dispersed, the blue sky was appearing here and there; and Emanuel saw crowds of people flocking from the garden towards a tumulus in an adjoining field, from which the old director used to speak in the summer on national festivals.

"I suppose we must go and see what is going on!" he said.

"I thought it was time to be getting home," said Hansine.

"Yes, I think it is."

Just then three soldierly Skibberup youths passed them at quick march, with swinging arms and resounding steps.

"Are you going to sit there?" they shouted in passing. "I suppose you don't want to hear!"

Then they got up and followed them.

CHAPTER IV

The crowd of people who gradually assembled round the stone on the barrow consisted mainly of Veilby and Skibberup people. The visitors from Copenhagen and the Norwegian author had left an hour ago to catch their train, and others whose homes were distant had driven off one after another.

Still there were some strange faces among them, and notably one which attracted much attention; young, stout, and pale, with a suspicious look and thick powerful lips. It belonged to the much talked of Ole Madsen, a laborer's son, a curate in West Jutland, who had lately become the great hope of the People's Cause. He was standing with his hands behind his back, talking to Hansen the weaver; his long black coat and flat black hat gave him a certain resemblance to a Roman Catholic priest.

Emanuel's arrival was observed by most of those present, and he couldn't avoid feeling that he was expected to speak. He had himself, at the sight of so many of his congregation, felt a necessity to address them . . . openly to lay his doubts before them and to free his position from all misconstruction. Was it not his plain duty, he asked himself? Would it not be cowardice to delay for a single day expressing his new views on the People's Cause and its future?

He forced a way through the crowds and mounted to the speaker's place amid a deep silence.

He began by a tribute to the friend round whose bier they had met today. He said they must all be deeply grateful to the Almighty for this man whose life had been one of pure love, utter unselfishness, and faithful affection.—But had the deceased never been disappointed in his hopes, he then asked; had his faith never suffered shipwreck? He had got the impression, he added, that the old High School director, in his later years, had been a little depressed and no longer looked to the future with those bright hopes which before had helped him lightly over all the adversities of life. Nor was it any use to deny that the People's Cause was at the moment passing through an hour of tribulation. Its friends had a great defeat behind them—great expectations dashed to the ground—and, like every defeat, this one had also sown suspicions and dissensions among the vanquished. But instead of attempting to hide the truth, and to get out of its gravity by lies, and hurling complaints at one another, for each one's share in the common misfortune; they should all examine themselves closely, and try to find out where they had trespassed, where they had made a mistake, and what in the future was to be done to remedy the defect.

There began to be some disturbance among the crowd. He had already been interrupted once or twice by somewhat uproarious shouts.

He continued, however, without noticing them.

"I won't mention the mistake in 'tactics' which we have made by undervaluing our opponents' strength, by not sufficiently remembering that the community we wish to overthrow is built up upon timbers and piles having their foundations in old time. Nor will I allude to the fact that we have perhaps been too ready to stamp with selfishness those who did not in all points share our views. There is no doubt among these, not a few who acted with the most upright desire to work out good and to seek out God's ways, and from whose toleration we might perhaps take example."

"Dr. Hassing!" a voice in the crowd called out, an allusion which was understood and immediately raised a laugh.

Emanuel turned pale. He recognized his former man Niels' harsh voice, and was obliged to stop a moment to calm and control himself.

Then he continued:

"But what I specially wish to allude to, is the great internal rupture which the People's party—and here I mean the peasant class in particular—in my opinion is suffering under, and which has been fatal to it. We have been far too pleased with ourselves. We have been far too certain that we were in the right . . . and therefore we could not understand that the Lord did not give us what we asked for at once. Nay, let me use the right word . . . we have thought too much of ourselves, we have been too presumptuous; we have latterly been too busy sweeping at our neighbor's door, dusting his house and searching his heart, and in so doing we have forgotten our own."

He went on talking for a little time—quietly and with self-command—although the interruptions became more frequent and noisy. But when at last he was hardly allowed to speak, he concluded abruptly by hoping that all friends of truth and justice among the vanquished, might learn that not self-righteousness but self-esteem, not arrogance but toleration, were the means to raise them and lead to eventual conquest.

When he stepped down he read in the glances he met on every side, and in the way in which the crowd fell back before him, that by his words he had broken every bond, between himself and the congregation. . . .

Loud shouts of approval suddenly burst out. Hansen the weaver was mounting to the speaker's place in his deliberate manner. The sight of the old champion, who for so many years had not spoken at any meeting, acted at this moment like an electric shock, and the people crowded round him in expectant excitement, so as not to lose a word or an expression of his face.

He stood, just as in former days, for a long time silent, with one hand on his back, holding his chin in the other, while his glance roamed over the crowd with a smile. At last he said slowly in his innocent voice:

"Well, that was a very queer speech we've just heard from Emanuel. I stood there pinching my ears and thinking I couldn't be hearing right; and at last I said to myself: 'You're asleep, Jens! you're dreaming that you're listening to our old friend Archdeacon Tönnesen.' "

"Hear, hear! Bravo!" the Skibberup people thundered.

"This is just how it is, ye see; I can't help thinkin' of another speech Emanuel made, ever so many years ago, . . . it was the very first time he spoke to us in our old Meeting House. He sang a different song then . . . then peasants were the very best sort o' folks Emanuel knew. . . . Ah, we were that nice and that honest, it was a'most too much of a good thing. Why, I daresay a good many of you can mind that speech; folks thought a good deal of it then. I don't mind sayin' that for my part I wasn't near so taken with it; and so Emanuel's words today aren't so much of a surprise. It's always like that with folks that fill their mouths too full; they have to spit some of it out again!——Well, then there was what Emanuel said about our being so taken with ourselves, and everything had gone wrong because of it. We ought to learn of the good people in the towns, he said, and then the Almighty would be sure to give us what we asked for.—Oh, no, I've not got much faith in that. My idea is, on the contrary, that we've been far too ready to let ourselves be led by the nose by these Copenhagen people who've turned up here in the last few years, calling themselves friends of the People's cause, and without more ado made themselves leaders, . . . and in my opinion that's why everything's gone wrong. It's been a sort of a fashion among the town folks to make themselves friends of the people, and I daresay we country folks were a bit flattered that so many fine clever people busied themselves about us; we were ready to go out of our five senses just to please them. We thought it a mighty fine proud thing when a lawyer in gold spectacles or his fine wife came and patted us on the back and called us 'little friend.' Then when into the bargain they came and settled here like one of ourselves, and even married one of our girls, . . . why, then we were so mightily honored we didn't know which leg to stand on.—But it was a kind of disease, and I always thought if we only gave it time it would wear itself out again. And I fancy I've seen signs lately that we were comin' to the end of the farce we'd been such innocents as to let ourselves be fooled by. And I think that we can begin, little by little, our old honest work of fighting against the tyranny of the educated, and spiritual pride . . . don't ye think so too, friends?"

"Yes, yes!—hear, hear!" again resounded from the audience, who for a time had been silent.

Emanuel's face was deeply flushed. The weaver's insults, and the approving shouts of his former friends, hit him like the lashes of a whip, and he had the greatest difficulty in preserving his self-command.

At the same time a voice within him said, What are you enraged by? Isn't it your own work of which you see the consummation here? You are only reaping what you sowed. Don't complain, go away quietly . . . go away and be ashamed of yourself!

"Let us get away from here," said Hansine, by his side.

"Then there's all that about toleration that Emanuel talked so much about," continued the weaver. "Well, toleration is all very well. But as the saying has it, 'you mustn't let any one sit so close to you that he sits your thighs off.' It's not so long ago when the peasants in one place, denying the faith of their childhood, elected a freethinker, a regular bad atheist; and then, when some people thought it was going rather too far, what happened?

"Didn't our dear pastors and the learned gentlemen at the university say, 'Blow it all—don't let us ask people about their faith; it would be impertinent and rude. What will our opponents think of us?' . . . . Now that's the sort of new-fangled learning we've had so much of from Copenhagen, right down materialistic principles, one may say . . . but they don't agree with my reading of the catechism. And I'll just repeat here what our guest, Pastor Ole Madsen, whispered to me a moment ago during Emanuel's speech. 'Beware of false prophets,' he said. And for my part I'll add, beware of all that talking too much about toleration . . . for they've generally got something or other on their conscience. Mark that!"

Although the smile had hardly left his face a moment, one could tell both by his voice and the way he pointed to the sky every time he named the Almighty, with what suppressed passion he spoke—and the crowd stood round open mouthed, as if rooted to the spot.

Emanuel and Hansine had left, and gone back towards the school. On the way they met Ane, who had left the field before them to fetch her things, and who now came back to say good-bye. Emanuel bid her good-bye absently, and immediately went on—he was impatient to get home. But Hansine held Ane's hand a long time, and said in her quiet calm manner:

"Then it's a bargain—when you hear from me?"

"But are you really in earnest?" exclaimed Ane, both pleased and uneasy. "I didn't quite believe it before."

"Yes, I mean it—if you will have me?"

"Won't I, my chickie? You may be sure I will. . . . But what do you think Emanuel will say?"

"I don't know, but I will write to you. Good-bye! So long!"

Emanuel meanwhile had stopped a little way off, and turned round to wait for Hansine. He saw the dark mass of people crowded round the barrow, and the weaver's swaying figure sharply outlined against the horizon, and he was filled with deep sadness. He remembered the time when he came out here in the belief that here, at any rate, he would find the human heart in all its pristine purity and simplicity; and now, up there, stood a master in intrigue and scandal triumphing over him! He thought how he had come out to preach the gospel of love; and up there stood the apostle of hatred, stretching out his blood-red hands towards heaven, urging on strife and oppression.

Emanuel and Hansine did not speak to each other on the long road from the school to the shore. Only, after they got into their boat, and when Emanuel had rowed a little way out into the fiord in the quiet evening air, Hansine, who was sitting in the stern, smoothing the fringe of her shawl, said:

"Have you nothing to say to me, Emanuel?"

He stopped rowing and rested his arms on his oars while he looked out to sea.

"Yes; there is no other way now. . . . We must go away," he answered, out of his own thoughts.

"What have you thought of doing?" she asked, in a little while.

"Indeed, I don't know. I suppose I must try and get another living . . . a small place, somewhere or other in Jutland, on the heath or among the sand dunes; I suppose they won't deny me that?"

"You shouldn't do that, Emanuel."

"What do you mean? . . . Why should I not?"

"No; for it will soon be just the same as it is here. It won't be long before you will be dissatisfied and only want to get away."

He looked at her with a searching glance; she had put in words his own gnawing thoughts, which he had not had courage to divulge. The prospect of beginning a fresh life in a new solitude—in a new, wide, silent desert,—made him shudder.

"What do you want me to do then?"

"I think you should go where your longings draw you, Emanuel; . . . it's no use trying to hide it from each other any longer; we may as well talk about it plainly. . . . You are longing to get back to your family and the other ways in which you feel at home, and it's only natural. So I think you shouldn't struggle with yourself any longer, Emanuel; it will be no good. I think you will be able to get some work either in Copenhagen or some other large town, so that you can be together again with your old circle of friends. I can quite understand that you need it."

Emanuel lifted his head and looked at her in astonishment.

"But do you want to do that, Hansine?"

"I?" she said, bending still deeper over the fringe of her shawl, which she had been smoothing all the time:

"I want to do whatever will be best for all of us."

CHAPTER V

The very next day Emanuel drove over to the diocesan town to see the Bishop, and to ask him to accept his resignation. Hansine walked restlessly up and down the long alleys nearly all the afternoon —wrapped in a little woolen shawl, as if she were cold,—waiting for his return.

Every moment she went up the little mound from whence the road was visible to see whether the carriage was in sight.

At last, just before sunset, he came; and half-an-hour later they were both walking in the chestnut avenue at the bottom of the garden, where they had gone to be undisturbed.

Hansine sat down on the rustic seat, which had been here ever since former days, while Emanuel, excited by his journey and full of experiences and news, walked up and down before her, telling her everything.

At first the old Bishop addressed him rather sharply. He said he was ungrateful, nay treacherous, and declared with great decision that his request could not possibly be granted. But he softened by degrees, and in the end sorrowfully agreed to everything.

"So now we are free, Hansine!" he concluded, stopping in front of her. "We can leave as soon as we get the permission."

She was leaning forward, with her arms resting on her knees, looking at the toe of her shoe, with which she was scraping up the damp earth.

"Well . . . that's just what I want to tell you, Emanuel," she began—and it was evident that she had difficulty in getting the words out; "I can't go to Copenhagen with you."

"What's that? I don't understand you at all! What do you mean?"

"I mean . . . not at once," she corrected herself, when she saw that Emanuel had not the slightest idea of her purpose. "Everything there is far too strange; I should only be a burden to you until you have arranged your affairs, and made a position and a home. . . . I should not be able to help you in anything. And, besides, I need a little quiet time to myself. Everything has been so disturbed lately."

"Well, there's perhaps something in that," said Emanuel, beginning to walk up and down again with his arms behind him.

"But I must tell you that this will hardly be a pleasant place of abode for you. I saw that in just driving through Skibberup; we no longer live among friends, but among bitter enemies."

"Oh, yes; I've thought of all that. I think I could go and stay with Ane for a while. We talked about it the other day; she said there were two rooms in their new house which they did not use; and I was welcome to have them she said."

"With Ane? Out in Skallingland! Among those dreadful people! Whatever are you thinking about, Hansine?"

"Oh, I don't suppose they are as bad as they are made out, . . . they're not—Ane said so—and she doesn't seem to have come to any harm."

"But it won't do, all the same, Hansine; . . . it won't do, for the children's sake. Isn't it both your wish and mine that they should get away from the influences by which they have been hitherto surrounded . . . and, in Sigrid's case, it's high time they did. She's a dear, sweet child, but she easily picks up bad habits, I've noticed."

"I've been telling you that for a long time, Emanuel."

"Yes, but then, I don't understand why you want to——"

"Well, what I thought was, that you'd better take them with you to Copenhagen. You will have to set up a home there . . . and I think it would be good for the children's sakes if I were to keep away from them for a while. For, you know, I can't set them in the right way about anything; I should rather hinder them in taking to their new friends, and in the education and cultivation which we both think right for them. So I thought that your sister . . . she would help you with their education; you know she lost her own child a little while ago, and I daresay she would make a good foster mother to them."

She maintained the same quiet, controlled voice the whole time, but she had grown very pale, and kept her eyes on the ground.

Emanuel was silent. She had again expressed the same thoughts which had occupied him, but which he had not had the heart to mention to her, for fear of hurting her feelings. He saw well that it would be very difficult for Hansine to manage a house under such strange circumstances, and that she would not be that support to the children which they would require, especially at first. He saw, too, that with her peculiar, incomprehensible, and often repellent ways to strangers, she would prepare for herself—and perhaps also for him—many difficulties; moreover, he had been thinking all day with much anxiety how his friends would receive her, and on the whole, how they would take his return. He glanced at her, and when he saw her emotion, he went up to her and clasped her head tenderly.

"Put all these thoughts away, my dear. Don't let us give way to all these worries. This is just the time for us to cling closer to one another. We must share both good and evil in the fight for our home and happiness. . . . Perhaps it won't always be easy; but if we only hold together we shall pull through somehow, you will see!"

She had no longer the strength to gainsay him—was not even capable of preventing his bending over her and kissing her.

. . . They did not allude to the matter for the next few days, but they both prepared for departure. Hansine could see that it continued to occupy him, and as he became more unsettled and anxious every day about the step he was going to take, she held more firmly than ever to her decision.

It was not long before he led the conversation back to the same subject of his own accord. He said that perhaps, after all, it would be wiser not to set up housekeeping as long as their future was so unsettled, especially as long as he was without prospects or income. It had occurred to him that till he had found work, either clerical or teaching in Copenhagen or some other town, he and the children might stay with his father, who lived alone in a large house, and would probably be glad to have them. He consoled her by saying that the separation would be short; as soon as he got to the capital he would try to get a post which would again enable them to live together in comfort and contentment.

Urged on by Hansine, he wrote a long letter the same day to his father, in which he fully—and so as to parry the sympathy of his family—somewhat self-consciously explained why he was returning with his children to Copenhagen, while his wife remained in the country. In conclusion, he asked if he and his children might enjoy the hospitality of his old home till he could make a new one for himself.

CHAPTER VI

Both he and Hansine waited impatiently for the answer. It was very unpleasant for them now in Veilby Parsonage. They quickly perceived that the people especially those of Skibberup, had taken up his words as a challenge.

The postponed church council had been held without any notification having been sent to him; and altogether he was made to feel that they wished to be rid of him. They even talked of calling in an independent priest to the ministry, and a deputation was being prepared to go to Ole Madsen, who, it was expected, would return a favorable answer.

At the service on Sunday the Ness Church was, just as in Provst Tönnesen's time, quite empty; orders had actually been sent out that no one was to attend, and Hansen the weaver had so completely regained his old supremacy that no one dared to oppose his commands.

From time to time, however, Emanuel received proofs both of grateful affection and of anger at the behavior which was being shown to him. When it became known that he had sent in his resignation, some of the Veilby people even took courage and began to collect money for the purchase of a silver coffee-pot and an arm-chair, which—just as in the case of Provst Tönnesen—they proposed to present to him on his departure.

The old feud between the Veilby and Skibberup people had broken out again more fiercely than ever, and the formerly harmonious congregation now found itself in a complete state of disruption. The chairman of the Parish Council, after his downfall, had gone back to his old life of drinking and card-playing, and he was drawing more and more of his friends after him to his orgies. Niels, on the other hand, who was always looked upon as a martyr to the good and holy Cause, had taken the first upward step towards the goal of his dreams.

At the ever increasingly popular prayer-meetings of Maren Smeds he was beginning to educate himself as a wandering preacher, and to this end he had procured a wide-brimmed hat and dark-blue spectacles.

At the Parsonage the preparations for departure were in full swing. Emanuel, who had suddenly lost all interest in his work and only wished to be rid of the trouble of the fields and stables as soon as possible, sold all his standing crops to a neighbor, who, for part of the purchase money was to look after the land until his successor was appointed. He also turned cows, horses, and agricultural implements into money, and with it paid the rather numerous petty debts which, in the course of years, he had been foolish enough to contract indiscriminately among many of his former friends; and which more than anything had contributed to weaken his influence in the congregation.

Wild with delight at the prospect of Copenhagen, Sigrid rushed in and out, shaking her golden locks, and infecting with her mirth little Dagny, who had grown in the summer and now trotted about alone. As soon as Emanuel appeared, Sigrid sprang caressingly to him to get him to tell her about the delights which awaited her. Every day in the dusk after dinner he had to sit with her on his knee, telling her about the Copenhagen streets, and all the people, the lighted shops, the tinkling tram-cars, the women shouting their wares, and the black dust men by the round tower, the harbor with the ships, the king's red liveried coachman, and the illuminations at Tivoli . . . and he was always so taken up with his stories, which woke so many slumbering memories in him, that it grew quite dark before he noticed it.

Meanwhile Hansine sat quietly in her arm-chair, stitching at the children's Sunday clothes and knitting them new stockings, "so that their grand relations in the capital should not be ashamed of them," as she once said. Emanuel could not understand how it was she remained so pale now, when they had every hope for a brighter future. He had even once or twice discovered her in tears; and when he asked what was the matter, she would not answer. He also wondered at the shyness, nay, almost repulsion with which she met all his advances. No sooner did he sit down by her and try to take her hand than she discovered an errand in the kitchen or elsewhere.

He came to the conclusion that it was nervousness at the break-up of their home and the approaching separation which she wanted to hide from him, and he tried in every way to soothe and cheer her. But it almost seemed as if his sympathy wounded her, and at last he found it best to leave her in peace.

The anxiously expected answer from Copenhagen came almost as soon as it could.

It was one of his father's usual missives on a large, square sheet of paper, inside of which there was a scented and much crossed note from his sister Betty. Emanuel, who sat down at once to read it aloud to Hansine, was so much moved by all the love and longing for him which they both breathed, that his eyes filled with tears in reading them.

His father's letter was in his usual rather stilted style. He wrote that he was now an old man with not many steps to the grave, and that a greater pleasure could not have been given him than the prospect of again seeing his eldest son, whom he for so long had missed. Without in the least reproaching him for his self-conceit, he offered him a hearty welcome to his house.

"Your two old rooms shall be ready to receive you at the shortest notice," he wrote, "and I need hardly add that your children will be beloved guests; rooms shall be prepared for them in your immediate promixity, and we shall do all in our power to make them happy among us. As you perhaps know I rented a not inconsiderable piece of garden ground a few years ago which belongs to the property, it was at one time rented by the late Konferentsraad Tagemann (whom I daresay you remember); so there is a sufficient playground for your children, and I shall see that the carpenter is sent for to put up a swing and anything else necessary for their amusement. Nor will they be in want of playmates, the Löbners on the third floor, and the Winthers on the ground floor have nice, well-behaved children, so I hope they won't miss the free country life too much. I quite understand your wife's decision to remain in the country for the present, and quite agree with it; she would hardly be satisfied with the strange life of a large town at once.

"This is all for today. Your brother Carl sends his love; he wishes to point out that all 'Kammer-yunkers' are not 'so wicked'—he particularly wishes me to use this word—as you perhaps think, and he is looking forward to the day when he can invite you to the guard-room of the Amalienborg Palace to convince you of it.

"My love to all of you.—Your affectionate Father."

"Only think," burst out Emanuel at the end, with a beaming glance at Hansine, who was sitting in her arm-chair bent over her work. "I am to have my old rooms with the view over the canal, the Exchange, and Kristiansborg Palace! What fun it'll be! . . . and isn't that grand about the garden? Just think how the children can play about there! Don't you think it sounds delightful?"

Hansine only nodded. Her bosom swelled, and she closed her eyes like a person going through a mental struggle.

The letter from Betty was stamped with the depression caused by the loss of her child.

She wrote:—"You don't know how empty and sad our home has become since the Lord took my little Kai from me. I am longing for your little girls, so that I may again hear children's voices and laughter around me. Tell your wife not to be anxious about them—I know a mother's fears. We will guard them as well as we can while she is away from them. But I long most of all for you, dear brother, whom I have not seen for so many years. Miss Tönnesen, who saw you lately and who visits me a good deal, tells me you are so brown and have a big beard. How delighted I shall be to see you! And you'll be kind to me, won't you, Emanuel? I do so need your comfort. I am longing to lean my head against your shoulder and have a talk with you. Yes, Emanuel,—our Lord visits us. May we have the strength to bear our burdens!

"I don't think you need be anxious about your future; neither father nor my husband think so either. Yesterday, after father had received your letter and sent it up for me to read, we were dining out with Mr. Justice Munck; the Dean, who is a friend of ours, sat next to me, and I was so pleased with your letter that I couldn't help telling him that you were moving in to town. Curiously enough he seemed to have heard something about it beforehand, and seemed quite pleased about it. I asked him at last outright whether he thought you could get one of the smaller livings here in town, and he didn't think it at all unlikely. 'Your brother has such a good degree,' he said, 'and we want young and tried men here.' He laid special stress on *'tried.'* Altogether he talked so nicely about you (he remembers you when you lived at home) that I don't think the old views, which you have now changed, will go against you."

CHAPTER VII

The day of departure came at last, in the beginning of September.

It was a very busy day, and full of emotion. Early in the morning Emanuel went to the Skibberup churchyard to take leave of Laddie's grave, and from there to see his father- and mother-in-law, and Hansine's brother Ole, who now managed his parents' property. These farewells were somewhat cool; Else especially was much affected by the general feeling in Skibberup, and although by Hansine's desire the visit to Skallingland was spoken of as only of short duration, a distrustful expression came into her light eyes every time the stay with Ane was mentioned.

The deputation before referred to arrived at the Parsonage in the morning, with a plated coffee-pot and an armchair; and at last, well on in the afternoon, the carriage came which Emanuel, to avoid being under any obligation to his neighbors, had ordered from a livery stable in the town, . . . it was a landau with silver mountings, and a coachman in livery.

Emanuel rushed about with all a traveler's feverish excitement among boxes and trunks. He wore a new black cloth coat, and his hair and beard were newly trimmed. He was followed everywhere by Sigrid, who would not let him out of her sight, just as if she was afraid he would leave her behind. She had hardly closed her eyes all night, but had asked what time it was every half hour; and ever since early morning she had faithfully carried about her own private treasures—a little tin pail, a broken doll's head, and two match boxes filled with colored pebbles—nor could she be persuaded to lay them down a moment.

Abelone, whom Hansine had persuaded to go with the children and stay with them for a time, went about crying nervously; and in the empty stable, Sören the cowherd was sitting on the edge of a manger pondering on the manifold changes of life.

Hansine was perfectly calm all day, and made herself useful everywhere. Nobody could read in her face that she was absolutely convinced she was today seeing her husband and children for the last time. . . . She knew that the children would soon forget her among all the strange people and new things which would occupy their minds; and when they grew older and accustomed to their surroundings, they would feel it a hindrance and a shame to have a mother who wore a peasant's cap and who spoke in peasant's dialect. But she had promised herself that they should never suffer for the faults of others. They should fully and entirely share in the bright joys of life, in which she had once dreamed she might herself share. And Emanuel? To him also she would soon be as a heavy burden which he would long to shake off. She had seen latterly, in a hundred ways, how in his thoughts he was already living in a world very far removed from hers, and which she would never be in a condition to share with him. She knew that he could not be long in his old circle without feeling the deep gulf which separated them; and it would therefore come to him as a relief when she one day wrote to him that she would never go back to him, that he was free, and that it would be fruitless on his part to attempt to make her alter her decision.

She reproached him with nothing. She only blamed herself for her arrogance in thinking that she could fill a place on the upper benches. Nay, she was not even surprised at what had just come to pass. Her wonder was that it had not happened long before. The experiences of the last seven years had so often appeared curiously unreal to her. She would sometimes be overcome by the impression of still being the young girl in her father's house, and that her marriage, and all her life in Veilby Parsonage was only a long uneasy dream, from which she would be awakened by the crowing of some cock. When the moment of departure came, she kissed the children, and said goodbye to Emanuel, in so quiet a manner that it might really have been thought that the parting was only to be a short one. She followed them to the carriage, wrapped up the children well, and told Abelone to be sure to put on their clean pinafores before they reached Copenhagen.

When at parting, Emanuel was overcome by emotion, and continued to clasp her to him, and to kiss her on the forehead, she said to cheer him, that he was not to worry about her, she would get on very well.

"Look after the children, Emanuel," she said, at the last moment,—and then, as if in these words she had poured out all her remaining strength, she turned and went up the steps before the carriage started.

"Go up on to the mound in the garden—so that we may wave to you—till the last!" Emanuel called after her.

But she did not turn, and went quickly into the house.

The coachman cracked his whip, and the horses started off. When the carriage rolled under the arched gateway, Sigrid shouted hurrah!

On the way through the village the people mostly called out "Lykkelig Reise" as they passed; many even took off their hats in involuntary awe of the landau and the liveried coachman.

When the carriage reached the highroad, Emanuel said, "Out with the pocket handkerchiefs, children!"

As soon as they saw Hansine on the little mound, in the corner of the garden, they all began to wave. Why doesn't she wave back, thought Emanuel. "Wave children . . . wave!" he said, with his eyes full of tears.

But the figure on the mound did not move; . . . They had no answer to their "Paa Gensyn" (au revoir).

Hansine stood like a statue till the last glimpse of the carriage had disappeared in the distance;——then she went quietly down. Suddenly a dizziness came over her, and she sank heavily on to one of the little wooden steps which led from the path to the mound. Hour after hour, she remained sitting with her face buried in her hands, while the autumn wind moaned sadly through the trees above her. At sunset she rose and went towards the house. She was to spend the night at her parents' house, in the old room where she used to sleep as a girl. Ane's husband would come the next day to fetch her in his boat and take her to her future home.

She fetched a little bundle of clothes from the empty bedroom, then went to the stable, and said good-bye to Sören, who was now sole master of the place, and left the Parsonage.

THE LIFE AND WORKS OF HENRIK PONTOPPIDAN

By ALFRED JOLIVET

HENRIK PONTOPPIDAN was born on July 24, 1857, in the small Danish town of Frederica, where his father Dines Pontoppidan was a minister. His earliest childhood memories, however, dated from 1863, when his father moved to the nearby town of Randers. For the rest of his life, Henrik retained a great affection for Randers, and wrote and spoke of it with tenderness. But it was in Randers, in 1864, that he lived through one of the most tragic episodes of Danish history: the occupation of the town by German and Austrian troops. Henrik was too young to grasp the significance of the event; the teeming soldiery merely amused him, and he could neither understand nor share the unhappiness of his parents. It is interesting, however, to note the feelings that this memory evoked in the grown man. The occupation and sack of Randers was perpetrated while England and the rest of Europe turned a blind eye, and in his memoirs Pontoppidan recalled a jest of the English Prime Minister, Lord Palmerston: "So complicated is the Schleswig question that only three men can understand it: the Prince Consort, who is dead; a German professor, who has gone mad; and myself, who have forgotten it." The adult Pontoppidan comments bitterly: "What a cost to England and the world was Palmerston's lapse of memory, and the adoration of Queen Victoria for her husband, the unofficial German ambassador to the English court. It gave Bismarck full liberty of action."

Pontoppidan's father was a follower of the Danish theologian and poet N. F. S. Grundtvig (1783–1872), who preached that all culture, and especially Danish culture, must be intensely nationalist in origin and spirit. He exchanged ideas with other local pastors who were also interested in "Grundtvigianism," though he disapproved of their endless controversies and of certain aspects of the Danish past as exemplified in the folklore and ballads taught in the high schools. But when Grundtvig died, Dines Pontoppidan gave an address in the town hall of Randers on the influence of Grundtvig on the Danish church, praising his virtues and the beauty of his religious poetry, but noting that two essential qualities of Christianity, humility and contrition, were absent from his work. Henrik himself believed that these qualities were the essential ingredients of his father's character, though they were apparently overlaid by a cold outward formality.

In his memoirs, Pontoppidan recalls a significant and revealing childhood incident: the death of a workman, his friend, who died from an injury while sawing wood. "I wept bitter tears," he wrote, "at the loss of this friend, and I often missed him. I once went with one of our maid servants to see him in his wretched dwelling, and afterward often thought about it. One of his children was on his lap, chortling with pleasure, and he was playing with the child. I had never known this myself, and although the child's clothes were patched and the house squalid, I could not help envying their home and their father, and wishing I were in their place."

Pontoppidan's mother seems to have had a greater direct influence on him than his father. Though often ailing and fatigued, she had great patience and fortitude and radiated warmth and affection to the family's sixteen children. Her hard life taught her compassion for those less fortunate than herself. She was a cultivated woman, well read in history and economics, and she condemned contemporary society for its failure to solve the problem of poverty.

Despite financial difficulties in his own family, Henrik was sent to the Polytechnic, or college of applied science, in Copenhagen. There, at first, his sole ambition was to obtain an engineering degree. He believed that a new era had dawned in Danish history, an era in which technology would change the world; and in this changing world the would-be Engineer Henrik Pontoppidan hoped to play his part. Meanwhile, he led the life of a poor student, wandering from one boarding house to another, until the day when he was lucky enough to find lodgings with an old couple in the Nyboder part of the town. With pathetic delight, he wrote home that they treated him like a son, and years later, in the novel *Lykke-Per* (Lucky Peter, 1898–1904), he described the gratitude with which he always remembered them.

He visited the museums and galleries of Copenhagen, taking advantage of the days when admission was free. He attended High Mass in the Royal Chapel when Bishop Martensen officiated in his velvet cope and full regalia. In his memoirs, Pontoppidan writes that he went to see Martensen rather as one might go to the zoo to see a rhinoceros. He also describes the impression made on him by the sermons of that veritable Savonarola, Pastor Frimodt of the Indre Mission. Pontoppidan went out of curiosity, to hear Frimodt's flamboyant descriptions of Hell—a place that clearly awaited most of his congregation. The new Savonarola would single out one of his flock and shriek, "And you, you old sinner! Yes you, the one with the beard and white hair! Listen to me! The Day of Judgment is approaching. Have you prepared to meet your Maker?"

Pontoppidan also heard of another orator in Copenhagen, the great critic and historian, Georg Brandes; but it was only later that he came to understand his importance. During this period, it was the political rather than the literary struggle that interested him. He followed Parliamentary debates and attended some of the daring speeches of Berg, the leader of the opposition. He observed the dismay of Berg's opponents when the opposition party threatened the dissolution of Parliament, but he observed, too, that the government leader Jacob Estrup was soon governing the country against the popular will. Pontoppidan speaks of the Estrup regime in his memoirs: "Where now, before the Houses of Parliament stands an equestrian statue of the King, there should be a statue to Shame, to commemorate the perfidious attempt to restore absolutism. The King cannot understand the irreparable damage done to the nation by the years of illegality."

Under these varied influences, Pontoppidan's interest in an engineering career flagged. He wanted to be free of school and to see the world, and left his native land for the first time to make a journey to Switzerland. He spent some time near Interlaken walking in the mountains, and the many descriptions in his memoirs of the grandeur of Swiss scenery show how well he observed nature in all its aspects. On his return to Denmark, he tried unsuccessfully to find employment as a schoolmaster, then finally took a post teaching science at the public high school near the rural town of Hilleröd, where his brother Morten was headmaster. The country life attracted Pontopiddan, for here for the first time he could meet the peasants and talk to them. "It was above all the conditions of the poor that interested me," he writes. "I was concerned primarily with the inequality in this world's distribution of goods." In this region, inhabited mainly by landless farm laborers, he could satisfy his curiosity. He was drawn to the peasants, and yearned to be one of them, which may help to explain his first marriage, in 1881, to a peasant girl whose calm dignity greatly appealed to him.

In 1881, he began to publish regularly in periodicals. His short stories were favorably received by editors, and he made the acquaintance of the powerful publisher Hegel, head of the Gyldendal firm. At Hegel's sumptuous dinners he met many famous authors of the day, but he hated the showy display of these occasions and the guests were to him little more than figures of derision. But then his affairs took a crucial turn. His brother Morten was sentenced to a term in prison for political activity; the government subsidy for Morten's school was withdrawn, and Pontoppidan was forced to seek another career. Toward the end of his days of teaching at Morten's school, Pontoppidan had begun to read avidly, attempting to place his own philosophy of life on a more solid basis. He read the philosophers Kierkegaard, Hoeffding, and "others hard to digest," and he was dazzled by the panorama of European literature. He reread the Russian authors, admiring their straightforward style, and slowly formed his own ideas on prose style, contending that it should always be simple, modeled precisely on the ideas it intends to express, and the impressions it intends to give.

In 1884, Pontoppidan settled with his wife and two children in Oestby, his wife's native town. He installed a study in the house of his wife's parents and deepened his knowledge of peasant life. It was now that he decided, with some apprehension, to commit himself to the hazardous career of writing. Toward the end of his life, Pontoppidan wrote, "One must know how to take risks. Deviations and errors often involve risks we must take in this life, a life to which only adventure can reconcile us."

During these early years, his talent was given over to short stories and descriptions, but he was already contemplating more ambitious work. As early as 1883, he had written to Hegel suggesting the idea of a long novel whose principal theme would be the rivalry between the disciples of Grundtvig and those of the Indre Mission. This novel, *Det Forjaettede Land* (*The Promised Land*) (1891–1895), was eventually completed many years later.

In 1887 the family moved to Copenhagen, where Pontoppidan wrote for the periodical *Politikon,* and from this time his domestic difficulties began. Finally his first wife left home to return to her parents in Oestby. A few years later, Pontoppidan obtained a divorce, and in 1892 he married Antoinette Kofoed. He always retained a tender and grateful memory of his first wife, but his attempt to communicate directly with the people, to ally himself with the soil of his country, had failed.

Difficult as they were in personal matters, the 1880s brought Pontoppidan his first literary success. As noted earlier, it was in 1881 that he began his career as a writer. He sent a collection of his stories to the influential critic Bourchenais, who read them with interest and published one in the widely read weekly *Ude og Hyemme*. The story attracted the attention of a Copenhagen publisher, who offered to bring out the whole collection. It was published that year under the title *Staekkede Vinger* (Clipped Wings), a title that summarizes Pontoppidan's general views about existence. Men appeared to him as ambitious dreamers, lacking the courage and energy to pursue the plans they conceived, and in his later novels and stories we frequently come upon the motif of the impotent dreamer. But the idea is not peculiar to him, and it would detract from the richness of his output to see in his work no more than variations on this theme.

In his early stories, all set in the countryside, Pontoppidan depicted with great force the unfortunate lot of the farm laborers he had come to know and understand. At the same time, he attacked the pharisaical attitude of certain peasants who were intent on enriching themselves and made no effort to alleviate the sufferings of others.

Then, in 1890, Pontoppidan turned his literary effort to politics. In that year he published a collection of short stories, *Clouds,* dealing with the Danish political conflict. Here Pontoppidan takes a firm stand against the illegality of the national government. His disapproval and scorn are revealed in the way he describes events and men: he invariably shows the government in an unfavorable light, though he is by no means always in agreement with the progressives.

After this literary excursion into politics, Pontoppidan finally finished the long novel about the Danish countryside that he had conceived of nearly eight years earlier. At that time, he had written of it to the publisher Hegel, saying, "It will be a broad canvas, in clear colors depicting the countryside . . . I shall attempt to write lively and picturesque descriptions of something which has never been satisfactorily portrayed in our literature, great public gatherings, festivals of church and state, Christmas celebrations, and such like." This project had taken a long time to mature in his mind, and now it culminated in a great trilogy. *Det forjaettede Land* (1891–1895), published in English as *Emmanuel, or Children of the Soil* (1892) and *The Promised Land* (1896), is a very long novel in which Pontoppidan's talents came to full fruition. To begin with, he brilliantly describes the Danish countryside. Far more important, however, is his description of the country people's mentality, as expressed in their religious celebrations, their religious conflicts and their political activities. The numerous characters and the springs of their actions are drawn with precision and awareness. Pontoppidan's probings of morality, however, are focused on a few characters, who never leave the center of the stage and give the novel its unity and power.

As almost always in Pontoppidan's work, the hero, Emmanuel, fails to realize his ideals: through his own weaknesses, he fails to meet the challenge of a task too ambitious for his powers. At first a curate, then a pastor, Emmanuel takes a post in a part of Sjaelland, an isolated outpost. There, fired with enthusiasm, he works to bring about a great reconciliation between the peasants and those who have always enjoyed the monopoly of culture and power. For him, physical labor and the simple, honest customs of the countryside are the fertile soil from which new life will spring for both the individual and the nation. To give substance to his ideals, he marries a peasant girl, just as Pontoppidan himself did.

But Pontoppidan knew that there were aspects of country life that were neither idyllic nor edifying. Throughout the work there are scenes that give full play to his irony, pillorying the selfishness and boorishness of country society. Unlike Pontoppidan, who always saw both sides of a question, Emmanuel is blinded by his generous enthusiasms, and in the first part of the trilogy the reader can gauge for himself the flaws of Emmanuel's character and his misguided enthusiasm for his cause.

Seven years elapse between the first and second parts of the story, a period during which Emmanuel tries to put into effect his ideal of the simple life by working in the fields. At the beginning of the second part, we find him working in the fields, wearing a coarse smock and heavy boots laced to the knees, with disheveled hair and unkempt beard. But his appearance deceives no one but himself. From his silhouette and narrow, sloping shoulders it is obvious that he is not a peasant. His arms and hands lack the coarseness and strength of those accustomed from childhood to bearing burdens. Nor has his face the dark, leathery color of the true peasant's; instead, it is flecked with small white blotches. His agricultural projects have nearly all been unsuccessful; they earn him only the pity of his wife and parents-in-law. Meanwhile, the peasants involve him in their political activities, and he emerges from these activities as a slightly ridiculous figure.

A tragic event, the death of Emmanuel's son, dominates this part of the novel. The child had been ill for two years, and despite his wife Hansine's entreaties, Emmanuel refused to call a doctor for the boy, putting all his faith in God and nature. Blamed by his wife for his son's death, tortured by his own sorrow, Emmanuel begins to lose his faith. At the funeral of the headmaster of the local high school, the weaver Hansen attacks him ferociously, demanding that Emmanuel give up his post. Then his wife tells him that they must part, and that Emmanuel must return to Copenhagen to be with his own kind. The second part of the novel ends with their separation.

The third and last part of the book takes place at a high school at Sandinge and its immediate surroundings. The subject is no longer the struggle between two cultures, but an exposure of the trends of thought developing within the Danish Church; the story of Emmanuel's personal life is over. Pontoppidan takes a number of priests as spokesmen, and uses their discussions, lectures, and speeches to reveal their individual characters. The great failing of these men is their misuse of words. They have all come to Sandinge to discuss the crisis which divides the Danish Church, for they all repudiate the literal readings of the Bible and each of them searches for his own interpretation. But giving speeches and hearing themselves talk is their real *raison d'être*. Pontoppidan clearly feels that the Church had lost its spiritual authority and that, to regain it, it must return to the temporal domain.

Emmanuel's destiny is associated with these religious discussions. He comes to Sandinge to express his own opinions, but while the colloquies are being prepared he withdraws more and more from the world, beginning to follow what he imagines is the example of Christ. He is no longer strong enough to confront an audience such as the one at Sandinge, and when he tries to speak before the professors and pastors, he collapses speechless, convinced that God has abandoned him. He does not survive this shock long, and dies.

Emmanuel's strange transformation to

a Christlike figure in the last part of the novel lends the ending a certain grandeur. The problem stated at the outset, the confrontation of the peasants and the literate classes and the search for a compromise between them, has been abandoned, yet the novel as a whole presents a vivid picture of Danish history in the last quarter of the nineteenth century—a picture of the changes within the Church, and of the political struggles that led to nothing and were naturally followed by religious agitation.

Between *Emmanuel, or Children of the Soil* and *The Promised Land,* and his second great novel *Lykke-Per* (Lucky Peter, 1898–1904), Pontoppidan wrote a shorter work, *Nattevagt* (*The Night Vigil*), published in 1894. Its subject is once again the conflict between politics and religion. The novel is set in Rome, where Pontoppidan had spent some time in 1892, and despite its brevity, it is rich and varied. Pontoppidan's feelings on the subject had intensified, and in this book he made one of his most interesting contributions to the social and political portrait of Denmark.

In 1898, Pontoppidan started the long novel *Lucky Peter.* Its writing occupied him until 1904, but the novel was published piecemeal, in eight parts (two in 1898, two in 1899, one in 1902, one in 1903, and one in 1904). In 1905 he revised the book, condensing it into three parts; it is in this form that it has been published since, and Pontoppidan expressed the wish that critical studies of "Lucky Peter" would be based on the final revision.

The title itself resists precise translation. The Danish word *lykke* has two meanings: "luck" and "happiness"—and if it is luck that favors the hero in the first part of the novel, it is happiness, a calm and stoical happiness, that he later seeks. Per, the hero, spends his childhood and early adolescence in a provincial presbytery. Later he goes to Copenhagen to study engineering, and conceives the ambitious plan of using the Jutland canals for the transport of freight, thereby creating a free port in competition with Hamburg. He comes into contact with the literary circles of Copenhagen, and soon becomes the son-in-law of a wealthy financier. Just when his fortune seems assured, a chance occurrence disgusts him with the circles in which he now lives. He leaves Copenhagen and retires to Jutland, and there, after a second marriage he spends the rest of his life as a humble roadmender.

Pontoppidan's third major novel is *De døde rige* (*Kingdom of the Dead,* 1912–1916). In it, he wrote of the present and the future of his nation, through a strong effort of a radical politician to awaken a "people who are sleeping." Numerous characters are carefully studied, and their several stories are developed in a complex plot involving an election campaign and a series of parliamentary scenes. But a prevailing tone of pessimism and despair, becoming more pronounced and acute as the novel approaches a tragic culmination, gives the book a certain unity. Pontoppidan was seriously ill when he wrote this novel, and believed that his death was near. He worked feverishly to set down what he considered essential truths. "I'm not an author," he said, "but a loyal soldier." And *Kingdom of the Dead* reflects its author's mood in a bitter picture of Danish political life.

In his last novel, *Mands himmerig* (*Man's Heaven,* 1927), Pontoppidan returns to some of the same themes. Niels Thorsen, a journalist, is deeply involved in politics. His wife, Asta, has married him over her family's objections. Repelled by his violence, her mind poisoned by scurrilous gossip, she believes herself deserted and dies by her own hand. But it is neither intrigue nor the violent character of Thorsen that provide the main interest of this novel. Its importance lies in the *reason* for his violence. A vicious intrigue ousts Thorsen from the editorship of the great Danish liberal newspaper *Friheden* (Liberty), and in a plot far simpler than that of the *Kingdom of the Dead* the author launches a violent attack against certain corrupt and scandal-mongering newspapers. Thus, while *Man's Heaven* repeats some of the themes of the *Kingdom of the Dead,* there is an important difference: it is not concentrated on the Church, but attacks the country as a whole. In this brief novel, Pontoppidan's final pessimism is even more marked. Both of his last two novels end with the death of the hero, after total defeat.

After completing this last effort, Pontoppidan added finishing touches to a final volume of short stories, published in 1930, and produced a revised edition of his earlier short stories. In 1932, he began editing his memoirs, published in five volumes between 1933 and 1943. He died at Ordrup in 1943.

Alfred Jolivet is honorary professor of Scandinavian languages and literature at the Sorbonne.

Translated by Anthony Rhodes.

THE 1917 PRIZE

By A. JOLIVET

It was 1917. The World War was in its third year and still raging. After the terrible slaughter at Verdun, when the antagonists had sunk into apathy, a renewed frenzy of fighting had broken out, covering a much wider area than the land round the forts of Vaux and Douaumont. In February, Germany had launched total submarine warfare in the oceans, which was to bring the United States into the war. In Russia, the imperial colossus tottered on its feet of clay. The February Revolution in Petrograd was pursuing its fateful course, beginning with the Czar's abdication and culminating in the Communist seizure of power in October. Clouds of catastrophe were gathering on every horizon.

At the time, awarding a Nobel Prize for Literature hardly seemed appropriate. The hitherto honorable task of choosing the laureates had become a wearisome burden without glory, one which was no longer able to arouse interest. The small scene which was being played out at the same time as the immense drama of the century was bathed in an atmosphere of dull indifference. There were no Prize celebrations on December 10, therefore.

In addition, there were political worries. Sweden felt it was important to remain strictly neutral. But this posture was not without risk. Sweden's neutrality was, to say the least, delicate: the nearness of the German seaboard on the Baltic and her diplomatic relations with Germany produced serious tension between Sweden and the Allies in 1917. The Allies' suspicion of Swedish policy contributed toward provoking a governmental crisis in March. In Sweden it became urgently necessary to prove a neutral stand did not necessarily mean going along with Germany's warlike designs.

Sweden stiffened her attitude toward Germany in 1917, and, as it happened, neither France nor England proposed any Nobel candidates. The Germans proposed only one of their writers, Paul Ernst, a star of lesser brilliance. The Swedish Academy looked for a graceful means of getting out of the difficulty unscathed.

In December of 1914, the Kings of Denmark, Norway, and Sweden had met at Malmö. The presence side-by-side of the three neutral monarchs revealed the existence of a new cohesion in this corner of the planet. It also marked the end of the dissension that had formerly troubled the Nordic atmosphere, and it quieted the repercussions that had occurred after the separation of Sweden and Norway in 1905. The famous meeting of the three kings, repeated again in Christiania in 1917, showed a happy willingness for cooperation and the wish to support each other in this time of strain. People began to think of themselves more emphatically as Scandinavians. And so the Nobel Prize for Literature was awarded in 1917 to two Danish writers, Karl Gjellerup and Henrik Pontoppidan. Gjellerup, who had had a German philosophical education and had strong Germanic spiritual affinities, had lived in Dresden since 1892. His books had a wide circulation in Germany. Like Gjellerup, Pontoppidan had also been one of the group of young men enlightened by Georg Brandes.

Now the question arose as to whether the prize should be divided or not. In the eyes of certain Academicians this was an abomination, an intolerable half-measure. Albert Nobel had expressed the wish in his will that his money should be a substantial means of support, not merely a source of tips. A certain number of Academicians wanted to give the whole Prize to Gjellerup, and were deeply disappointed when the idea was abandoned. Others pointed out that a division was justified and that this praiseworthy concession to literary fairness would be appreciated by future generations. Neither Gjellerup nor Pontoppidan were after all of such far-reaching importance. The division was necessary as a sort of happy medium that allowed the problems of a delicate situation to be resolved.

Thus it was that the Swedish Academy, when it met in plenary session on November 8, 1917, decided to award the Nobel Prize for Literature to Karl Gjellerup "for his varied and rich poetry, which is inspired by lofty ideals" and, more laconically, to Henrik Pontoppidan "for his authentic descriptions of present-day life in Denmark."

Translated by Dale McAdoo.

Salvatore Quasimodo

1959

"For his lyrical poetry, which
with classical fire expresses
the tragic experience of life
in our own times"

Illustrated by MET IVERS

PRESENTATION ADDRESS

By ANDERS ÖSTERLING

PERMANENT SECRETARY
OF THE SWEDISH ACADEMY

SALVATORE QUASIMODO, the Italian poet who has been awarded this year's Nobel Prize for Literature, is a Sicilian by birth. He was born near Syracuse; to be more exact, in the little town of Modica some distance from the coast. It is not difficult to imagine that a region so rich in memories of the past must have been of the utmost importance for his future calling. The relics of the ancient Greek temples on the island, the theaters near the Ionian Sea, Arethusa's fountain, so famed in legend, the gigantic ruins at Girgenti and Slinunte—what a playground for a child's imagination! Here in days gone by the heroes of Greek poetry were guests at the court of King Hieron, here the voices of Pindar and Aeschylus linger like an echo through the ages.

Even if, as far as material matters are concerned, Quasimodo was reared in comparative poverty, the milieu in which he spent his youth was nevertheless something to be grateful for. Admittedly, many restless years of travel were to pass before he became conscious of his talent and began to find his way in the classical heritage that was his. In due course, however, his studies were to show their influence in his great contribution as a translator of the literature of classical antiquity which now forms the homogeneous background of his own work as one of the foremost poets in the Italian language. There can hardly be any doubt that his strict classical education acted as a stimulus, not to servile imitation, but to energetic self-discipline in the use of language and the achievement of artistic style. Although regarded as one of the principal innovators in modern poetry, Quasimodo is, nevertheless, bound to the classical tradition and occupies this place with all the natural confidence of a true heir.

Quasimodo made his debut as early as 1930 but it was not until the forties and fifties that he established his position as one of Italy's most outstanding poets, and by this time his reputation had become international. He belongs to the same generation as Silone, Moravia, and Vittorini, that is, the generation of left-wing authors who were able to prove their worth only after the fall of Fascism. Quasimodo is like these writers in that for him, too, the fate of present-day Italy is a reality in which he is deeply involved. His literary production is not very large. In actual fact it consists of five books of poetry, which reveal his development to complete individuality and originality. I quote the characteristic titles of the volumes: *Ed è subito sera* (And Suddenly It's Evening) published in 1942, *Giorno dopo giorno* (Day after Day) in 1946, *La vita non è sogno* (Life Is Not a Dream) in 1949, *Il falso e vero verde* (The False and the True Green) in 1956, and finally *La terra impareggiabile* (The Incomparable Earth) in 1958. Together they form one homogenous work in which not a single line is unimportant.

Quasimodo has sung of the Sicily of his childhood and his youth with a love that, since he went to live in the north of Italy, has gained an ever-increasing depth and perspective—the windswept island scenery with its Greek-temple columns, its desolate grandeur, its poverty-stricken villages, its dusty roads winding through olive groves, its strident music of pounding surf and shepherds' horns. Nonetheless, he cannot be called a provincial poet. The area from which he draws his themes gradually increases, while at the same time his human pathos breaks through the strict poetic form which first fettered him. Above all, the bitter experiences of World War II provided the impulse for this change and made him an interpreter of the moral life of his fellow countrymen in their daily experience of nameless tragedies and constant confrontation with death. In this later period he has created a number of poems that are so monumental that one would like to believe that they will be accepted as a lasting contribution to the world's great poetry. Naturally, Quasimodo is far from being the only Italian poet to be deeply affected in this way by the martyrdom of his country and its people, but the Sicilian poet's dark and passionate earnestness rings with a special and individual note when he ends one of his lyrics with the cry:

However much everything else is distorted
The dead can never be sold.
Italy is my country, o stranger,
It is of its people I sing, and of the sound
Of secret lamentation that comes from its sea,
I sing of its mothers' chaste grief, of all its life.

Quasimodo is of the bold opinion that poetry does not exist for its own sake but has an irrefutable mission in the world, through its creative power to recreate man himself. To him, the road to freedom is the same as the conquest of isolation, and his own progress points in the same direction. In this way his work has become a living voice and his poetry an artistic expression of the consciousness of the Italian people, as far as this is possible for poetry with an otherwise so concise and individual structure. In his poems, Biblical turns of phrase are to be found side by side with allusions to classical mythology, that mythology which is an ever-present source of inspiration for a Sicilian. Christian compassion is the basic quality of his poetry, which in moments of greatest inspiration attains universality.

Dear Sir—The following statement pronounced by the Swedish Academy is the reason for which you have been awarded the Nobel Prize: "For his lyric poetry, which with classical fire expresses the tragic experience of life in our own times."

Your poetry has come to us as an authentic and vivid message of that Italy which has had faithful friends and admirers in our nation for centuries. With our most cordial congratulations I ask you to receive the Nobel Prize for Literature from His Majesty the King.

ACCEPTANCE SPEECH

By SALVATORE QUASIMODO

I HAVE ALWAYS THOUGHT of Sweden as a country adopted by the men who received the Nobel Prize, that unique and brilliant distinction in contemporary civilization. No other nation, in fact, has succeeded in proposing, much less realizing, a similar prize. Although it originates in a country of a few million men, the Nobel Prize is a model of universality charged with an active and spiritual significance.

The Prize, an award not easily attainable, arouses the passions of men of every political faction in every nation—a sign of its omnipresence and of that gulf which the writer, or poet, or philosopher finds opening before him. Culture, however, has always repulsed the recurrent threat of barbarism, even when the latter was heavily armed and seething with confused ideologies. Here around me are the representatives of one of the most ancient Northern civilizations, which in the course of its rugged history has found itself fighting next to those who have determined the extent of human liberties. It is a civilization which has produced humanist kings and queens, great poets and writers. These poets, both past and contemporary, are known in Italy today, even if only for the volatile side of their restless temperaments and their brooding spirits. From an allegorical presence, inspired by the fabled memories of the Vikings, these difficult and musical names have come to be honored by us. They speak more forcefully to us than do the poets of other civilizations that are decaying or already buried in the dust of a Renaissance rhetoric.

My purpose is neither to eulogize nor subtly to congratulate myself, but rather to criticize the intellectual condition of Europe, when I affirm that Sweden and her people through their choices have consistently challenged and influenced the culture of the world. I have already said that the poet and writer help change the world. This may seem presumptuous or merely a relative truth, but, in order to justify tumult or acquiescence, one need only think of the reactions that poets provoke, both in their own societies and elsewhere.

You know that poetry reveals itself in solitude, and that from this solitude it moves out in every direction; from the monologue it reaches society without becoming either sociological or political. Poetry, even lyrical poetry, is always "speech." The listener may be the physical or metaphysical interior of the poet, or a man, or a thousand men. Narcissistic feeling, on the other hand, turns inward upon itself like a circle; and by means of alliteration and of evocative sounds it echoes the myths of other men in forgotten epochs of history.

Today we can talk of a neo-humanism on earth in an absolute sense—a neo-humanism without equal for man. And if the poet finds himself at the center of this temporary physical structure, which was made in part by his spirit and intelligence, is he still a dangerous being? The question is not rhetorical but an ellipsis of the truth. The world today seems allied with the side opposed to poetry. And for the world, the poet's very presence is an obstacle to be overcome. He must be annihilated. The force of poetry, on the other hand, fans out in every direction in organized societies; and if literary games escape the sensibilities of men everywhere, a poetic activity that is inspired by humanism does not.

I have always thought that one of my poems was written for the men of the North, as well as for those of the Dark Continent or of the East. The universality of poetry is crucial to its form, its style, let us say (that is, the concentrated power of its language). But universality is also what was not there before and what one man contributes to the other men of his time. Such universality is not founded on abstract concepts or on a harmful morality—even worse when moralism is involved—but rather on a direct concreteness and on a unique spiritual condition.

My idea of beauty is embodied not only in harmony but also in dissonance, for even dissonance can attain the precision of a poetic form. Whether we think of painting or sculpture or music, the esthetic, moral, and critical problems are the same; and likes and dislikes are similar. Greek beauty has been imperiled by contemporary man, who has destroyed form only to seek a new form for his imitation of life—an imitation, that is, which will reveal the very workings of nature. I speak of the poet, of his singular imperfection of nature, who builds his own real existence piece by piece out of the language of men. This language, however, is constructed from a sincerely reasoned syntax, not from a deceptive one. Every experience in life (whether lived or felt) initially involves an unexpected moral disintegration, a spiritual imbalance manifesting itself gradually, and a fear of prolonging a spiritual condition which has already collapsed under the weight of history. For the man of letters as for the transitory critic, the poet always keeps an inaccurate diary, always plays with a terrestrial theology. Indeed, it is certain that this critic will write that such poems are but ponderous restatements of an *ars nova*—restatements of an art, of a new language which did not exist before these poems were written (thus the history of poetic form is overturned). Perhaps the latter is a way of rendering solitude bearable and of naming the coldest objects that enclose it. The poet's evil influence? Perhaps, because no one ever fills the silence of those men who may read just one poem of a new poet, certainly not the fragile critic, who fears that a sequence of fifteen or twenty verses may be true. The investigation of the concept of purity is yet to be done in this century of divisions which are, in appearance, political; a century in which the lot of the poet is confused and hardly human. His latest rhapsodies are always viewed with suspicion for their understanding of the heart.

I have spoken here not to propose a poetics or to establish esthetic standards but to salute a land for its sturdier men, who are very precious to our civilization, and who come from the adopted country of which I spoke before. I now find myself in this country.

I salute and profoundly thank your Majesties the King and Queen of Sweden, Your Royal Highnesses, and the Swedish Academy. Its eighteen members, wise and stern judges, have decided, in awarding the Nobel Prize to my poetry, to honor Italy, which has been very rich during the first half century, up to the most recent generation, in works of literature, art, and thought fundamental to our civilization.

DISCOURSE ON POETRY

By SALVATORE QUASIMODO

Translated by Allen Mandelbaum

Philosophers—the natural enemies of poets—and those who steadily catalogue critical thought, assert that poetry (and all the arts), like the works of nature, undergoes no changes during or after a war. An illusion, because war alters the moral life of a people. Man, at his return from war, no longer finds measures of certainty in an inner *modus* of life, a *modus* he has forgotten or treated ironically during his trials with death.

War summons up, with violence, a hidden order in the thought of man, a greater grasp of the truth: the occasions of reality inscribe themselves in its history. Valéry, in 1918, closes a period of French poetry, and Apollinaire begins another, the modern period. The sway of D'Annunzio (and it was he who had sounded the call to arms) crumbles in that same year, and there begins the reaction against his poetry, his diction. In 1945, silence insinuates itself into the Hermetic school of Italian poetry. Since then, critics have begun to put the so-called "time of waiting" on trial. Does the most recent chapter of Italian poetry represent the maturity or the decadence of a language? Criticism cannot answer; and it tries to draw up balance sheets or pseudo-histories of poetry between the two wars, indicating its relations with a humanist tradition. These are provisional tombstones that will be lifted one day when the chronicle of formal ashes gives way to the history of contemporary poetic man. Grown arid in a method that is too abstract or too "methodological," a portion of criticism has—for more than twenty years—called on "taste" to recognize or deny what is poetry. More steeped in Romantic vices than it was aware, it attached itself to "forms," believing it had thus evaded Crocean criticism. By means of judicious deformations (the false scheme of "literary generations," for example), a recent anthology of twentieth-century Italian poetry presents us with a waxwork museum—from 1905 to 1945—in which several figures (from the *Crepuscolari*—the poets of the Twilight School—to the heads and tails of the Hermetic school) are arranged in a sequence that has a purely verbal life, without any systematic base. It seems to me that Hermetic criticism began its first exercises in reading around 1936 with a study by Oreste Macrì on the "poetic of the word" in my poetry. The philosopher demonstrated his enthusiasm for a philological method; perhaps that was the right way, following the lesson of history, to arrive at some conclusions about the origins of the Italian poetic language of today. Another critic, Luciano Anceschi, the anthologist noted above, followed the lessons of his teacher, Giuseppe De Robertis, in attributing to Dino Campana and then to the Twilight poets the first revolts against D'Annunzio and the first timid utterances of a new *ars poetica.* All this, in order to bring the innovations of Ungaretti (of *L'Allegria,* be it understood, which is not yet a Hermetic volume) into line with tradition. From premises such as these, a hazy, baroque perspective leads the critic to unsteady judgments, to bewildering documents on the validity of a poetic period in Italian literary history that is concrete and positive. One cannot deny that there was, indeed, a Hermetic school; but the critic who tried, ambitiously, to inquire into the innovators, instead of presenting a "semantic of constructions" (i.e., of images) in order to establish the origins of that school, has gone back to the abstract geometry of pure art, to an Arcadia. Evident here is the absence of any critical orientation towards recent poetry, that poetry crystallized by the last war; while other minor critics turned against the silence of the poets with new symbolisms and existential pronouncements. Has all this meant a criticism by means of emblems? A purely formal criticism? The results fade away in approximations. Here the Twilight poets, there the Futurists, and there again the poets of *La Voce;* a chronicle that cannot distinguish poetry from literature. The Hermetic poets, in fact, make their appearance as ascertainable motifs of a literary movement. They continue a phase that had been interrupted in the years before 1918 by the "shadow" Sergio Corazzini, the phantom Dino Campana, the hobgoblin Camillo Sbarbaro (these epithets only reflect the unsolidity of the images that critics portray). And when, in dealing with the poets between the wars, the critics present us, not with men but phantoms—they can only remind us that too many centuries of Italian poetry carry the precious echoes of Arcadia, voices quenched by the Communes, the Signorias, the Princely States, the Courts, the ecclesiastical powers. This is the heritage of conventional encounters, where the poet is the "unloved lover" with platitudes—from fire to ice—that are as punctual as death. The image of the poet that would emerge from this: a man of sentimental risks, a lesser nature suspended in love—love that all others, except him, possess. This is the aesthetic and doctrinaire image that would rescue, from the origins of Italian literature until today, seven or eight poets, seven or eight men. Because it is so faithful to traditional operations (dealing always, except for two or three adequate and communicable examples, in the narrow range of a literary—not a poetic—voice), this criticism can only give rise, if anything, to a question: Who are these poets, and what do they represent in the contemporary world? Do they toy with shadows in pure forms or, rather, do they join life and literature through the growth of their awareness and their response to the pressures of time?

The critical itinerary is necessary. The last war overtook a poetic language that was drawing near to the objects of the earth in order to reach the universal. Allegories had been dissolved in the solitude of the dictatorship. But criticism preferred to resolve the poetic process in intellectual terms: it believed that one could single out poetic personalities, the existence of the shaping word, in symbols and in Petrarchesque, baroque gyrations. But where literature "reflects," poetry "makes." The poet participates in literature only *after* his experience as an "irregular." The poet shatters, both naturally and unnaturally, a metrical and technical habit, and modifies the world with his freedom and truth. The voice of Homer exists before Greece, and Homer "forms" the civilization of Greece. Even a complete "history of forms as the history of the word" does not, then, exhaust the history of the poets. The poet is a man who is linked to other men in the field of culture and is important for his "content" (that is the grave word) not only for his voice, his cadence (immediately recognizable when it is imitated).

The poet does not "say"; he sums up his own soul and consciousness and makes these—his secrets—"exist," forcing them out of anonymity into personality. What, then, are the words of these poets between the two wars? Are these poets masters, who have a right to citizenship in the contemporary world, or are they rather pilgrims, only engaged in stylistic operations, worn-out literary categories? No one has answered this question, and the critics (many between the two wars) have repeated unspecific schemes, and given us facsimiles rather than images of men. Poetry is the man, as I have said: and the filing cards enumerated by "taste" are barely an introduction to the drama of a part of Italian history, only notes to be developed. The logic of the fantasy, as criticism, cannot confront poetry, because poetry does not "measure" good inventions; its responsibility is not to falsehood but to truth.

In 1945, alongside formalist criticism, that had been empirical, wavering, unsure of itself in making judgments, there emerged, even if in limited form, a realist criticism, not yet Marxist, but tending towards the orthodox formulation of that doctrine. The history of poetry between the two wars, which had remained in the encyclopedic "limbo" of varied aesthetic tendencies, descended now to other and more scientific scrutiny. We know how risky is the theoretical machinery of an aesthetic before it is systematized; and the Marxist aesthetic, too, is in a phase of development, making use of the writings of Marx and Engels on art and literature that have to be interpreted in the light of the growth of contemporary critical thought. But from a new conception of the world, we have the right to expect inquiries that are more aware of the presence of man.

From 1945 on, and always for the historical reasons indicated earlier, the new generation, reacting against existing poetics, found itself unexpectedly without any apparent masters for the continued writing of poetry. This generation refused the humanist tradition—recognizing the maturity but not the finality of that tradition—and gave rise to a literary situation that can only excite admiration in those who are interested in the fate of Italian culture. The search for a new poetic language coincides this time with an impetuous search for man: in substance, the reconstruction of man defrauded by war, that "remaking of man" to which I referred, precisely in 1946, but not in a moralistic sense, because morals cannot constitute poetry. A new poetic language, when another is about to reach its maturity (as was the case in 1945 with the language of the Hermetic poets), necessarily involves an extreme violence. Formalist criticism (and not only this), faced with the poetic documents of the new generation, speaks disparagingly of a "translation style," considering the desire for "discourse" of the postwar poets only in its external aspects (at times ametrical and prosaic).

But does the "translation style" have no native origins, does it mean the imitation of foreign spirits and poetics? This is a point to be made clear. In reaction against the traditional Italian Arcadia, the contaminated elegiac amorous exercises, the reborn Petrarchism, there emerges the first lexicon of a new poetry, whose syntactic efforts include spacious rhythms and "forms" (the lexicon of the poetry between the wars had already been made specific, through rigorous inquiry, by Francesco Flora). This may involve mistaken hexameters, that answer to the "presumption" of a literary genre. But we are witnessing the growth of a social poetry, that addresses itself to the various aggregates of human society. Not, of course, sociological poetry, because no poet dreams of invoking his soul and his intelligence to fashion "sociological theory." Dante, Petrarch, Foscolo, Leopardi wrote social poems, poems necessary at a given moment of civilization. But the poetry of the new generation, which we shall call social in the sense indicated above, aspires to dialogue rather than monologue. It is already a demand for dramatic poetry, an elementary "form" of theater. (In the same way, the *Contrasto* of Ciullo d'Alcamo and the *Lamenti* of the Sicilian school marked a breaking-away from the Provençal school, which—except for a few poets—was another Arcadia.) The new poetry may become dramatic or epic (in a modern sense) but not, I repeat, gnomic or sociological. Civil poetry, one knows, is beset by deep traps, and sometimes it has toyed with "aestheticisms." Remember Tyrtaeus, who invites the youths to fight in the front ranks for their homeland, because the cadaver of an old man is ugly, while the body of a dead boy is always beautiful. The new generation is truly *engagé* in every sense in the literary field. The new "contents" are heavy at times, but the content is conditioned by the course of history. The poet knows today that he cannot write idylls or horoscopes. Fortunately, he is not beset by critics alongside him indicating more or less probable outcomes for poetry, as happened between the two wars: a criticism that anticipates poetic solutions, a philosophy become the master of poetry. Hegel wrote that art was dying because it was being resolved into philosophy, that is, into thought: and today it may seem that poetry tends to disappear in the "thought" of poetry.

Returning now to that "translation style," the term used with contempt to indicate the texture of poetry around 1945, let us note that both formalist criticism as well as historical materialist criticism intended by that a language drawn directly from the translation of a poetic text from a foreign language. Was this term accurate or was it not, rather, a loose formulation by critics when faced with a "taste" for speaking of the world and the things of this world that used a new technique, prelude to a concrete language that reflects the real and disturbs the traditional planes of rhetoric? Our poetic tradition has always seemed to the foreign reader to be layer on thick layer of impenetrable schemes, in which man spends his precious time in elegiac occasions, detached from the authentic passions intrinsic to his nature. After forty years of critical silence about Italian poetry, Europe has again begun to read our poetic manuscripts; not those poems that mime the Hermetic school, but those that answer or pose questions to men, the poems of '43, '44, '45 and of dates even closer to us. Is this interest owing only to a projection of sentiments and objects common to the man of today? Is it, then, an attention of an ethical and problematic nature? I do not believe so: it is precisely the "formal reasons," those least apparent now to us, that make our poetry participate humanly in the world. Our poetry gains attention not because of its linguistic exercises, but because of its poetic responsibilities, those that had been obscured after Leopardi. It is the sign of an active presence of our civilization and—with it—of Italian man (this, the true tradition, beyond the courtly flutes of nature subdued in a perennial Arcadia).

The secret of a poetic language reveals itself late to criticism; that is, when the model has already branched out into imitation, when its best memory falls to fragments, becomes a "school." It is then that minor poets propose, in guise of beauty, well-balanced literary mannerisms, superimposed on the repetition of "common" images, no longer original. Can man, as he is, be the content of a rigidly deterministic poetic? In describing the poetic experience of these past years, some have spoken of "ethical realism," with the "real" (or the truth) referring to what is represented, and the "ethical" to the aim of the representation. It is easy to catalogue; but man's precarious existence, the harshness of his political mind, his struggle against pain—all have brought man near to man and the poet to his listener. At times the modern poet is eloquent (ancient hortatory eloquence has a different metaphorical voice); he seems, that is, to discourse with a world gathered up in a narrow landscape (the poet's own land): eloquent, even if the tone of his voice is subdued, familiar. These poets are often men of Southern Italy—of Lucania, Abruzzo, Puglia, the islands—but also of Piedmont, of Veneto. Their inheritance was close-to-the earth and feudal; erect and clear, they have opened a dialogue on their fate. They have no childhood, or memory of childhood, only chains to burst and concrete realities with which to enter the cultural life of the nation. The muses of the woods and valleys are silent in them: their peasant mythologies are filled, rather, with the roar of landslides and floods. One day we shall chart a geographical map of the South; and it matters not if it will still touch Magna Grecia, whose sky extends over imperturbable images of innocence and blinding senses. There, perhaps, the "permanence" of poetry is being born. Luckily, those regions have no "lettered" dialect poets to reduce them to the brief space of a vignette, and their syntactic and linguistic "migrations" already carry a particular lexicon, the announcement of a language.

In Tuscany, unfortunately, one can still find some Guittone d'Arezzo, who schools in his precious doctrine the last chimeras of the realms of the absent beloved, where the existential lathe still turns. But in that other poetic and popular geography (though the critics still grant it little space) the presence of man —his gestures, his works—is constant. We shall not speak of ethical realism: the poets only teach us to live: shaping the material into new forms is difficult enough. It took a generation to meditate then carry out the impulse to break up and reconstruct the hendecasyllabic measure. And this, after the accidental loss of the faculty of rhythmic reading, in accord with the traditional metric writing. Poets are recognized by their particular pronunciation of metrical measures, and their voice (their song, we should say) consists of that cadence. The unit of their expression can, prosodically, be long or short; that "voice" will be revealed in any structure. We have a voice for every poet; and in that "translation style," too, what counts is the poetic pronunciation.

Speaking of the language of the "real," in an essay of mine on Dante, I recalled the enduring force of the "simple style." This was also a reference to its intensity, because the language of the *Comedy,* though it had its origins in the *dolce stil nuovo,* was purified through its contact with human and concrete contents. Dante's figures aimed at a drama that was no longer that of the classic world, although his mode of representing or inventing his figures had its roots in the classics. The lesson of Dante served Petrarch and the major writers of the Cinquecento; it was truly a lofty sign of Italian literary civilization. And today it is not only in one direction that we can read Dante in order to forget Petrarch and his obsessive cadences mirrored in the little space assigned to them by the feelings.

Is the social poetry of Dante, his other world so firmly set in the landscape of this earth, still subject to doubt, or can it be the "legal" point of departure for the new poets? The "translation" style can surprise anyone who is accustomed to the traditional movement of the lyric; but it begins a discourse that is unusual in Italian poetry, shattering forever the harmonious approaches to Arcadias. It may well create other rhetorics, but it will draw our poetry out from bondage, our poetry that has but recently entered the literary domain of European man, blocked off as it was, till yesterday, by walls of silence: the same walls that Italian criticism has raised around this poetry. Beyond them, at times, criticism seeks the major figures of the new tendency, using antiquated aesthetic yardsticks (not all, however), and only recognizes "contents," judgments, hopes. Dreams are but the sounds of life, cruel answers to the most frequent and disturbing questions. And forms? Where now is the *"dolce color d'orïental zaffiro"* ("sweet hue of oriental sapphire"), *"la fresca aura dei lauri"* ("the cool air of the laurels")?

The two criticisms—formalist and historical materialist—theorize and would create the poets in accord with the limits of their ideas on art. They hope to reduce poetry to a science; but they know it will be the poet, then, to force their science to yield to his rôle of an "irregular."

The motives of my discourse may seem polemical—with reference, too, to my own poetic situation—but the critical documents we now have for the future literary history of the twentieth century in Italy are mediocre witnesses, catalogues of literary artisanship. Poets—I cite the words of Croce—"are little disposed to organic and philosophical consideration, but are acute and subtle in particular questions." They can, then, discuss the examples cited by anthologists and discriminate, if nothing else, between literature and truth; i.e., between literature and poetic creation. And they can consider the figure of the poet in the contemporary world, in his attempt to join life to literature. The relation life-art is at the center of the problems of modern thought: but the supreme aesthetic orders repulse the poet (whom I have called elsewhere "the imperfection of nature") precisely because he has begun a dialogue with man.

"Chiare, fresche, dolci acque!" ("Clear cool, sweet waters!") Would this were a time of such tender utterances, a time in which memory would allow a poetic active enough to re-see the world in its gentle measures and sentiments. But here, now, the present generation, that dares to read new numbers in the tables of poetry, learns day by day what it means to write verses—so simple before the civil and political struggles. Gramsci saw clearly from the darkness of his prison the "literary" principles of the world. The position of the poet cannot be passive in society; he "modifies" the world, as we have said. His forceful images, those that he creates, beat on the heart of man more than does philosophy or history. Poetry is transformed into ethic, precisely because of its beauty: its responsibility is in direct proportion to its perfection. To write verses means to undergo judgment: and implicit in the aesthetic judgment are the social reactions to which a poem gives rise. We know the reservations one must make on these statements. Yet a poet is a poet when he does not renounce his presence in a given land, at a precise time, politi-

cally defined. And poetry is the freedom and truth of that time and not the abstract modulations of sentiment.

For criticism to put the works of the "time of waiting" on trial now, in a formative period like the present, is absurd, especially when new aesthetic theories are on the horizon and the continuation of a worn-out poetic school can only give us a false sense of "enduring." War has interrupted a culture and proposed new values for man; and though the weapons have been laid aside, the dialogue of the poets with men is necessary, even more than the sciences and the agreements between nations, which can be betrayed. Italian poetry after 1945 is—in its kind—of a choral nature. It flows with spacious rhythms, speaks of the real world with ordinary words; sometimes it presumes to the epic. It has a different fate because it has opened itself to forms that negate the false Italian tradition. Its poets now pay out their silence amid political alarms and the chronicles of moral decadence.

POEMS

By SALVATORE QUASIMODO

Edited and translated by Allen Mandelbaum

And suddenly it's evening
1920–1942

NEW POEMS: 1936–1942

The Magpie Laughs, Black Upon the Orange Trees

Perhaps it is a very sign of life:
around me, children in a game
of cadences and voices dance
with easy movements of the head
along the meadow of the church.
Piety of evening, shadows
rekindled on the grass so green,
loveliest in fire of the moon!
Memory grants you brief sleep;
but now, awake. Behold, the well
churns for the first tide. This is
the hour. Mine no longer, burnt
and distant semblances. And you,
south wind thick with orange blossoms,
drive the moon where children sleep
naked, force the foal to fields
damp with the tracks of mares, bare
the sea, lift the clouds from the trees.

The heron now moves waterward
and slowly sniffs the mud among the thorns;
the magpie laughs, black upon the orange trees.

Street of Agrigentum

There a wind endures that I recall
kindled in the horses' manes, slanting
in races across the plains, a wind that stains
and wears away the sandstone and the heart
of mournful telamones, overturned
on the grass. Ancient soul, now gray
with rancor, with this wind do you return
to sniff the delicate moss that cloaks the giants
downward thrust from heaven. How alone
you are within the space still left you!
And more you grieve one hears again the sound
that moves far off and broadly towards the sea,
where Hesperus already creeps with morning:
the marranzano quivers sorrowfully
in the throat of the waggoner, who climbs
the hillside neat beneath the moonlight, slowly
amid the murmur of saracen olive trees.

l. 14: The marranzano is a musical instrument, similar to the jews'-harp, used in Sicily.

The Gentle Hill

Birds far-off and open in the evening
tremble on the river. And the rain insists
and the hissing of the poplars illumined
by the wind. Like everything remote
do you return to mind. The light green

of your dress is here among the plants
burnt by lightning flashes where the gentle
hill of Ardenno rises and one hears
the kite hawk on the fans of broomcorn.

Perhaps in my return deluded, I
confided in that flight of locked-in spirals,
the harshness, the defeated Christian pity,
and this naked pain of sadnesses.
You have a flower of coral in your hair.
But your face is an unchanging shadow;
(thus death does). From the darkened houses
of your borough, I hear the Adda and the rain,
or perhaps a quivering of human steps
upon the banks among the tender canes.

The Rain's Already With Us

The rain's already with us
tossing silent air.
The swallows skim spent waters
on the Lombard lakes,
fly like gulls at little fish;
beyond the garden enclosures, the scent of hay.

Again a year is burned,
without lament, without a cry
upraised to win us—suddenly—a day.

The Tall Schooner

When birds came to stir the leaves
of the bitter trees beside my house

(blind nocturnal birds
boring their nests in the barks)
I faced the moon,
and saw a tall schooner.

At the island's rim the sea was salt;
the earth extended, ancient conches
glittered thrust into the rocks
on the roadstead of dwarf lemon trees.

And I told my love (my child was stirring in her,
and, for that, she had the sea within her soul continuously):
"I'm tired of all these wings that beat
in time to oars, and of the owls
that howl a dog's lament
when wind of moon is in the cane brakes.
I want to leave, I want to leave this island."
And she: "O love, it's late: let's stay."

Then slow I set myself to count
the strong surges of sea water
the air bore up into my eyes
from the mass of the tall schooner.

On the Banks of the Lambro

Intact, that day vanished from us
in the water with tumbled sails.
The pines deserted us, the semblance
of smoke above the houses
and the waterfront on holiday
with flags that fluttering neighed
like foals.

In the serene tone
that rises here at death of moon
and whets Brianza's hills, you still
moving longingly
have leaf-like pause.

The bees dried of honey
lightly climb with spoils of grain,
the Pleiades already change their light.

At the river that now, with a wheel's
splash, stirs up the hollow of the valley,
childhood, with the sexes played, renews.

I yield to its blood
bright on the brow,
to its voice in servitude of sorrow
mournful in the silence of the breast.
All that is left me is already lost.

North and east upon my island
is a wind borne from beloved
stones and waters: in the spring
it opens the tombs of the Suabians;
the kings of gold attire themselves with flowers.

Semblance of eternity for piety,
in things endures an order
that recalls the exile:
On the rim of the avalanche
the rock forever hesitates,
the root resists the teeth of the mole.
And within my evening, birds
odorous of orange sway
on the eucalyptus trees.

Here autumn still is in the pith
of plants; but in the womb of earth

that holds them, brood the stones;
and long flowers pierce the hedges.
Remember not with loathing now the almost
human warmth of hairy corollas.

You, listening, smile in revery:
And what sun smooths the hairs
of young girls, racing;
what mild joys and dark fears
and gentleness of striven tears,
resurge within the time that levels!
But like autumn, your life is concealed.

This night, too, sets
in the wells of the slopes; the bucket rolls
towards the circle of the dawn.
The trees beyond the windows like
flowered ships return.
O love,
how distant, dead it was from earth.

Elegos for the Dancer Cumani

The wind of the woods
races brightly to the hills.
Precociously day breaks: just as the blood
dismays the adolescent.

And the water's track is dawn
upon the shore. In me exhausted was
the torment of the sand,
to heart-beats, roving the night.

The durable most ancient cry pains:
pity for the youthful animal

struck dead among the grasses
of bitter morning after the new rains.

The earth is in that desperate breast,
and there my voice has measure:

You dance to its closed number
and time returns in fresh figures:
sadness too, but so to quiet
turned, that through sweetness it burns.

In this silence swiftly consuming
confound me not ephemeral,
leave me not alone in light;

now that in mild fire in me,
you are born Anadyomene.

Delphic Woman

In the air of lunar cedars,
at the sign of gold we heard the Lion.
The earthly wail foretold.
Unveiled is the vein of corolla
on the temple that slopes to sleep
and your voice orphic and marine.

As salt from water
I issue from my heart.
The age of laurel vanishes
and the unquiet ardor
and its pity without justice.

At your naked shoulder
odorous of honey

perishes exiguous
the invention of dreams.

In you I rise, o Delphic woman,
no longer human. Secret
the night of the warm moons' rains

sleeps in your eyes:
to this quiet of skies in ruins
occurs the inexistent childhood.

In the movements of starred solitudes,
to the bursting of the grains,
to the will of the leaves,
you will be howl of my substance.

Horses of Moon and of Volcanoes

TO MY DAUGHTER

Islands I have dwelt in,
green on immobile seas;

of burnt seaweed, of sea fossils
the beaches where run in heat
horses of moon and of volcanoes.

In the landslide season,
the leaves, the cranes assail the air;
in the light of alluvion, gleam
skies dense and open to the stars;

the doves fly
from the naked shoulders of children.

Here the earth is done:
with toil and blood
I make for me a prison.

For you shall I have to cast me down
at the feet of the mighty,
make soft my plundering heart.

But driven-off by men, again
I lay me down in the flash of light,
a child with open hands
on the banks of trees and rivers:

there, for matings of the gods, the quarry
fruitful makes the grecian orange tree.

Again a Green River

Again a green river plunders me
and accord of grass and poplars,
where the gleam of dead snow is forgotten.

And here within the night, mild lamb
has howled with head of blood:

there floods, in that outcry, the time
of the long wolves of winter,
of the well, homeland of thunder.

The Scrawny Flower Already Flies

I shall know nothing of my life,
obscure monotonous blood.
I shall not know whom I have loved, whom I do love

now that here—straitened, lessened to my limbs—
in the wasted wind of March
I enumerate the evils of deciphered days.

The scrawny flower already flies
from the branches. And I wait
the patience of its irrevocable flight.

Before the Statue of Ilaria Del Carretto

Now your hills beneath a tender moon,
along the Serchio young girls
in red and turquoise dresses lightly move.
Thus, gentle one, in your sweet time;
and Sirius grows dim, each hour grows
more distant, and the seagull rages
on the derelict beaches. The lovers walk
lighthearted in the air of September, their gestures
accompany the shades of words
you recognize. They have no pity; and you,
held fast by earth, o what do you lament?
Here you remain alone. My shuddering
is yours perhaps: mine, too, with wrath and terror.
Remote the dead and even more the living,
my comrades vile and taciturn.

Now Day Breaks

The night is done, the moon
slowly melts in the serene,
sets in the canals.
September lives so in this land
of plains, the meadows are as green

as in the valleys of the south in spring.
I have left my comrades,
have hid my heart within the old walls,
to rest alone remembering you.
How you are more distant than the moon,
now day breaks
and on the stones the hoofs of horses beat!

An Evening, the Snow

Again I hear the animal moan
of distant you behind a closed door:
thus, in the highland villages at the wind of snow,
the air that wails among the shepherds' folds.

Brief game that jars the memory:
the snow has fallen here and gnaws
the rooftops, swells the arches of old Lazzaretto,
and the Great Bear plummets red among the mists.

Where is the colored thigh of my rivers,
the brow of the moon within the summer
thick with assassinated wasps? There rests—the mourning
of your humbled voice in the darkness of shoulders
that lament my absence.

What Seek You, Shepherd of the Air

And again the call of the ancient
shepherd's horn, harsh on the torrents
white with the sloughs of snakes. Perhaps
it sweeps from the plateaus of Acquaviva,
where the river Plàtani rolls shells
underwater among the feet of olive-skinned

children. O from what land does the gust
of the prisoner wind erupt and echo
in the light that crumbles now: what seek you,
shepherd of the air? Perhaps you call the dead.
You, love, beside me, do not hear—confused
by the sounding sea, attentive to the low cry
of fishermen hauling in their nets.

Imitation of Joy

Where the trees make evening
even more abandoned,
how languidly
your final step has vanished,
like the flower that scarce appears
on the linden, insistent on its fate.

You seek a motive for the feelings,
experience silence in your life.
Mirrored time reveals to me
a different destiny. Beauty flashing
now in other faces, saddens me
like death.
I have lost every innocent thing,
even in this voice, surviving
to imitate joy.

Verge of Puberty

Pillager of pains and of inertias,
night; a shield for silences,
the age of sadnesses
oblique, regerminates.

And I see young boys in me,
still graceful on the hip,
at the slope of conch shells,
uneasy at my altered voice.

ERATO AND APOLLYON: 1932–1936

Song of Apollyon

Earthly night, at your meager fire
I was pleased in me at times
and descended among the mortals.

And I saw man
bent over the breast of the beloved
listening to his being born,
and—altered—to the earth consigned,
his hands clasped,
his eyes scorched and his mind.

I loved. Cold were the hands
of the nocturnal creature:
she ingathered steep terrors in that vast bed
where at dawn I heard me wakened
by the beat of doves.

Then the sky bore leaves
on her still body:
somber rose the waters in the seas.

My beloved, I here grieve
deathless, alone.

Apollyon

In somber sleep, the mountains
lie supine exhausted.

The hour of full
death is born, Apollyon;
my limbs are tardy still; the heart
is heavy, unremembering.

I stretch my hands to you
from forgotten wounds,
beloved destroyer.

The Ànapo

On your banks, my Ànapo,
I hear dove water; in memory moans
to its sorrow
loudest rustling.

Rising softly to the shore,
after playing with the gods,
an adolescent body:

Mutable his face,
on a shin bone in the movement of the light
swells a vegetal grume.

Bent over the deep ferments
he re-endures each phase,
bears within him death in nuptial seed.

—Lord, what hast Thou done with the tides
of the blood?—Cycle of returns
vain on his flesh,
night and the surge of the stars.

Sterile substance laughs humanly.

Descended into cool oblivion,
he lies in the dark of grass;
the beloved is a shadow and eavesdrops
in his rib.

Mild animals,
their pupils of air,
they drink in dream.

In Your Light I Shipwreck

I am born in your light I shipwreck,
evening of limpid waters.

The air, consoled,
burns with serene leaves.

Uprooted from the living,
a makeshift heart,
I am vain limit.

For Thy tremendous gift
of words, I pay
assiduously, Lord.

Awake me from the dead:
each one has taken his land,
his woman.

Thou hast seen within me,
in the darkness of my bowels:
no one has found my desperation
in his heart.

I am an only man,
an only hell.

Often a Riviera

Often a riviera
gleams with solemn stars,
beehives of sulphur on my head
sway.

Time of bees; and the honey
is in my throat
fresh with sound again;
at noon a raven wanders
on gray sandstones.

Delightful airs: to which the solar quiet
teaches death, and night
words of sand

of homeland—lost.

Ulysses' Isle

The ancient voice is still.
I hear ephemeral echoes,
oblivion of full night
in the starred water.

Ulysses' isle
is born of the celestial fire.
Slow rivers carry trees and skies
in the roar of lunar shores.

The bees, beloved, bring us gold:
time of the mutations, secret.

Sardinia

At daybreak, with the moon alight,
as soon as you emerge, the azure
water moans.

At another rivermouth
more grieving substance
breathed life into the wail of the gulls.

I share your birth;
and, here, the ancient islander
searches for his only eye—
blasted—on his forehead, tries
his masterly arm
in the casting of stones.

Granite rocks undone by the air,
waters that grave slumber
ripens in salt.

Pity has lost me;
and here I find the sign
that speaks with love
to the squalid exile;
in the names of memory: Siliqua
with its slabs of crude earth,

in the bone heaps of stone
in squat cones.

Ephemeral desert: in the heart there plays
the mass of the hills of younger grass;

and the fraternal air comforts love.

Dead Heron

In the warm swamp, thrust into the slime,
dear to the insects, in me grieves
a dead heron.

I devour me in light and sound;
struck down in squalid echoes,
from time to time a breath, forgotten,
moans.

Mercy, that I not be
without words and forms
one day, in memory.

Quarries

Syllables of shadows and leaves,
on the grass, abandonedly
the dead make love.

I hear. Dear is the night to the dead,
for me—a mirror of sepulchers,
of quarries of greenest cedars,

of mines of salt,
of rivers whose Greek names,
spoken, are soft verses.

Insomnia

NECROPOLIS OF PANTÀLICA

A glad gust of winged things
jarring the green light:
the sea in the leaves.

I am awry. And all that's born in me to joy
time lacerates, leaving only
its faint echo in voice of trees.

My self-love—lost,
memory, not human:
on the dead, celestial stigmata glisten,
grave starshapes fall into the rivers:
An hour grows languid with soft rain
or a song stirs in this eternal night.

Years and years, I sleep
in an open cell of my earth,
seaweed shoulders against gray waters:

in the still air meteors thunder.

On the Hill of the "Terre Bianche"

Surviving the day
with the trees I humble me.

Enough of arid things:
friends to feeble green,
to chill clouds
resigned in rains.

The night is filled by sea,
and the howl bears down malignly
sunk in little flesh.

An echo of the earth consoles us
at the tardy harrowing, beloved;

or the geometric quiet of the Bear.

For My Human Smell

In the murdered trees
infernos wail:
summer slumbers in the virgin honey,
the lizard in its monstrous infancy.

For my human smell
I ask pardon of the air of angels,
of the water—my heart celestial—
in the fertile darkness of the cell.

In the Just Human Time

She lies in the wind of deep light,
beloved of the time of doves.
Alone among the living, choicest one,
you speak of me of waters of leaves;
your voice consoles
the naked night
with gleaming joys and ardors.

Beauty deluded us, the vanishing
of every form and memory.
the fleeting motion unveiled to the feelings
mirroring the inward fires.

But from your deep blood,
in the just human time,
we shall be reborn without sorrow.

Of the Sinner of Myths

Of the sinner of myths,
recall the innocence,
o Eternal; the ravishments,
and the fatal stigmata.

He bears your sign of good and evil,
and images wherein laments
the fatherland of earth.

SUNKEN OBOE: 1930–1932

To My Earth

A sun bursts swollen into sleep,
and trees howl;
adventurous aurora
where you, unmoored, set sail,
and mild marine seasons
ferment shores that verge on birth.

I here, infirm, awake,
bitter with an other earth
and with the mutable mercy of song
love germinates in me
of men, of death.

My grief bears new green,
but the hands are airy
on your branches,
on women whom sadness
shut in desolation
and time never touches,
that grays me, strips my bark.

In you I cast myself: a coolness
of naves settles in the heart:
naked steps of angels
sound there, in the dark.

Word

You smile that I grow lean for syllables,
bend the hills and heavens, azure hedge
around me, murmuring of elms
and voices of trembling waters;
that I beguile my youth
with clouds and colors
deepened by the light.

I know you. All astray in you
does beauty lift the breasts,
scoop to the loins and in soft motion
widen through the timorous pubes,

then redescend in harmony of forms
to the feet comely with ten conch shells.

But if I take you, lo:
you, too, are word to me and sorrow.

Woods Sleep

Womb dry with loves and births,
long years I moan
uninhabited, beside you.

Asleep—serene
woods of green, of wind,
plains where sulphur
was the summer of myths,
immobile.

You had not come to live upon me,
omen of enduring pain:
The earth was dying on the waters,
ancient hands in rivers
gathered reeds.

I cannot hate you: so light
is my hurricane heart.

Minor Curve

Lose me, Lord, that I not hear
the silent sunken years despoil me,
that pain to open motion alter:

living's minor
curve is left me.

And make me wind that sails joyous,
or barley seed or seed of leper
that utters itself in full becoming.

And be it easy to love Thee
in grass that strives to light
in wound that pierces flesh.

I try a life:
everyman walks unshod and wavers
in search.

Again you leave me: I am alone
in the shade that spreads into evening,
nor does passage open for
soft outpouring of the blood.

Metamorphoses in the Urn of the Saint

The dead mature;
with them, my heart.
Self-pity
is earth's final humor.

Stirring in the glass of the urn,
a light of lacustrine trees:
Dark mutation devastates me,
unknown saint: in the scattered seed moan
green maggots:
my visage is their springtime.

A memory of darkness
is born at the bottom of walked-in wells,
an echo of buried drums.

I am your suffered
relic.

My Patient Day

My patient day
to Thee, Lord, I consign,
my not cured infirmity,
my knees cleft by boredom.

I abandon me, I abandon me:
wail of springtime
is a forest
born within my eyes of earth.

Where the Dead Stand Open-Eyed

We shall follow silent houses,
where the dead stand open-eyed
and children, made adult already
in the smile that saddens them,
and branches beat at speechless windows
in the middle of the nights.

We, too, shall have voices of the dead,
if ever we have been alive
or the heart of the woods and the mountains
that drove us to the rivers,
had us be no more than dreams.

Green Drift

Evening: grieving light,
lazy bells founder.
Tell me no words: in me is still
the love of sounds, and mine the hour
as in the time of colloquies
with the air and with the woods.

Slumbers descended from the skies
into lunar waters,
houses slept the sleep of mountains,
or the snow stopped angels on the alder trees
and stars at windows
veiled like paper kites.

Green drift of islands,
landfalls of schooners,
the crew that followed seas and clouds
in the chant of oars and cordage
left me the prey:
white and naked, and to touch her
secret sounded
voices of the rocks and rivers.

Then the lands did rest
on aquamarine depths:
uneasy weariness and life of other movements
fell in engulfed firmaments.

To have you is dismay
that repays for all laments,
softness that recalls the islands.

First Day

A peace of outspread waters,
awakens me within the heart
of ancient hurricanes,
small uneasy monster.

Weightless in my darkness are
the stars that crumbled with me
in sterile globes of two poles,
between swift daybreaks' furrows:
love of rocks and clouds.

My blood is Thine,
Lord, let us die.

Seed

Trees of shadows,
islands shipwreck in vast aquaria,
infirm night,
on nascent earth.

A sound of leaves
of cloud that opens
on my heart:

No thing dies
that in me lives not.

You see me: I am wrought so lightly,
made so within things
that I tread with the heavens;

that when Thou willest
Thou mightest hurl me into seed
already weary of the weight that sleeps.

Lamentation of a Friar in an Ikon

I live on enough aridity,
my God;
my green squalor!

A night drones loud
with warm insects;

lament unfastens
my rotted tunic of wool:

I card my flesh
gnawed by ascarides:
love, my skeleton.

Deep, concealed, a cadaver
chews earth steeped in urine:

I repent
of having given Thee my blood,
Lord, my refuge:

mercy!

Comrade

I know not what light wakened me:
nuptial ellipse of white and azure
plummets, avalanches in me. Blessed birth,

you have come to touch me,
assembling, in the silences, the shapes of childhood:
mildest eyes of an impaled sheep,
a dog of mine they killed,
and he a harsh and ugly comrade
with scrawny shoulder blades.

And the boy I loved
above all others; agile
at tipcat and quoits
and silent always and unsmiling.

We grew in the sight of steep skies
traveling lands and mists of planets:
mysterious trips by lantern light
and late-come sleep enclosed me, absorbed
in the serene songs of the chicken roosts,
in the first clatter of shoes near the ovens—
the ungirdled servant girls.

You have given me lament
yet the light does not reveal your name,
only that white lamb's-name
of the heart that I have buried.

Repose of Grass

Drift of light; shifting whirlpools,
airy zones of suns,
abysses rise: I bare the sod
that is mine, recline. And sleep:
for ages, the grass reposes
its heart with me.

Death wakens me:
more one, more only,
beating deep of the wind:
of night.

To the Night

From your womb
unremembering I rise
and weep.

Angels tread, mute
with me; things have no breath;
every voice is turned to stone,
silence of buried skies.

Your first man
knows not, yet grieves.

Without Memory of Death

Springtime raises trees and rivers;
lost in you, beloved,
I cannot hear the deep voice.

Without memory of death,
joined in the flesh,
the drone of final day
awakens us, adolescents.

No one listens to us;
the light breath of the blood!

Become a branch,
my hand
flowers on your thigh.

Of plants stones waters,
the animals are born
to the breath of the air.

Sunken Oboe

Miser pain, delay your gift
in this my hour
of longed-for abandons.

Chill, again an oboe utters
joy of everlasting leaves,
not mine, and disremembers;

in me, evening falls:
the water sets
on my grassy hands.

In a dim sky, fleeting
wings sway; the heart migrates
and I am fallow

and the days, rubble.

The Water Decomposes Dormice

Lucid dawn of funereal panes.
The water decomposes dormice
in the vegetal dark,

from the clots of beech trees
filtering unknowing
into the hollow trunks.

Like the dormice, time dissolving:
and the final splash scorches,
pillages with softnesses.

Nor in you is shelter,
you abandoned unto slumber
after fresh joy:
in vain, made sex, I gain new blood.

In the Ancient Light of the Tides

Island city
submerged in my heart,
thus I descend in the ancient light
of the tides, near tombs
on the shore of waters
set loose by a joy
of dreamt-on trees.

I call me: a sound is mirrored
in amorous echo:
soft, its secret startles
in broad avalanches of air.

In me there yields a weariness
of precocious rebirths:
the usual pain of being mine
in an hour beyond time.
And I hear your dead

in the jealous throbs
of vegetal veins
made less deep:

an intent breathing of nostrils.

Of Young Woman Bent Back Among the Flowers

One divined the occult season
from the anxiousness of nightly rains,
from clouds that varied in the skies,
wavy light cradles:
and I was dead.

A city hanging in mid-air
was my final exile,
around me called
the soft women of ago,
and, by years renewed, my mother
her gentle hand choosing roses,
with the whitest ones she garlanded my head.

Night outside,
in curves of gold, the stars pursued
precise and unknown paths
and things, made fugitive,
drew me to secret corners
to tell of gardens opened wide
and of the sense of life;
but I was grieved with the final smile

of young woman bent back among the flowers.

Island

I HAVE ONLY YOU,
HEART OF MY RACE.

Love of you soddens me,
my earth, if evening sheds
dark perfumes of orange trees,
or oleanders, if—serene—
the torrent flows with roses
that almost reach its estuary.

But if I return to your shores
and, in song, a soft voice calls,
fearful, from the road—
I know not whether childhood or love,
longing for other skies turns me,
and I hide in the forgotten things.

Prayer to the Rain

Fine odor of sky
on green,
rain of early evening.

Nude voice, I listen to you:
in you, the furrowed heart has sweet
first fruits of sound and refuge;
and you awaken me, mute adolescent,
surprised by other life and every motion
by sudden resurrections
that darkness utters and transfigures.

Piety of the celestial time,
of its light
of suspended waters;

of our heart
of veins that open
on the earth.

Amen for the Sunday in Albis

Thou hast not betrayed me, Lord:
of every grief
was I brought forth first-born.

The opening words of the introit for the Sunday in Albis, the first Sunday after Easter, are *Quasi modo: "Quasi modo geniti infantes . . ."* ("As newborn babes . . ."), I Pet. 2, 2.

WATERS AND LANDS: 1920–1929

And Suddenly It's Evening

Each alone on the heart of the earth,
impaled upon a ray of sun:
and suddenly it's evening.

Wind at Tindari

Tindari, I know you mild
among broad hills, above the waters
of the god's soft islands,
today you assail me
and bend into my heart.

I climb peaks, airy precipices,
engulfed in the wind of the pines,
and my lighthearted company
moves far-off in air,
wave of sounds and love,
and you, beloved, take me,
you from whom I drew evil
and fears of shades and silences,
asylums of softness once assiduous
and death of soul.

To you unknown's the earth
wherein each day I sink
and nourish secret syllables:
other light unleafs you through your windows
in your nocturnal dress,
and joy not mine reposes
on your breast.

Harsh is exile,
and my search for harmony
that was to end in you, alters today
into precocious dread of death:

and every love is a screen for sadness,
silent tread into the darkness
where you have set me
bitter bread to break.

Tindari, serene, return;
soft friend awaken me
that from a stone I thrust me skyward,
feigning fear to who knows not
what deep wind has sought me out.

Deadwater

Still water, slumber of the marshes,
that steeps venom in broad patches,
now white now green in lightning flashes,
you are like my heart.

Here, the ilex grays, the poplar;
within, the acorns and the leaves grow still;
and each has its single-centered circles
unraveled by the dark drone of the southwester.

Thus, as memory on water
widening its rings, my heart;
she stirs from one point and then dies:
to you, deadwater, she is sister.

Ancient Winter

Desire for your bright hands
in the penumbra of the flame:
they smelt of oak and roses;
of death. Ancient winter.

The birds were seeking grain
and suddenly were snowed under;
thus—words.
A little sun, an angel's glory,
and then the mist; and the trees
and us, made of air in the morning.

Grief of Things That I Know Not

Thick with white and black roots,
odorous of worms and ferment,
severed by the waters—earth.

Grief of things that I know not
is born in me; one death is not enough
if often on my heart, behold,
a sod lies heavy with the grass.

The Dead

It seemed to me that voices opened,
lips sought water,
hands were lifted to the skies.

What skies! Whiter than the dead
that ever wake me softly;
their feet unshod; they go not far.

Gazelles were drinking at the springs,
wind to seek out junipers
and branches to lift the stars?

Avidly I Stretch My Hand

In poverty of flesh, as I am
behold me, Father; dust of streets
the pardoning wind lifts lightly.

Yet if once I could not thin
my voice still crude and primitive,
now avidly I stretch my hand:
give me sorrow daily bread.

Day after day
1943–1946

On the Willow Branches

And how could we have sung
with the alien foot upon our heart,
among the dead abandoned in the squares
on the grass hard with ice, to the children's
lamb lament, to the black howl
of the mother gone to meet her son
crucified on the telegraph pole?
On the willow branches, by our vow,
our lyres, too, were hung,
lightly they swayed in the sad wind.

Perhaps the Heart

The acrid odor of the lindens
will sink within the night of rain.
The time of joy, its fury, will be vain,
its lightning bite that shatters.
There scarce remains the indolence,
the memory of a gesture, of a syllable,
but like a slow flight of birds

in fumes of fog. And still you await,
I know not what, my lost one; perhaps
an hour that decides, that recalls
the end or the beginning; henceforward,
equal fates. Here black the smoke
of fires still dries the throat. O if
you can, forget that taste of sulphur,
and the fear. Words wear us out,
they rise again from a stoned water;
perhaps the heart is left us, perhaps the heart . . .

O My Sweet Animals

Now autumn spoils the green of hills,
o my sweet animals. Again we'll hear,
before night falls, the last lament
of birds, the call of the gray plain
that goes to meet that high sound
of the sea. And the smell of wood
in the rain, the smell of dens,
how it lives among the houses,
among the men, o my sweet animals.
This face that turns its slow eyes,
this hand that points to the sky
where thunder drones, are yours, my wolves,
o my foxes burnt by blood.
Each hand, each face, is yours.
You, love, tell me all was vain:
life, the days corroded by a water
assiduous, while from the gardens
rises a children's song. Are they distant,
then, from us? But they yield in the air,
barely shadows. This your voice.
But I perhaps do know all has not been.

To Pilgrim Me

Here, I return to the silent square:
on your balcony sways solitary
the banner of a bygone holiday.
—Appear again—I say. But the echo
from abandoned quarries of rock deceived
only the age that yearns for sorcery.
How long since the invisible—if I
should call, as once, in silence—answers not.
You are here no more, no more your greeting
reaches pilgrim me. Never twice
does joy reveal itself. And light extreme
beats on the pine that recalls the sea.
Vain, too, the image of the waters.

Our land is distant, in the south,
warm with tears and mourning. Women
there, in black shawls,
speak of death in lowered voices
at the portals of the houses.

Man of My Time

You are still the one with the stone and the sling,
man of my time. You were in the cockpit,
with the malign wings, the sundials of death,
—I have seen you—in the chariot of fire, at the gallows,
at the wheels of torture. I have seen you: it was you,
with your exact science persuaded to extermination,
without love, without Christ. Again, as always, you
have killed, as did your fathers kill, as did

the animals that saw you for the first time, kill.
And this blood smells as on the day
one brother told the other brother: "Let us
go into the fields." And that echo, chill, tenacious,
has reached down to you, within your day.
Forget, o sons, the clouds of blood
risen from the earth, forget the fathers:
their tombs sink down in ashes,
black birds, the wind, cover their heart.

Letter

This steady silence in the streets,
this lazy wind, that now slides down
among dead leaves, or climbs again
to the colors of alien ensigns . . .
perhaps the anxiety to tell you a word
before the heavens close again
upon another day, perhaps
our vilest ill, inertia . . . Life
is not in this tremendous, somber
heartbeat, is not pity, is
no longer but a game of the blood
where death's in flower. O my soft
gazelle, recall that geranium kindled
on a bullet-riddled wall.
Or now does even death no longer
console the living, the death for love?

The Wall

And on the stadium wall already,
among the clefts and tufts of hanging
grass, the lizards lightning flash;

the frog returns to the canals, a steady
song within my distant village
nights. You do recall that here
the great star greeted our arrival
from the shades. O love, how much
time has fallen with the leaves of the poplars,
how much blood into the rivers of the earth.

Of Another Lazarus

From remotest winters, a sulphureous
gong that hammers thunder on the smoking
valleys. And as in that time, the voice
of woods is modulated: "Ante lucem
a somno raptus, ex herba inter homines,
surges." And your stone is overturned
where hesitates the image of the world.

Day After Day

Day after day: accursed words and the blood
and the gold. My similars, I recognize you, monsters
of the earth. At your bite is pity fallen,
and the gentle cross has left us.
I can return no more to my elysium.
We shall raise tombs along the sea, upon the lacerated fields,
but yet not one sarcophagus that marks the heroes.
Death has often played with us:
in the air one heard a monotonous beating of leaves,
as on the heath when, in sirocco,
the marsh hen climbs upon the cloud.

Inscription on a Tomb Perhaps

Here, remote from everyone, the sun
beats down on your hair, rekindling honey there,
and from its shrub, the summer's last cicada
now calls us back—us, the living—
as does the siren wailing deep
alarm upon the plain of Lombardy.
O voices scorched by the air, what do you search?
The weariness still rises from the earth.

From the Fortress of Upper Bergamo

You have heard the cry of the cock in the air
beyond the ramparts, beyond the towers
chill with a light that you knew not,
lightning cry of life, and murmur
in the cells of voices and
the birdcall of the dawn patrol.
For yourself, you spoke no words:
you were in the narrow circle:
and the antelope and the heron stilled
lost in a gust of malignant smoke,
talismans of a world scarce born.
And the February moon did pass
plain upon the earth, for you
but a remembered form, alight in its silence.
You, too, among the cypresses
now soundless walk; and here the wrath
is stilled in the green of the youthful dead
and the distant pity is almost joy.

Milan, August 1943

In vain you search among the dust,
poor hand, the city is dead.
Is dead: the final drone has sounded
on the heart of the Canal;
and from the aerial, high on the convent,
where he sang before the sunset,
fallen is the nightingale.
Dig no wells in the courtyards,
no longer do the living thirst.
Touch not the dead, so red, so swollen:
leave them in their houses' earth:
the city is dead, is dead.

January 19, 1944

I read to you an ancient one's soft verses,
and the words that were born among the vineyards,
the tents, on the riverbanks of eastern lands,
how sad and desolate they fall in this
profoundest night of war, where no one
crosses the sky of the angels of death,
and the wind is a ruinous roar when it tosses
the metal sheets that here, on high,
divide the balconies, the melancholy
rises from dogs that howl in the gardens
at the rifle shots of the patrols
on the empty streets. Someone's alive.
Perhaps someone's alive. But we, here,
attentive to the ancient voice,
seek a sign that overarches life

the obscure sorcery of earth,
where even among the rubble tombs
the malign grass raises up its flower.

The Ferry

From where do you call? Your echo's faint
within this fog. Again it's time:
from the huts, the eager dogs
rush to the river, to track the scent:
bright with blood, a polecat sneers
upon the other shore. I know
that ferry: there on the water, black
stones emerge; how many ships
pass in the night with sulphur torches.
Now you are truly distant, if your voice
has the measureless tone of echo
and I can barely hear its cadence.
But I see you: you have violets,
so pale, in your clasped hands, and lichens
near your eyes. Thus, you are dead.

Life is not dream
1946–1948

Lament for the South

The reddish moon, the wind, your color
of a woman of the North, the expanse of snow . . .
My heart is now upon these meadows,
in these waters clouded by the mists.
I have forgotten the sea, the grave

conch shell sounded by Sicilian shepherds,
the cantilenas of the carts along the streets,
where the carob tree trembles in the smoke of stubble fields.
I have forgotten the passage of the herons and the cranes
in the air of green plateaus
for the lands and streams of Lombardy.
But man will anywhere cry out a homeland's fate.
No one will take me South again.

Oh, the South is tired of hauling the dead
on the banks of malarial marshes,
is tired of solitudes, of chains,
is tired of the curses,
in its mouth, of all the races
that have howled death withing the echo of its wells,
that drank the blood of its heart.
For that, its children return to the mountains,
constrain their horses under starry blankets,
eat acacia flowers along the tracks
newly red, still red, still red.
No one will take me South again.

And this night charged with winter
is still ours, and here do I repeat to you
my absurd counterpoint
of sweetnesses and furors,
a lament of love without love.

Epitaph for Bice Donetti

With her eyes on the rain and the elfs of the night,
there—in Field Fifteen at Musocco—
lies the woman of Emilia
whom I loved in youth's sad time.
But a while ago, she was tricked by death
as quietly she watched, from her gray house

on the outskirts, the autumn wind toss
the plane tree's branches and the leaves.
Her face is still quick with surprise,
as surely it was in childhood, astonished
by the fire-eater high on the wagon.
O you who pass, drawn by other dead,
before grave number one-hundred-sixty,
stop a moment to salute her—
she who never grieved over the man
who here remains, hated, with his verses,
one like all others, a workman of dreams.

Dialogue

"At cantu commotae Erebi de sedibus imis
umbrae ibant tenues simulacraque luce carentum."
We are filthy with war and Orpheus swarms
with insects, he is pierced by lice,
and you are dead. The winter, that weight
of ice, the water, the tempest air,
were with you, and the thunder of echo
in echo in your earthly nights.
And now I know I owed you stronger
approbation, but our time
was fury and blood: others were foundering
in the mud, had hands and eyes
undone, were howling for mercy and love.
But as it is always late to love;
forgive me, therefore. Now I, too,
cry out your name in this noon hour
lazy with wings, with cords of cicadas
stretched within the cypress barks.
We know no longer where is your shore:
there was a passage marked by poets,

near springs that smoke with landslides on
the high plateau. But there I saw,
as a boy, shrubs of violet berries,
sheep dogs, somber birds,
and horses, mysterious animals,
behind the man, their heads held high.
The living have forever lost
the way of the dead, and stand apart.

This silence now is more tremendous
than that which separates your shore.
"Frail shadows came." And here
the Olona flows tranquilly,
no tree moves from its well of roots.
O were you not Eurydice? Were you not Eurydice?
Eurydice lives. Eurydice! Eurydice!

And you, still filthy with war, Orpheus,
like your horse, without the whip,
lift up your head, earth quakes no more.
How with love, win, if you will, the world.

ll. 1–2: "Touched by the song, from the deepest Erebus
frail shadows came and semblances bereft of light."
Virgil, *Georgics,* Bk. IV, 471–472

Colors of Rain and Iron

You said: death, silence, solitude,
like love, life. Words
of our makeshift images.
And the wind rose light each morning
and the season colored with rain and iron
passed over the rocks, over
our mewed-up murmur of the damned.
The truth is distant still.

And tell me, man cleft upon the cross
and you with hands thick with blood,
how shall I answer those that ask?
Now, now: before another wind does rise,
another stillness fill the eyes, before
another rust flourishes.

Almost a Madrigal

The sunflower bends to the west, and day
already sets in its ruined eye,
the air of summer thickens, curves
the leaves, the smoke of the factories.
With the clouds' dry flow, the lightning's screech
this last game of the heavens moves
far-off. Again, love, as for years,
we pause at the changes in the trees
crowded in the circle of the canals.
But it is still our day, and still
that sun that takes its leave
with the thread of its affectionate ray.

I've no more memories, I do not want to remember;
memory rises up from death,
life is without end. Each day
is ours. One day will stop forever,
and you with me, when it seems late for us.
Here on the edge of the canal, our feet
swinging back-and-forth like children's,
let us watch the water, the first branches
in its darkening green.
And the man who approaches in silence
hides no knife within his hands,
but a geranium.

Thànatos Athànatos

And shall we have to deny thee then,
God of the tumors, God of the living
flower, begin with a no to the obscure
rock "I am," consent to death
and on each tomb inscribe our only
certainty: "thànatos athànatos"?
Without a name to tell the dreams
the tears the furors of this man
defeated by still-open questions.
Our dialogue alters; now the absurd
becomes possible. There, beyond
the smoke of fog, within the trees
the power of the leaves is watchful,
true is the river pressing on the banks.
Life is not dream. True is man
and his jealous plaint of silence.
God of silence, open solitude.

Letter to My Mother

"Mater dulcissima, now the mists descend,
the Naviglio dashes against its dikes,
the trees swell with water, burn with snow;
I am not sad in the North: I am not
at peace with myself, but I expect
pardon from no one, many owe me tears,
as man to man. I know you are not well, that you live
like all the mothers of poets, poor
and just in the measure of their love
for distant sons. Today it is I
who write to you."—At last, you will say, two words
from that boy who fled by night in a short coat,
a few lines in his pocket. Poor, so quick of heart,

one day they'll kill him somewhere.
"Surely, I remember, I left from that gray station
of slow trains that carried almonds and oranges,
at the mouth of the Imera, river full of magpies,
salt, of eucalyptus. But now I thank you—
this I would—for the irony you laid upon
my lips, mild as your own.
That smile has saved me from laments and griefs.
And it matters not if now I've some tears for you,
for all who wait—like you—
and know not what they wait. Ah, gentle death,
don't touch the clock in the kitchen that ticks on the wall;
all my childhood has passed on the enamel
of its face, upon those painted flowers:
don't touch the hands, the heart of the dead.
Perhaps someone will answer? O death of mercy,
death of modesty. Farewell, dear one, farewell, my
dulcissima mater."

The false and true green
1949–1955

The Dead Guitars

My land is on the rivers and thrust against the sea,
no other place has voice so lingering
where my footsteps wander
among the rushes heavy with snails.
Surely it is autumn: in the wind in snatches
the dead guitars pluck the chords
on the black mouth, and a hand stirs the fingers
of fire.
In the mirror of the moon
young girls with breasts of oranges dress their hair.

Who weeps? Who whips the horses in the red
air? We shall stop beside this shore
along the chains of grass and you, beloved,
bring me not before that infinite
mirror: there within behold themselves
boys that sing and steepest trees and waters.
Who weeps? I not, believe me: on the rivers
race exasperated flailed by a lash,
the somber horses, the lightning flashes of sulphur.
I not, my race has knives
that blaze and moons and wounds that burn.

The False and True Green

No longer wait for me with the coward heart
of the clock. It matters not if you set free
or fix the squalor: all that's left
are hard and ragged hours, the beat
of leaves upon your windowpanes,
steep above two streets of clouds.
I keep the slowness of a smile,
the dark sky of a dress, the rust-
colored velvet around your hair
and loose on your shoulders, and your face
sunk in water that hardly stirs.

Strokes of leaves rough with yellow,
birds of soot. Other leaves
now cleave the branches, darting out
entangled: April's false and true
green, that unleashed sneer of certain
flowering. And do you flower not,
put on no days, nor dreams that rise
from our beyond? Where are your childlike
eyes, your tender hands
to seek my face that flees me?

There rests, the shyness of writing diary
verses or casting a howl into the void
or into the incredible heart that still
struggles with its ruined time.

In a Distant City

He didn't emerge from the sky, but on the meadow
of pale seaweed in the northern garden—
a raven sudden sprang from the steep
leaves: not a symbol, in the summer
bent with rainbows and rains: a true raven
like an acrobat on the trapeze
at Tivoli.
            Fragile, astute image
entering into the day that ended in us
with carousels and paddle wheels
and strophes of sailors'
ballads and the departing wail
of a steamer opening furious wings
of foam or the tears of harbor
women.
            The hour struck on this farthest
shore of Europe, insistent, frenzied
for innocence.
                        The raven was still a happy
sign, like other signs
when I tried out my mind in its every
limit and form, holding back
an outcry to attempt the still
world, amazed that I, too,
could cry out. Perhaps a game, a waiting,
a violence: but for a touch of irony
one loses all, and there's more to be feared in the light
than the shadow.
                        My love, did you await

a word unknown to you or my word? Then the raven
turned, lifted his swift feet from the grass
and vanished in the air of your green eye.

For a touch of irony one loses all.

How Long a Night

How long a night, how pink and green the moon
at your outcry among the orange blossoms,
if you pound at a gate like one of God's kings,
pungent with dew: "Open, beloved, open!"
The chorded wind from the Iblei, from the cones
of the Madonie, wrests hymns and laments
from the drums of grottoes ancient as
the agave and the bandit's eye. And the Great Bear
still won't leave you and shakes its seven
bonfires blazing on the hills,
and these are with you still—the sound of the red
chariots of Saracens and Crusaders,
perhaps the solitude and, too, the dialogue
with the starred animals, the horse
and the dog, the frog, the hallucinating
guitars of crickets in the evening.

Near a Saracen Tower, for His Dead Brother

I listened to a glistening
shell of my sea
and in the far-off sound I heard
hearts growing with me, beating
equal time. Of gods and beasts, of timid ones
or demons: contrary fables of the
mind. Perhaps the attentive

bite of the dark
snares for foxes wolves
hyenas, under the moon with tattered sails,
snapped for us,
hearts of delicate violets, hearts
of spiny flowers. O they should not have risen
and fallen with the sound: the somber thunder
up from the rainbow of air and stone,
into the ear of the sea droned
a mistaken childhood, heritage of
dreams awry, to the earth
of abstract measures, where everything
is stronger than man.

Laud: April 29. 1945

SON

—And why, mother, do you spit at the cadaver
head down, lashed by his feet to the crossbeam?
And don't the others, hanging there
beside him, disgust you? Ah, that woman,
her macabre can-can stockings,
her throat and mouth of trampled flowers!
No, mother, stop: cry to the crowd
to go away. This is no lament, it is sneer,
it is joy: the horseflies are already fast
at the knots of the veins. You have fired
now at that face: mother, mother, mother!

MOTHER

—We have always spat at the cadavers,
son: hanging at the window grates,
at the mast of the ship, incinerated
for the cross, torn limb from limb
for a little grass at the edge of the estates.
And be it solitude or tumult,

eye for eye, tooth for tooth,
after two thousand years of eucharist,
our heart had wanted to open
that other heart that had opened yours,
my son. They have hollowed your eyes, shattered
your hands for a name to be betrayed.
Show me your eyes; give me here your hands:
son, you are dead! Because you are dead,
you can pardon: son, son, son.

SON

—This repugnant sultry heat, this smoke
of rubble, the fat green flies
in clusters on the hooks: the wrath and the blood
flow justly. Not for you
and, mother, not for me: again tomorrow they will
pierce my eyes and hands. For centuries
mercy is the howl of the assassinated.

Auschwitz

There, at Auschwitz, distant from the Vistula,
love, along the northern plain,
in a camp of death; funereal, chill,
the rain upon the rusty poles
and the tangled iron of the fences:
and neither tree nor birds in the gray air
or above our revery, but inertia
and pain, that memory bequeaths unto
its silence without irony or ire.

You seek no idylls, elegies: only
motives for our destiny, you tender
here before the contrasts of the mind,
uncertain at a clear
presence that is life's. But life is here,

in every no that seems a certainty:
here we shall hear the angel weep, the monster,
hear our future hours
beating on the beyond, that now is here
in movement and eternity, not in
an image of dreams, of possible piety.
And here the metamorphoses, the myths.
They bear no name of symbols or a god,
are chronicle, are places of the earth,
they are Auschwitz, love. How suddenly
to smoke of shadow altered
dear flesh of Alpheus and Arethusa!

From that inferno opened by a white
inscription: "Labor will make you free"
issued continually
the smoke of thousands of women, from the kennels
forward thrust at dawn against the target
wall or suffocated howling mercy
unto water with the skeletal mouth
under the showers of gas.
You will find them, soldier, there within
your history, within the forms of streams,
of animals, or are you, too, but ash
of Auschwitz, medal of silence?
Long braids remain enclosed in urns of glass,
still crowded by amulets and infinite
shades of little shoes and shawls of Jews:
they are relics of a time of wisdom,
of man who makes of arms the measure, they
are the myths, our metamorphoses.

Upon the plains, where love and lamentation
rotted and piety, beneath the rain,
there, a no within us beat, a no
to death, at Auschwitz dead, that from that pit
of ash, death not repeat.

The incomparable earth
1955–1958

I say that the dead slay the living
—AESCHYLUS: *Choephoroe,* V. 886

Visible, Invisible

Visible, invisible
the waggoner on the horizon
in the arms of the road calls out,
answering the voice of the islands.
I, too, am not adrift,
the world revolves, I read
my history as a night watchman
reads the hours of rain. The secret has happy
margins, stratagems, difficult attractions.
My life—smiling, cruel inhabitants
of my ways, my landscapes—
has no handles at its doors.
I don't prepare myself for death,
I know the origin of things,
the end is a surface on which journeys
the invader of my shadow.
I do not know the shadows.

The Incomparable Earth

Long since I owe you words of love:
or they're the words, perhaps, that flee
each day when they are barely struck,

words that are feared by memory
that alters the inevitable
signs into hostile dialogue
that sinks with the soul. Perhaps
my words of love are drowned by the thud
of the mind or the fear of the arbitrary
echo from even the frailest image
of a fond sound: or they touch the invisible
irony, that's like an axe,
or—love—my life, by now beleaguered.
Or color dazzles them, perhaps,
when they clash with the light
of the time that will come to you when my
time can no longer call love dark
love already weeping
the beauty, the impetuous rupture
with the incomparable earth.

Today the Twenty-First of March

Today, the twenty-first of March, the Ram
enters the equinox, battering his
male head against the trees and rocks,
and you, love, at his blows, remove
the winter wind from your ear bent down to hear
my latest word. The first froth
floats upon the plants, pale-
almost-green it does not shun
the omen. Tidings run
to the gulls that gather
among the rainbows: they emerge,
their language splashed
with spray that tolls
in the grottoes. At my side,
you drown their outcry, open the bridge

between us and the gusts
that nature, underground, prepares
in a flash that has no wisdom;
you pass beyond the thrust of the buds.
Now spring is not enough for us.

In This City

This city has even got the machine
that grinds out dreams: with a quick
token, a little disk of pain,
in no time you're off, upon this earth,
unknown in a pack of raving shadows
on phosphorus sea weed, mushrooms of smoke:
a merry-go-round of monsters
revolving on conch shells
that fall to putrid pieces when they play.
It's in a bar down there at the turn
of the plane trees, here in my metropolis
or elsewhere. Come, the switch is on!

Mycenae

On the road that runs through Mycenae, lined
with eucalyptus, you can find
sheep's-milk cheese and scented wine
"A la belle Hélène de Ménélas,"
a tavern that veers the mind from the blood
of the Atreides. Your kingdom, Agamemnon,
is a bandit's den beneath Mount Zara,
jutting over crooked gullies,

its stone not scarred by roots. The poets
speak much of you, of the crime invented
in your house of crisis,
of Electra's funereal frenzy,
that nurtured—with the eye of sex,
for ten long years—her distant brother
to matricide; the diabolical
speak of the logic of the queen,
wife of the absent soldier,
Agamemnon, mind and sword betrayed.
And only you are lost,
Orestes, your visage vanished without
a golden mask. To the Lions at the gate,
to the skeletons of that scenic harmony
philologists have raised up from the stones,
my greeting of a Greek Sicilian.

To the New Moon

In the beginning God created the heaven
and the earth, then in His exact
day he set the lights in heaven
and on the seventh day He rested.

After millions of years, man,
made in His image and likeness,
never resting, with his
secular intelligence,
without fear, in the serene sky
of an October night,
set other luminaries like
those that turned
since the creation of the world. Amen.

An Answer

If the anchor of Ulysses burns in the mind . . .
If, on the shore of Acis' sea,
among the boats, my black eye set
to the prow against the evil fate,
I could, from the null of the air,
here from the null that sudden shrills
and hooks like the beak of the swordfish,

from the null of the hands that change like Acis,
form out of the null a living
ant and thrust it into the sandy
cone of its labyrinth, or a virus
that would give eternal youth to my
most faithful enemy,
then would I perhaps be like to God—

in equal steadiness of life
and death, not contraries:
wave and lava here, larvae
of light for the already future
glistening winter morning—answer
to a claim of nature, an anguish
that blazes on a milestone number,
the first on the torrid road
that drives like a wedge into the beyond.

Other Answer

But what do you want, lice of Christ?
Nothing happens in the world and man
still hugs the rain in his raven wings
and cries out love and dissonance.

Since eternity, you've never
lacked for blood. Only the sheep
turned round on its way back with ragged
head and eyes of salt.
But nothing happens. And moss already—
the chronicle on the walls of the city
of a distant archipelago.

To My Father

Where Messina lay
violet upon the waters, among the mangled wires
and rubble, you walk along the rails
and switches in your islander's
cock-of-the-walk beret. For three days now,
the earthquake boils, it's hurricane December
and a poisoned sea. Our nights fall
into the freight cars; we, young livestock,
count our dusty dreams with the dead
crushed by iron, munching almonds
and apples dried in garlands. The science
of pain put truth and blades into our games
on the lowlands of yellow malaria
and tertian fever swollen with mud.

Your patience, sad and delicate,
robbed us of fear,
a lesson of days linked to the death
we had betrayed, to the scorn of the thieves
seized among the debris, and executed in the dark
by the firing squads of the landing parties, a tally
of low numbers adding up exact
concentric, a scale of future life.

Back and forth your sun cap moved
in the little space they always left you.
For me, too, everything was measured
and I have borne your name
a little beyond the hatred and the envy.
That red on your cap was a miter,
a crown with eagle's wings.
And now in the eagle of your ninety years
I wanted to speak to you—your parting
signals colored by the night-time lantern—
to speak to you from this imperfect
wheel of the world,
within a flood of crowded walls,
far from the Arabian jasmine
where you are still, to tell you
what once I could not—difficult
affinity of thoughts—to tell you (not only
the marshland locust, the mastic tree can hear)
as the watchman of the fields tells his master:
"I kiss your hands." This, nothing else.
Life is darkly strong.

A Copper Amphora

The thorns of the Indian fig
on the hedge, your bodice—
new and azure—torn, a pain
at the center of your hollowed heart,
perhaps at Lentini, near the swamp
of Iacopo, the notary
of eels and loves. What does the earth
recount, the whistle of the blackbirds
hidden in the noontime hungry
for fruit that's hard with violet

and ocher seeds. Your hair
over your ears where tempest droned
that now do not awake, your water-
color hair, its tarnished tone.
A copper amphora on a door
glistening with water drops
and red threads of grass.

Crooked Nature

Now the symmetrical leaf has fled
crooked nature, the anchor cannot
hold her any longer. Now winter, not winter,
a bonfire smokes near the Naviglio.
At that nocturnal fire, someone
can betray, deny—three times—
the earth. How strong the grip must be
if here for years—what years!—you watch
the soiled stars afloat in the canals
without repugnance, if you love
someone on this earth, and if
the fresh wood crackles, the wrinkled leaf's
geometry can blaze, to warm you.

An Open Arch

With a roar of smoke, the evening falls
to fragments in the earth, the owl
strikes it "tu," uttering only
silence. And the high, dark islands
crush the sea, upon the sands

night invades the conch shells. You
measure the future, the beginning
already gone, divide—with slow
breaking—the sum of a time now absent.
As the spume of the sea coils round the stones,
you lose the sense of the impassive
flow of the destruction.
While death dies it does not know
the closed song of the owl, it tries
its hunt for love, continuing
an open arch, revealing
its solitude. Someone will come.

THE LIFE AND WORKS OF SALVATORE QUASIMODO

By CARLO BO

WE MAY BEGIN this account with a recollection by the subject:

"I was born in Syracuse on August 20, 1901. My father was a railway worker. When the crossing bell announced the passage of one of the very rare trains through this sulphur-mining country, its tinkling seemed to last forever. The nearest villages were Megara Iblea and Sferro: they made one think of Greece and her harsh landscapes. I was baptized in Roccalumera, a few miles from Taormina. My grandmother was a true Greek, a native of Patras. I learned early to read and write, and I became acquainted with the poets. I did not yet understand them, but they left an indelible impression on me.

"I first went to school in Gela, where I felt the shock of the Messina earthquake. Three days later my father was sent into the desolated city. This was my first encounter with death. Looters were being shot. We were locked into the railway cars, and as new tremors occurred we were dispatched from one disaster to another.

"In Palermo I attended technical schools: I wanted to be an engineer. When I returned to Messina I began writing verse. In 1919 I left Sicily for Rome. There I attended the Polytechnic Institute and at the same time struggled constantly to support myself. And so I became a draftsman in a large construction company, a salesman for an iron works and a clerk in a large department store in Piazza Colonna. My career was terminated by the mounted police after I had organized a strike just before the new law forbidding them had become effective. By this time I had completed my studies, and once more I had to face the problem of a livelihood. My friends wanted to get me into newspaper work, but I preferred a state job with the civil engineering department. I was assigned to Reggio Calabria—a return to the south.

"From the time I was fifteen until I was twenty I wrote verse, and then, unhappy with it, I gave it up. When I was twenty-seven I felt the 'vocation' anew, in Reggio Calabria. Every Sunday I would take the ferry to Messina and spend the day talking with my friends."

Let us interrupt Quasimodo's own story of his life at this point. From the moment when his "vocation" regained dominance, his life belonged to history—a life characterized above all by his books and punctuated by the dates of their publication. But in what we have just heard from him we already have everything—or almost everything—that is required for a preliminary definition, an initial identification, of this poet. The element that dominates all others is insularity; it is symbolized by the mark of departure: Quasimodo cannot be explained without this essential word. It is immediately followed by two further marks: the mark of a difficult and arduous life, and the even more potent mark of death, the death he encountered during the awesome earthquake of Messina when he was seven years old.

Let us emphasize, first, the feeling of solitude, even if it is privileged and bathed in the light of grace and perfection; second, the feeling of life conceived of as effort or conquest or, better still, as a constant unending discharging of obligations; and, third, the transcendent vision of death ineradicably impressed on the first scenery that the poet observed. The various stages of the poet's development were grafted onto this root-stock, the traces of which remained discernible throughout his life. But for the moment it is enough to recall that Quasimodo had a second vocation, the vocation that we will call "scientific" and that led him to enroll in the Polytechnic Institute. This was no random choice such as students make when they emerge from junior high school; it was far more. It was a "vocation," and this word, in its narrow sense, implies some element of comparison; for the precision of Quasimodo's style and the clarity of his works cannot be explained without taking into account this period of education and inner development.

But we are getting ahead of ourselves; let us go back to Sicily, the island that made Quasimodo and that still possesses him today. Indeed, the poet has never shifted on this point: he has always striven to achieve a perfect agreement between his basic vision of the universe and the world of his childhood.

In 1950, at the threshold of full maturity, when he felt obliged to illustrate his "poetics," he could find no better means than to start from lines by an "old poet of his country," Jacopo da Lentino:

Miraculously
A love possesses me

Quasimodo then continues: "The word 'island' and Sicily are identified with each other in the final attempt at harmonizing the outer world and the hypothetical syntax of the lyric. I might say that my country is a 'living sorrow,' to which a portion of my memory retreats when an interior dialogue starts with someone I love—whether that person is distant in space or has passed to the farther shore of love. Or I might say that perhaps that is why my images always take shape in my own dialect and why my imagined interlocutor lives in my valleys and walks along the banks of my rivers. It is, so to speak, a statement that is always vague, a will to construct a mathematical system when there is as yet only the babble of one's first numbers. But then what poet does not bound his world within the horizons that his glance most clearly penetrates? My horizon is Sicily; she is the land of ancient civilizations, of cities of the dead, of prison quarries, of caryatids rising out of the grass, of salt and sulphur mines, of women who weep through the centuries for their dead children, of rages repressed or unleashed, of men made outlaws by love or by their concern for honor.

"I too have not strayed in my search for song; my scene is neither mythological nor Parnassian: it is the Anapo, the Imera, the Platane, the Ciane with its papyrus reeds and its eucalyptus; it is Pantalica with its burial caves that were hollowed out forty-five hundred years before Christ, 'close-tiered as the cells of a honeycomb;' it is Gela and Megara Iblea and Lentini: a love, as I said before, that cannot bid memory forsake these places forever."

To leave the island—for a poet who might have been satisfied with pure song—could have meant a negative limitation, a summons to shun all attractions and all psychological and moral concerns. A poet of that kind could never have passed the frontier of inert, unresponsive beauty. But from his very first attempts Quasimodo has striven to question and to perceive the beauty of human questioning. Let us not forget that, beyond the serenity of his early fields and rivers, there are suffering, the devastation of death, and, above all, the outrage incessantly inflicted on man by man: the crime of Cain. If we keep this point of departure clearly in mind, it becomes easy for us to understand how the translator of the Greek lyric and tragic poets was at last driven to render Shakespeare into Italian. His work as a translator was no accident, nor was it the gratification of an "emotion"; it was the fulfillment of a deep, basic need: I should say that it exemplified the rights that the poet claimed as his.

Quasimodo when young was not afraid even to use the exclamation, and this meant that Italian poetry was returning to the broader avenues of a fully human surrender. Let no one be deceived by the seeming discipline of the poems. This severity arises out of a different concern on the part of the poet: never to alter the volume of his own voice. Within the lyric framework Quasimodo endeavored from the start to deal with major themes yet without ignoring the reticence of the time or the fear of misleading. And so the Quasimodo of 1950 was right in claiming still another element for his work: the transformation of themes. But if the reader examines the matter carefully and restudies the album of the earliest landscapes, he will be forced to acknowledge that there is a very different sort of life in the background than what is barely hinted at in the foreground.

For a long period the poet limited his work to a cold recording of the mechanism of existence, the experience of living. Not that this was not necessary—I should say, indeed, that it was essential for purging the histrionics from a poetry that was beginning to lose all its strength and all its meaning and to dissipate itself in empty gestures. Italian poetry had emerged only with great difficulty from its long seizure of D'Annunzio's disease, and, since it was necessary to start again, it was equally important to keep to the minimum the effort required to set it back on its feet and rebuild its body. What the great poets of the nineteenth century had done was rightly interpreted from this point of view as an attempt not only at purification but at incarnation. It was left for Quasimodo, coming as he did after Ungaretti, Campana, Montale and others, to make the first moves into a freer air, no longer suspect or poisoned.

In its completion the word became an evocation of death, an allusion to the vanity of all things; whence the sadness that in Quasimodo's world takes on a special character. And it was at precisely this time, between the two wars, that Quasimodo made his return to the island viewed as a boundary, as an enclosure. In the presence of sorrow, death and the utter shipwreck of man's existence, geography assumed a form instead of losing it. And if some readers allowed themselves to be influenced by the fact that, in the gloomiest stage of our history, he could still with all serenity use the noun "song" and the verb "to sing," this is undoubtedly because they had forgotten the ultimate transformation that made it possible for him to go back to the island. So song remains the second key to his poetics, and, furthermore, in constant harmony with the first, his "vocation": both are words that suffer especial neglect and scorn in the poetics of our time.

Once this has been acknowledged, one must examine the fashion in which Quasimodo's poetics adheres to this tight rule of control and expresses an idea of restriction and constraint. The aridity of his tone derives in part from his early scientific training and aspirations, and, among all the callings that enjoyed his preference during his life—a career in engineering, a career in politics, etc.—from a certain point of view it has always been the vocation of song that has prevailed. The poet could do no less—even when it was a mere matter of giving testimony—than speak as if his voice could not resist being transmuted into song. Solemn song, dignified song—Quasimodo sins neither by amplification nor by abundance. At times, indeed, his concern with preserving total control has caused him to avoid conclusions, and many of his poems end on barely evoked symbols, on facts of life.

If "song" had meant liberation and, finally, betrayal and repudiation, his poems would be more numerous and more esteemed, and Quasimodo would have become famous. As a rule "song" is another word for escape, but in Quasimodo it means presence—and, let us not forget, religious presence. Clearly his is a religion that has neither date nor identifiable sacred writings. But if we say that it is a natural religion, we do not mean that the poet is merely a spectator or an idolator. For Quasimodo, singing fulfills a vital need, a recognized and accepted obligation. Thus, while he would wonder during the German occupation how he could sing with an alien hand gripping his throat, he certainly did not mean by that to lay claim to a position of privilege: he merely felt that he was a man who had been struck down in his religion, a man diminished, a man conquered.

As the years have accumulated, Quasimodo has learned to accord man a greater place. In the past, his terse argument used to be fractured by images or by some barely sketched aspect of reality. Today he seems to prefer to compress his self into a sentence. The early Quasimodo fashioned a skeleton that only time could have fleshed out and covered. Although, for obvious reasons, these operations have been minimal, little by little the poet appears to have fled into silence. In this sense his "vocation" is satisfied by the "enclosure" of the island, and Quasimodo has returned to his native land.

The past thirty years are filled with examples of many similar homecomings, but generally an intellectual hand guided the helm when these journeys were the result of pure speculation, whether ideological or emotional; for Quasimodo, perhaps one should consider the homecoming a kind of reincarnation in his native land. It is enough if one says *paesaggio,* countryside—something bigger than *paese,* village; something more than merely "family": it is precisely that something that expresses the idea of the struggle, the contradiction between man and things. Moreover, this way of disembodying his thought, of ridding it of all the waste thrown up by the moment, has enabled him not merely to attain to the essence of things but to acquire that religious dimension with which we do not here intend to occupy ourselves. In a seeming contradiction, finally, this Quasimodo in his newest stage recognizes that the poet has the duty of speaking in his own person, the function of altering things: as he says, "The poet does not 'describe' but rather accepts his own soul, his own understanding, and he gives his secrets 'life,' compelling them to emerge from the anonymous to the personal."

If we adopted this means of entering into it, we should better understand the arid body of his speech and the power of his intimations. Hence, to what we have said earlier of Quasimodo's return we must add that, for him, to go home, to return in the flesh to his native ambience in no way signifies abdication or renunciation, but, on the contrary, the prideful affirmation of the poet: he changes the world, and poetry becomes ethic precisely because of this splendid surrender. So Quasimodo has twice rediscovered himself—the first time, up to the period of *And Suddenly It's Evening,* in his quest for beauty, and then again during the past twenty years through his firm, unequivocal resolve to go back to man in all his aspects. Objects and themes, whether old or new, were no longer enough for him: they had to be submitted to a process of deep examination in the very heart of the man—which, in this context, means the hearts of all men. After this exploration was accomplished, he was able to go on to the shores of his private Eden, the Sicily of his childhood, in a literary world that, for the sake of convenience, we call "Theocritan"; but if you compare the two images, the two landscapes, you will see that in the end here is a whole man with the highest ambitions.

In our time who can say without being ridiculous that "the poet changes the world?" Quasimodo says so, and he does not question in the least the appropriateness of such a consoling notion that comes unimpaired to him from faith in his work and his idiosyncrasy of playing the high cards, and playing them fast.

"The poet wants man to live bravely": this statement of his sums up the story of a man who has conquered and lived to conquer, the story of a poet who, home again in his island of peace and death and of eternal life and ruin, has a message to convey to the men of his time.

Carlo Bo is rector of the University of Urbino in Italy.
Translated by D. D. Paige.

THE 1959 PRIZE

By KJELL STRÖMBERG

THE SWEDISH ACADEMY decided to award the 1959 Nobel Prize to the Sicilian poet Salvatore Quasimodo, "for his lyrical poetry, which with classical fire expresses the tragic experience of life in our own times."

In the Anglo-American press, the Swedish Academy's choice was generally approved. The New York *Times,* under the signature of Sir Maurice Bowra, the great Oxford expert on Latin literature, saluted Quasimodo as one of the few important poets to have appeared during World War II. He had revivified and enriched the language of Italian poetry more than any other poet of his country, and had reached objectives of the greatest consequence to humanity.

The Italian press in general was more reserved in its praise of the newly chosen laureate, although it expressed satisfaction that a compatriot should have benefited by this rich reward. Except for Pirandello, who was honored in 1934, no Italian writer had received the Nobel Prize during the last quarter of a century. When at last the now flourishing literature of the Apennine peninsula recovered its reputation, it was expected that several other names would be inscribed on the roll of honor, such as Ungaretti, Montale, Silone, and especially Alberto Moravia. The first of these was universally recognized as the master of that "laconic" school of which Quasimodo was also the product. Moravia was a distinguished novelist, who had been elected by his peers to be international president of the P.E.N. Club.

Emilio Cecchi, the leading literary critic in Italy, attacked the Swedish Academy outright in the *Corriere della Sera,* the biggest Milan daily newspaper, and accused the Swedes of a lack of knowledge of the Italian language and literature. It went on to say that this would explain "the banality, the uncertainty and the incompetence it has shown in its choice of certain laureates." In this newspaper's opinion, Pascoli, Verga, Gabriele D'Annunzio, and Benedetto Croce are among the Italian writers who deserved a Nobel Prize just as much, or even more than Sully-Prudhomme, Frédéric Mistral, Romain Rolland, Gide, or Bergson. In conclusion it noted that Italy was "quite obviously, not sufficiently represented on the roll of honor of the Nobel Prize, and that the few Italians who were awarded it are not the most deserving, with the exception of Carducci."

Nevertheless, it cannot be denied that the Swedish Academy had no lack of warm admirers of and astute connoisseurs of Italian literature, both ancient and modern. On the subject of Italian poetry alone there has never been a more devoted promoter nor a more faithful interpreter in Sweden than Anders Österling, the permanent secretary of the Academy. To him we owe some perfect translations, not only of Quasimodo, but of his masters and disciples, from the Middle Ages to the present day. It was Österling who wrote the report on Quasimodo for the use of his colleagues in the Academy. In his report Österling began by describing the deeply rooted origins of the laureate's poetry in the Latin soil and the still living ancient Greek traditions of Sicily, his native island. He showed how the poet passed through the hermetic style of his earliest masters and some contemporary models to reach the purified, simplified style, hewn out of stone and "unselfconsciously monumental," which characterizes his great postwar poetry, dominated by awareness of the presence of death everywhere and at all times.

When the choice was announced, the laureate had a statement ready for the press:

"I received the news with my habitual calm, because I knew that I had to reckon with strong opposition, in view of my special position in the domain of European poetry. My adversaries, that is to say the other candidates, held all the trump cards, so I had to fight my battle alone. The honor which has come to me through this tribute from the Swedish Academy is reflected in many directions. It relates in particular to the grave problem of the anxiety of modern man, which is at the heart of all my work."

Among the foreign personalities who sent their good wishes to Quasimodo was the president of the professional writers' association of the Soviet Union, in fact the very man who had expelled from its bosom Pasternak, the chosen laureate of the previous year. In his telegram of congratulation, the high Soviet dignitary expressed his pleasure that this time the Nobel Committee should have paid well-deserved homage to one of the world's greatest poets: "By your vigorous poems, which have been attentively read in the Soviet Union, you have acquired faithful new friends and readers in our country, where it is not forgotten that you were one of the first writers to devote a poem to our Sputnik."

At the press conference which he gave on his arrival in Stockholm, Quasimodo was bombarded with questions about his relations with Moscow. He strongly denied belonging to any political party whatsoever, and insisted that he had never allowed any political afterthoughts to influence his artistic creation.

Quasimodo was in Moscow by official invitation when the storm over Pasternak broke out; but he had had a serious heart attack and was confined to his bed in a hospital for months on end. He said he had never voiced the derogatory opinions he is supposed to have held on the subject of that unfortunate laureate; least of all did he concur with the view that "Pasternak was as far removed from the present generation as the moon is from the earth." He bluntly told the journalists at his Stockholm press conference that although Pasternak had had to suffer a few setbacks in Soviet Russia because of his Nobel Prize, they were a small thing compared to the martyrdom which he, Quasimodo, had had to undergo for the same reason, consisting of unjustifiable attacks on him in the Western press and most particularly in the Paris newspapers. As for the famous poem in honor of the Sputnik, it was not "the Russian machine itself" that he had wanted to glorify, but "this new moon created by the genius of men, with God's help."

Quasimodo replied in Italian, and paid a resounding tribute to Sweden. He then gave a learned dissertation on the part played by poetry in the world of today and of its increasingly difficult relation with politics. The day after the Prize-giving ceremony he gave a public lecture, also in Italian, in the great reception hall of the Swedish Academy, in which he developed and examined the theme of "Poetry and Politics" from every angle, both possible and impossible. "The politician expects man to die bravely, the poet would rather he knew how to live bravely, which is what makes the poet the enemy of the established order." A few hours later, Quasimodo was received, together with the other laureates of the year, by the King himself, to whom the poet chose to present a specially bound copy of his *Complete Works*.

Translated by Camilla Sykes.